NRAES–177

CROP ROTATION ON ORGANIC FARMS
A PLANNING MANUAL

CHARLES L. MOHLER AND SUE ELLEN JOHNSON, EDITORS

Natural Resource, Agriculture, and Engineering Service (NRAES)
Cooperative Extension
PO Box 4557
Ithaca, NY 14852-4557

NRAES–177
July 2009

ISBN 978-1-933395-21-0

Library of Congress Cataloging-in-Publication Data

Crop rotation on organic farms : a planning manual / Charles L. Mohler and Sue
Ellen Johnson, editors.
    p. cm. -- (Cooperative Extension NRAES ; 177)
 Includes bibliographical references and index.
 ISBN 978-1-933395-21-0
 1. Crop rotation--Handbooks, manuals, etc. 2. Organic farming--Handbooks,
manuals, etc. I. Mohler, Charles L., date II. Johnson, Sue Ellen, date III. Natural
Resource, Agriculture, and Engineering Service. Cooperative Extension. IV.
Series: NRAES (Series) ; 177.
 S603.C756 2009
 631.5'82--dc22
                                    200901605

Disclaimer

Mention of a trademark, proprietary product, or commercial firm in text or figures
does not constitute an endorsement by the Cooperative Extension System or the
publisher and does not imply approval to the exclusion of other suitable products
or firms.

*Requests to reprint parts of this publication should be sent to NRAES. In your
request, please state which parts of the publication you would like to reprint and
describe how you intend to use the material. Contact NRAES if you have any
questions.*

To order additional copies, contact:

Natural Resource, Agriculture, and Engineering Service (NRAES)
Cooperative Extension
PO Box 4557, Ithaca, New York 14852-4557
Phone: (607) 255-7654 • Fax: (607) 254-8770
Email: NRAES@CORNELL.EDU • Website: WWW.NRAES.ORG

CONTENTS

ACKNOWLEDGMENTS

Production of *Crop Rotation on Organic Farms: A Planning Manual* was made possible with funding from Sustainable Agriculture Research and Education (SARE). *See page 155 for more information about SARE.*

This project was a collaboration between researchers, extension educators, and growers. The authors especially thank the twelve farmers who participated in the DACUM process, and whose efforts created the foundation for this project: Polly Amour, Four Winds Farm, Gardiner, NY; Paul Arnold, Pleasant Valley Farm, Argyle, NY; David Blyn, Riverbank Farm, Roxbury, CT; Roy Brubaker, Village Acres Farm, Mifflintown, PA; Jean-Paul Courtens, Roxbury Farm, Kinderhook, NY; Jim Gerritsen, Wood Prairie Farm, Bridgewater, ME; Brett Grohsgal, Even Star Organic Farm, Lexington Park, MD; Jack Gurley, Calvert's Gift Farm, Sparks, MD; Don Kretschmann, Kretschmann Farm, Rochester, PA; Drew Norman, One Straw Farm, White Hall, MD; Eero Ruuttila, Nesenkeag Farm, Litchfield, NH; and Will Stevens, Golden Russet Farm, Shoreham, VT. Tina Overtoom, The Center on Education and Training for Employment, The Ohio State University, was the DACUM facilitator, and Eric Toensmeier, then with the New England Small Farm Institute, assisted her. Many additional growers reviewed and verified the DACUM chart: Frank Albani, Jay Armour, Mike and Terra Brownback, Judy Dornstreitch, Pam Flory, Darrell Frey, Les and Debbie Guile, Rick Hood, Jason Kafka, Dwain Livengood, Bryan O'Hara, Robin Ostfeld, L. Smith, Ed Stockman, Paul Volcklawen, and several anonymous reviewers.

The authors also thank the following reviewers for the many improvements they suggested: Brian Caldwell, farm education coordinator, NOFA-NY; Kathryne L. Everts, associate professor, Plant Pathology, University of Maryland and University of Delaware; Caragh B. Fitzgerald, extension educator, Maryland Cooperative Extension; Eric Gallandt, assistant professor, Weed Ecology and Management, University of Maine; Vern Grubinger, vegetable and berry specialist, University of Vermont Extension and regional coordinator, Northeast SARE; Jerzy Nowak, professor, Horticulture Department, Virginia Polytechnic Institute and State University; Ginny Rozenkranz, extension educator, Maryland Cooperative Extension; Elsa Sanchez, assistant professor, Horticulture Systems Management, The Pennsylvania State University; Abby Seaman, senior extension associate, Cornell Cooperative Extension; Eric Sideman, organic crop specialist, Maine Organic Farmers & Gardeners Association; Eric Toensmeier; and growers Polly Amour; Kurt Forman, Clearview Farm, Palmyra, NY; Brett Grohsgal; Jack Gurley; Brett Kreher, Kreher's Poultry Farms, Clarence, NY; Don Kreher, Kreher's Poultry Farms, Clarence, NY; Will Stevens; and Jon Thorne, Anchor Run Farm, Wrightstown, PA.

Additionally, the authors are grateful to Steve Gilman, Ruckytucks Farm, Saratoga, NY; Dave Colson, New Leaf Farm, Durham, ME; and Andy Caruso, Upper Forty Farm, Cromwell, CT for patiently working through early versions of the planning procedure. Steve Vanek, PhD candidate, Cornell University; Brian Caldwell; and Steve Gilman assembled the information for several of the crop rotation examples in Chapter 4. Klaas and Mary Howell Martens, Lakeview Organic Grains, Penn Yan, NY; John Myer, Myer Farm, Ovid, NY; Edwin Fry, Fair Hills Farm, Chestertown, MD; and Eric and Anne Nordell, Beech Grove Farm, Trout Run, PA assisted in the study of their farms. Cornell University students Jennifer Rodriguez, Hui Ouyong, Erin Finan, Danya Glabau, and Samuel Greenwood helped assemble information for the tables. Anusuya Rangarajan, senior extension associate, Cornell University, provided gentle and joyful guidance of the NEON project.

The book was edited by Jill Mason, MasonEdit.com and designed by Yen Chiang, NRAES. Marty Sailus, NRAES Director, managed book production from manuscript peer review through printing. Holly Hyde, editor, provided production support. Additional production support was provided Violet Stone, Cornell University Department of Horticulture.

Support for this project was provided through a grant from the USDA Initiative for Future Agriculture and Food Systems; and Hatch funds (Regional Project NE-1000, NY(C)–183458) from the Cornell Agricultural Experiment Station.

ABOUT THE AUTHORS
(LISTED IN ALPHABETICAL ORDER)

Jody Bolluyt, producer, Roxbury Farm, Kinderhook, New York

Sue Ellen Johnson, research leader, New England Small Farm Institute, Belchertown, Massachusetts; currently assistant professor and forage specialist, Department of Crop Science, North Carolina State University

Peter Lowy, intern, Roxbury Farm, Kinderhook, New York

Margaret Tuttle McGrath, associate professor, Department of Plant Pathology, Long Island Horticultural Research Laboratory, Cornell University

Charles L. Mohler, senior research associate, Department of Crop and Soil Sciences, Cornell University

Anusuya Rangarajan, senior extension associate, Department of Horticulture, Cornell University

Kimberly A. Stoner, associate agricultural scientist (entomology), The Connecticut Agricultural Experiment Station, New Haven, Connecticut

Eric Toensmeier, program specialist, New England Small Farm Institute, Belchertown, Massachusetts; currently farm project director, Nuestras Raices, Holyoke, Massachusetts

Harold van Es, professor and chair, Department of Crop and Soil Sciences, Cornell University

1

INTRODUCTION

CHARLES L. MOHLER

Crop rotation is a critical feature of all organic cropping systems because it provides the principal mechanism for building healthy soils, a major way to control pests, and a variety of other benefits. *Crop rotation* means changing the type of crop grown on a particular piece of land from year to year. As used in this manual, the term includes both cyclical rotations, in which the same sequence of crops is repeated indefinitely on a field, and noncyclical rotations, in which the sequence of crops varies irregularly to meet the evolving business and management goals of the farmer. Each field has its own rotation, and, consequently, each farmer manages a set of rotations.

Good crop rotation requires long-term strategic planning. However, planning does not necessarily involve identifying which crop will be grown on a field years in advance. Indeed, such specificity may prove futile as plans become disrupted by weather, changes in the market, labor supply, and other factors. Lack of planning, however, can lead to serious problems—for example, the buildup of a soilborne disease of a critical crop, or imbalances in soil nutrients. Such problems can result in an inability to meet the demands of a carefully cultivated market or in additional labor and expense. Problems caused by faulty rotation often take several years to develop and can catch even experienced growers by surprise. In fact, rotation problems usually do not develop until well after the transition to organic cropping. Since the crops grown by organic farmers are often different and more diverse than those grown in the preceding conventional system, the organic transition itself often rotates away from the previous crops and their associated problems. Most farmers are greatly tempted to plant excessive acreage of the most profitable crop or to overuse certain fields for one type of crop. Such practices can lead to costly problems that take many years

> "The purpose of this book is to help growers and farm advisors understand the management of crop rotations; avoid crop rotation problems; and use crop rotation to build better soil, control pests, and develop profitable farms that support satisfied families."

to correct. The purpose of this book is to help growers and farm advisors understand the management of crop rotations; avoid crop rotation problems; and use crop rotation to build better soil, control pests, and develop profitable farms that support satisfied families.

Although rotating among a diversity of cash and cover crops has numerous advantages, it poses substantial management challenges. The number of crops (and crop families) grown can be large, particularly on diversified vegetable farms and mixed vegetable-grain operations. Mathematically, this creates a huge number of potential crop sequences from which to choose. For example, if a farm produces ten different crops, these can be arranged in 90 two-year sequences, since each of the ten crops could be followed by any of the other nine. The same ten crops can be arranged in any of 5,040 unique four-year sequences! Of course, some sequences can be easily eliminated from the list of possibilities, based on experience or general rules of thumb, like avoiding successive vegetable crops in the same plant family, but the number of possibilities is still enormous. Further complications arise because, for market reasons, some crops are grown on a larger acreage than others. Large-acreage crops necessarily occur in multiple sequences with different small acreage crops. Moreover, since certain crops grow well only on particular fields due to soil type, availability of irrigation, topography, etc., the problem of choosing effective crop sequences and allotting them to particular fields becomes even more complex.

This manual is intended to assist growers in plotting a course through the maze of decisions involved in planning crop rotations. The idea behind the manual is not to provide a list of rigid dos and don'ts. Rather, the intent is to provide perspectives on how to approach the challenge of planning effective crop rotations and to provide current information on which to base decisions.

How This Manual Was Constructed

To ensure that this rotation planning manual reflects the realities of crop production on actual farms, the New England Small Farm Institute, on behalf of the Northeast Organic Network (NEON), assembled a panel of 12 expert organic farmers. The panel met for three days and worked through a formal facilitated process that produced a detailed analysis of how experienced organic farmers plan their cropping sequences. This process is discussed in chapter 2 (pages 3–20). Each expert farmer also detailed a highly successful crop rotation that they use, along with problems that sometimes occur with that rotation and how they meet such contingencies. These sample rotations are presented in chapter 4 (pages 47–57) and are supplemented with rotations from several farms that have been intensively studied by NEON. These sample rotations may not work well on farms that have different soil conditions, climates, financial resources, or types of crops, but they are intended to provide inspiration and insight in planning crop sequences.

Chapters 2 (pages 3–20) and 4 (pages 47–47) convey the practical experience of expert growers. In contrast, chapter 3 (pages 21–46) emphasizes the theoretical underpinnings of crop rotation. Five researchers who have extensive experience with organic agriculture provide their views on what crop rotation contributes to particular biological and physical aspects of organic cropping systems, including management of soil health, crop nutrition, diseases, insects, and weeds. An important aspect of these contributions is that they clarify what crop rotation cannot accomplish, as well as what it can do to solve various production problems.

Chapter 5 (pages 58–90) outlines procedures for sorting through the diverse types of data to arrive at decisions about crop rotation. These procedures distill the wisdom derived from the panel of expert growers into a method that can be applied to any farm. Step-by-step examples are provided.

Although this manual is primarily intended for organic farmers and the extension personnel who work with them, we hope it will also be useful to other growers. To this end, chapter 6 (pages 91–94) provides a brief discussion about crop sequences that can be used for transition from conventional to organic production.

Intercropping is not a necessary part of crop rotation, but intercropping greatly affects crop rotation planning. Consequently, chapter 7 (pages 95–100) discusses the basic principles of intercropping and how these interact with other aspects of crop rotation.

Finally, a series of appendices provide biological data relevant to planning crop rotations. These data have been assembled from a variety of sources, including scientific literature, extension publications, and farmer experience.

This manual is most applicable for farms from Maryland to Ohio and north through southern Canada. Most of the principles of crop rotation and methods for choosing among potential crop sequences are widely applicable beyond this region. Data tables on crops, weeds, insects, and diseases, however, are likely to be inadequate in areas far from the northeastern US.

How to Use This Manual

This manual can be used in several ways. First, it can be used simply as a reference. For example, one can check for possible pest or soil problems that may occur in a cropping sequence, or determine how long to leave a field out of a particular crop to avoid pest problems. Second, the manual can be used to see how experienced growers think about crop rotations, and how they manage particular crop sequences on their farms. Reading about what researchers have discovered about how crop rotation affects soil and pests will further increase one's understanding of crop rotations. Finally, the manual provides a method for systematically planning the crop rotations on a farm.

2

HOW EXPERT ORGANIC FARMERS MANAGE CROP ROTATIONS

Sue Ellen Johnson & Eric Toensmeier

Crop rotation is central to the success of organic farms. So how do successful farmers plan and execute crop rotations?

We asked twelve expert organic farmers this question when they gathered at a farmhouse in upstate New York for three snowy days in 2002. Between homemade organic meals, they detailed how they plan and execute crop rotations on their farms. The expert farmers, who together have over 200 years of experience, shared many concepts and insights about crop rotation management. Twenty other organic growers have since reviewed and added to the panel farmers' conclusions. Their cumulative knowledge and common practice are summarized in this chapter. Their specific actions and decisions related to crop rotation are outlined in the chart "Managing a Crop Rotation System" on pages 12–13. The chart delineates the key "responsibilities" and the necessary "tasks" that need to be executed to fulfill each key responsibility.

Why Rotate Crops?

Effective crop rotations are a foundation of organic cropping systems. Organic farmers recognize that crop rotation is necessary to maintain field productivity. Expert farmers design their rotations to (1) earn income and (2) increase soil quality or build "soil capital" (sidebar 2.1). Crop rotation and a crop rotation plan and records are required for organic certification of a field or farm.

Numerous books and articles outline the goals and benefits of crop rotations (see sidebar 2.2, page 4). The contribution of our panel of expert farmers is interesting in (1) the emphasis they give to business management decisions in crop rotation planning; and (2) the flexibility of their crop rotations, specifically the absence of fixed, long-term crop rotations. Their rotation planning is an ongoing annual process that incorporates information and objectives for multiple years. Many expert farmers do not have standardized, cyclical crop rotations for every field, yet our experts share an overall approach to designing, implementing, and adapting crop sequences on their farms. The tools in chapter 5 (pages 58–90) are designed to help readers develop their own expertise.

SIDEBAR 2.1

THE CONCEPTS OF SOIL QUALITY, SOIL CAPITAL, SOIL HEALTH, AND SOIL LIFE

The expert farmers used many terms interchangeably as they discussed rotations and their farm goals. Organic agriculture revolves around the concepts of soil life and soil biology. Organic practices, including crop rotation, are expected to enhance soil life and soil health. A basic tenet of organic agriculture is that biological diversity and soil organic matter are drivers of productive organic farming systems. Farmers believe that a soil high in organic matter leads to a healthy, biologically active soil that will have fewer crop fertility, pest, and disease problems. Farmers also use the term *soil capital* to express how soil building practices are an investment in long-term soil productivity.

Sidebar 2.2
What Some Good Books Say about Crop Rotation

Numerous books and articles do an excellent job of outlining rotation theory, guidelines, and practice. Many present crop-by-crop rotations. These may or may not reflect the real complexity of modern organic farming operations and successful farm management, but a sampling of the advice is listed below.

From *Cyclopedia of American Agriculture* (1907; L. H. Bailey, ed.), chapter 5, "Crop Management," pp. 85–88:

a. The rotation must adapt itself to the farmers business.
b. It must adapt itself to the soil and fertility problem.
c. The fertilizer question often modifies the rotation.
d. The kind of soil and the climate may dictate the rotation.
e. The labor supply has an important bearing on the character of the rotation course.
f. The size of the farm and whether land can be used for pasturage are also determinants.
g. The rotation must be planned with reference to the species of plants that will best serve one another, or produce the best interrelationship possible.
h. The rotation must consider in what condition one crop will leave the soil for the succeeding crop, and how one crop can be seeded with another crop.

From *Organic Farming* (1990; Nicolas Lampkin), chapter 5, "Rotation Design for Organic Systems," pp. 131–32:

"Usually a rotation contains at least one 'money crop' that finds a direct and ready market; one clean tilled crop; one hay or straw crop; one leguminous crop....

The starting point for the design of a rotation should be the capabilities of the farm and the land in terms of soil type, soil texture, climatic conditions."

Basic guidelines:

Deep rooting crops should follow shallow rooting crops....
Alternate between crops with high and low root biomass....
Nitrogen fixing crops should alternate with nitrogen demanding crops....
Wherever possible, catch crops, green manures, and undersowing techniques should be used to keep the soil covered....
Crops which develop slowly and are therefore susceptible to weeds should follow weed suppressing crops....
Alternate between leaf and straw crops....
Where a risk of disease or soil borne pest problems exists, potential host crops should only occur in the rotation at appropriate time intervals....
Use variety and crop mixtures when possible....
Alternate between autumn and spring sown crops....

Also consider:

suitability of individual crops with respect to climate and soil
balance between cash and forage crops
seasonal labour requirements and availability
cultivation and tillage operations

From *Building Soils for Better Crops* (2000; Fred Magdoff and Harold van Es), chapter 11, "Crop Rotation," pp. 102–3:

General Principles:

1. Follow a legume crop ... with a high nitrogen demanding crop.
2. Grow less nitrogen demanding crops ... in the second or third year after a legume sod.
3. Grow the same annual crop for only one year....
4. Don't follow one crop with another closely related species....
5. Use crop sequences that promote healthier crops.
6. Use crop sequences that aid in controlling weeds.
7. Use longer periods of perennial crops on sloping land.
8. Try to grow a deep-rooted crop ... as part of the rotation.
9. Grow some crops that will leave a significant amount of residue.
10. When growing a wide mix of crops ... try grouping into blocks according to plant family, timing of crops, (all early season crops together, for example), type of crop (root vs. fruit vs. leaf), or crops with similar cultural practices....

Basics of Crop Rotation

Rotations are one dimension of the art and science of farm management. The biological principles of crop rotation intersect with many other aspects of the farm operation and farm business. Crop rotation is both a principle of production and a tool of management (see sidebar 2.3). Expert farmers balance market options and field biology. Labor, equipment, the layout of beds and fields, along with other logistics of planting and harvest, all influence how rotations are designed and executed.

Expert farmers' rotations include key cash crops, "filler" or "break" crops, and cover crops. In every season, farmers must manage production across multiple fields and beds. Variation in the acreage of each crop, variation in field characteristics, and shifting business decisions result in multiple rotations or crop sequences on most organic farms. Consequently, farmers manage numerous crop rotations on the same farm.

"Model" rotations may suggest that every crop is grown on a fixed schedule on every field, with each crop rotating field to field around the entire farm. In reality, expert farmers in the northeast US rarely cycle every crop they grow through every field on any regular schedule. Instead, each field tends to have its own distinct sequence of crops, tillage, and amendments. Thus, each field tends to have a unique cropping history. On some farms, a few fields do follow an established, fixed rotation. Through trial and error the managers of these farms have settled on a cyclical rotation that works well for a particular field (see chapter 4, pages 49–54 for real field examples).

The challenge of a good crop rotation system is to grow the type and quantity of crops needed to ensure the farm's profitability while continually building soil quality for long-term productivity. Most vegetable farms grow many different crops and crop families. Every crop is not equally profitable, and some crops are highly profitable but have limited markets. The rotation of botanical families of crops prevents the buildup of pest populations, by (1) interrupting pest life cycles, and (2) altering pest habitats. Alternatively, fields (or beds) may be deliberately rotated through a fallow to manage a weed or pest problem. Sometimes tillage, the use of mulch, or compost applications are also integrated into a field's rotation plan (see chapter 4, pages 49–54 for examples). Cover crops are often used for building soil fertility and health but make no direct contribution to cash flow. Farms with limited acreage may rely on compost or other soil amendments rather

SIDEBAR 2.3
EXPERT FARMERS' DEFINITIONS OF CROP ROTATION

The NEON expert panel did not formally define crop rotation, but individual farmers provided their own working definitions:

- Don Kretschmann—"Rotation is the practice of using the natural biological and physical properties of crops to benefit the growth, health, and competitive advantage of other crops. In this process the soil and its life are also benefited. The desired result is a farm which is more productive and to a greater extent self-reliant in resources."

- Roy Brubaker—"[Rotation is] a planned succession of crops (cash and cover) chosen to sustain a farm's economic and environmental health."

- Will Stevens—"I've come to view crop rotation practices as a way to help me use nature's ecological principles in the inherently non-natural world of agriculture. Striving to have as much 'green' on the ground as possible throughout the year is one step in that direction. I view crop rotation as a series of 'rapid succession' cycles, (ideally) minimally managed. Through this approach, the power and sustainability of natural systems can be expressed through the health and prosperity of the farm system."

- Jean-Paul Courtens—"Rotations balance soil building crops (soil improvement crops) and cash crops, and can allow for bare fallow periods to break weed cycles and incorporate plant matter into the soil."

than cover crops (see sidebar 2.4).

Farmers with large land bases often include longer-term, soil-restoring perennial cover or hay crops in their rotations. After a period of intensive cropping, fields cycle out of annual production and into perennial hay or green manure cover crops. During the intensive cropping period, the season-to-season sequences vary with contingencies, and biological principles may be neglected. The perennial hay or cover crop is then expected to correct

problems that may have built up during intensive cropping. These cycles often run six to ten years or more.

On many successful farms, long-term, fixed, cyclical rotations are far less common than simple two- or three-year crop sequences. Expert farmers frequently rely on numerous "trusted" short sequences or crop couplets to achieve their crop rotation objectives. Instead of planning long, detailed cyclical rotations, experts use a suite of interchangeable short sequences to meet their farm's goals for cash flow and soil quality. Biological principles are the main determinants of these short sequences. Samples of short sequences are shown in the "Real Fields on Real Farms" chart in chapter 4 (pages 49–54).

During a field season, a bed or field may be planted with a series of different short-season crops. Sometimes, because of market demand or other farm practicalities, growers make multiple plantings of a crop in the same bed within a given growing season, which is more problematic biologically. The same crop or sequence is rarely replanted in the same bed or field the following year, however, due to the likelihood of pest and disease outbreaks. Cover crops are often planted to follow or precede a cash crop and occupy a field only for the winter or a portion of the growing season. In all cases, experts are very conscious that such intensive cropping needs careful biological monitoring and management.

Crop Rotation and Farm Management

Crop rotations require multidimensional thinking. Rotation management requires understanding both the whole farm and each individual field and balancing field- and farm-scale decisions (figure 2.1). On successful farms, rotation planning is a rolling, responsive process. Expert farmers are continually balancing annual and multiyear (short- and long-term) decisions. Business decisions must be optimized for annual returns and cash flow. Expert growers indicate that in any given season, market opportunities and logistical needs may override biological concerns.

Experts manage multiple, interacting factors as they implement crop rotations. Organic farmers rely on rotations and long-term soil quality to deal with problems and ensure the productivity of fields more than they rely on fertilizers and pest control products. Their understanding of biological principles sets the boundaries of their management practices. Many expert farmers push and test the

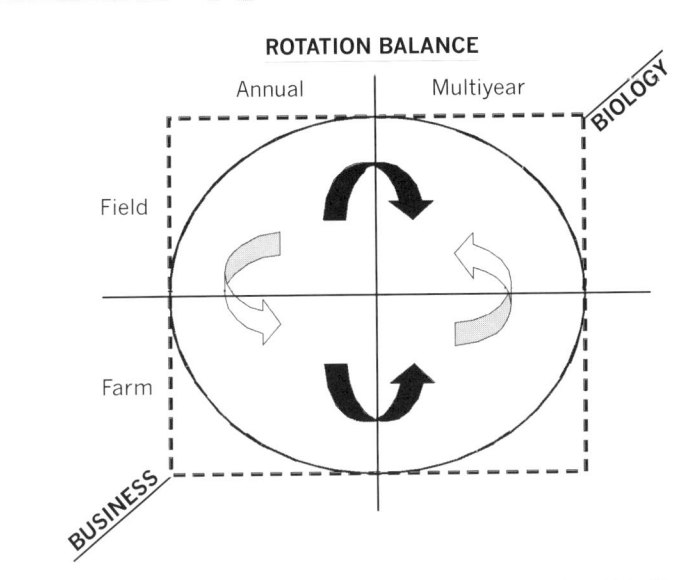

ROTATION BALANCE

FIGURE 2.1 Rotation planning balances the management of field- and farm-level decisions on an annual and a multi-year basis. Annual farm-level decisions tend to prioritize business concerns. Multi-year decisions tend to prioritize and accommodate biological demands.

FIGURE 2.2 Expert organic vegetable farmer panel, convened January 30 to February 1, 2002. From upper left: Jean-Paul Courtens (NY), Eero Ruuttila (NH), Paul Arnold (NY), David Blyn (CT), Roy Brubaker (PA), Don Kretschmann (PA), Jack Gurley (MD), Brett Grohsgal (MD), Polly Armour (NY), Drew Norman (MD), Will Stevens (VT). Not pictured: Jim Gerritsen (ME).

biological principles of crop rotation to the limit to meet management and business demands.

Expert farmers plan and implement rotations on an annual, seasonal, and last-minute opportunistic basis. Their annual plans are based on clear priorities. Each year the paramount challenge is to grow adequate quantities of profitable crops to keep the farm viable. At the same time farmers are deciding the rotational sequence on each field, they must consider how to rotate equipment and labor efficiently across the entire farm operation. Crop cultural and harvest characteristics—including the logistics of labor-intensive weeding or multiple harvests; vehicle access; and keeping crops like pumpkins or flowers secure from vandals, thieves, and wildlife— have to be managed across farm *and* field. Meanwhile, meeting market demands and maintaining cash flow are farm business issues that must be integrated with field decisions. Inevitably, expert farmers also adapt to the weather conditions of specific years, often by changing their crop mix and, consequently, their rotations.

Most farms have a few key cash crops that generate significant income. Year by year, expert farmers focus on planting their key crops in the most suitable fields for those crops without compromising the soil health and long-term productivity of those fields. Generally, these crop-to-field matches are first made based on market and logistical considerations (see sidebar 2.5, page 8). Then expert farmers review whether there are biological reasons to go in a different direction. They cross-check "what not to do" (see appendix 2, pages 104–123) biologically with both their experience and their knowledge. Farmers take special care to manage the production and soil capital of their best fields. Relying on their knowledge of their fields and the crops they grow, and some general principles (for example, avoid planting related crops in the same field year after year), expert farmers determine the crop for each field each year.

In any given year, field history, along with the weather, determine the suitability of a field for a particular crop. On many farms in the northeast US, any one field (or bed) is usually not interchangeable with all the others on the farm. Fields, even beds, have unique attributes because of soil parent material and landscape position. Even if soils are similar, microclimates, access to irrigation, and distance to roads or packing facilities cause some fields to be better suited for certain crops. Some fields are simply more productive; others have particular histories or problems that preclude certain crops or rotations.

Expert farmers understand that each field's biological management is central to the long-term success of the overall farm business. They monitor and manage crop rotation to limit negative impacts on any one field.

SIDEBAR 2.5

OPPORTUNISTIC DECISIONS: BUSINESS OVERRIDES BIOLOGY

Unexpected opportunities and circumstances often confront farmers. Expert farmers go through the following steps as they manage these situations:

1. Recognition of a market opportunity or logistical contingency (such as a change in weather, equipment, or labor availability).

2. Feasibility assessment to determine whether the market can be met successfully. Considering the available land, labor, equipment, and irrigation, will the change increase the overall profitability of the farm operation? What is the cascade effect across the farm?

3. Biological cross-check to determine the field or variety. For example, a more disease-resistant variety may be selected if taking advantage of the economic opportunity means that the rotation time between susceptible crops would be decreased. *Biological "rules" may be stretched to meet the market, but they are not repeatedly ignored on the same fields.*

Biological guidelines come into decisions at every convenient opportunity (for example, a field that was too wet for a planned early spring crop is now open for a cover crop). Biological guidelines also enter into decisions when a problem becomes evident and must be addressed (for example, a soilborne disease such as *Phytophthora*).

Frequently, expert farmers design crop sequences to set up for future key crops, in addition to meeting the current season's production needs. For example, for a successful early seeding of a small-seeded crop like carrot the rotation sequence must be planned so that the residue of the previous crop will be fully broken down—providing the proper seedbed for the next season's crop. Other sequences may be designed so that substantial spring growth of an overwintering cover crop precedes a heavy-feeding cash crop. For example, a field could be planted with a summer-harvested crop such as sweet corn in the current year, so that a hairy vetch cover crop has time to establish in the fall and supply nitrogen for a heavy-feeding cucurbit the following spring. High-value crops that are difficult to grow are often pivotal in determining a rotation, because they are the most critical in terms of both the business and the biology of the farm.

Of course, plans don't always go as expected. Market opportunities or weather may dictate a change in a rotation (sidebar 2.5). Seed may not be available or viable. A field may have weed problems or a pest outbreak that is best addressed by rotation. The experts build flexibility and responsiveness into their annual plans.

Expert farmers often need to make decisions for individual fields on the fly, based on their experience and knowledge of each field and the overall farm. They know what can go wrong. They know the limits of their systems. As business managers, they are continually reviewing the farm and its operational capabilities. Many farmers rely on their mental categorization of crops and fields (described in sidebar 2.9, page 15) which makes the quick substitution of crops easier. A tool for crop categorization and allocation of crops to fields is introduced in chapter 5 (pages 58–90).

Expert farmers balance the farm business, farm management, and field biology. Since they manage their systems intuitively, they do not always distinguish farm planning from crop rotation planning. For example, choosing the crop mix is a market-driven business decision, which is coupled with the allocation of crops to fields, which is a biological and logistical decision.

The NEON "Managing a Crop Rotation System" Chart

Our panel of expert organic farmers participated in a structured, facilitated process that was designed to elicit an outline of step-by-step decisions and actions related to their own management of crop rotation (sidebar 2.6). This is summarized in the chart "Managing a Crop Rotation System" (pages 12–13) The content and wording of the chart are those of the expert farmers. The chart reflects both their common practices and how they think about those practices.

The primary purpose of the chart is to provide insight into the decisions and actions followed by experienced organic growers as they manage crop rotations. The responsibilities and tasks outlined in the chart demonstrate how expert farmers integrate crop rotation decisions into the overall planning and operation of their farms. The chart provides a general, overall guide to all of the steps needed to manage crop rotations on an organic farm. Chapter 5

(pages 58–90) presents tools based on the experts' recommendations that will help in executing several priority tasks on the chart.

How to Read the Chart

The left hand column of the "Managing a Crop Rotation System" (pages 12–13) chart represents eight broad "key responsibilities" necessary for managing crop rotations. Each key responsibility is associated with a set of necessary "tasks" described in the boxes that run across the page. These tasks must be completed to fulfill the responsibility. (Note that the tasks associated with a key responsibility sometimes take up more than one row.)

Bear in mind the following when consulting the chart:
- The word *crop* refers to both cash and cover crops unless otherwise specified.
- The responsibilities are listed more or less in the order in which they are performed. Managing a crop rotation, however, is neither a linear nor a cyclical

---

SIDEBAR 2.6

THE NEON EXPERT FARMER ROTATION WORKSHOP

The New England Small Farm Institute adapted a process called Develop a Curriculum, or DACUM (78a), to understand and present the decision process followed by expert farmers in planning and implementing organic vegetable rotations. The DACUM process was first created at Ohio State University to develop training materials based on the knowledge of experienced workers in business and industry. It was built around the idea that skilled individuals currently performing a job are better able than anyone else to describe the job and how they do it. The approach provided a structured forum for farmers to successfully communicate about management of their farms. The expert farmers created the chart "Managing a Crop Rotation System," which details the key responsibilities for management of successful rotations and the tasks associated with each responsibility. It gave scientists a unique perspective on how farmers manage their systems and how research is used by farmers.

The Expert Growers

Twelve expert organic vegetable growers (figure 2.2, page 7) who farm from Maryland to Maine were nominated by sixteen organic farming organizations and organic certifiers in the northeastern US to participate in the three-day NEON Expert Farmer Rotation Workshop in 2002. Each of them had been farming for eight or more years, and vegetables are the primary crops on all twelve farms. Their operations range in size from 5 acres to 200 acres. They employ an array of marketing strategies, from wholesale to community-supported agriculture (CSA). Twenty other growers with similar qualifications reviewed the chart and other materials produced by the workshop (e.g. lists in sidebars 2.7, 2.8, 2.9, and 2.12, page 11 to page 18). Together, the expert farmers and the reviewers are representative of the best farms in the northeast US. (Farmer profiles are presented in sidebar 4.2, page 48)

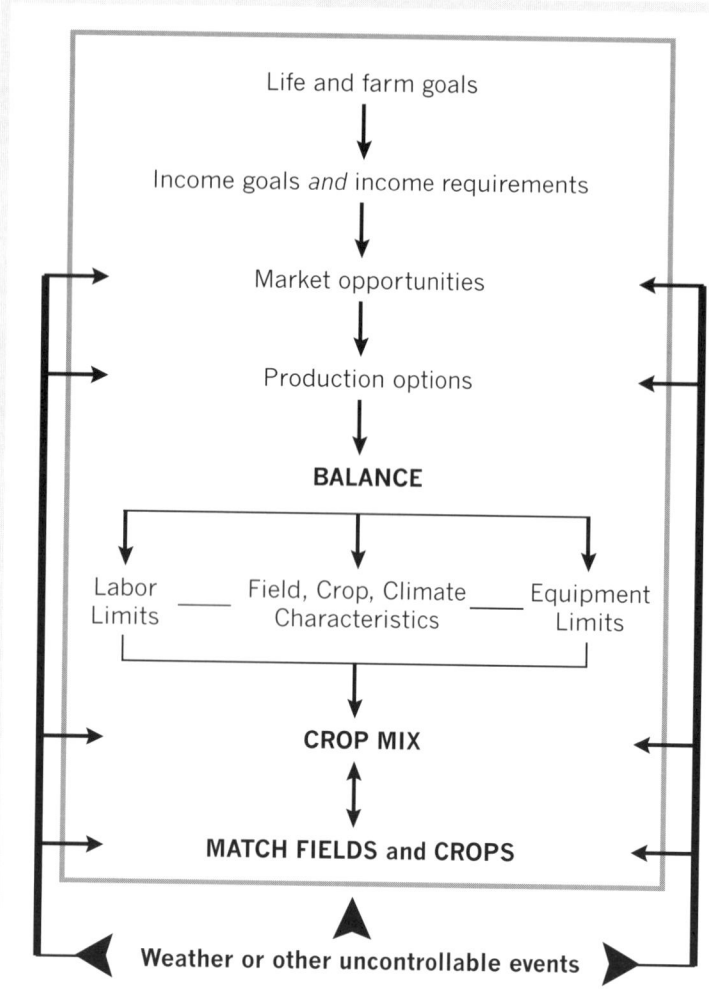

Figure 2.3 Schematic summary of crop rotation planning. When the weather or other uncontrollable event requires the rotation plan to be changed, expert farmers reevaluate options and revise the plan.

process. Although the chart is organized in a quasi-chronological order, farmers' decisions and actions move back and forth among many of the tasks and responsibilities listed. This back-and-forth process is schematically presented in figure 2.3.

- Many expert farmers do extensive planning and record keeping on paper. Most have some form of field maps. Some use computers. A few keep all details in their heads. Most of the panel farmers agreed that farmers should write down their field records and plans.
- Many of the key responsibilities and tasks require reflection and observation as well as information.

Expert farmers agree that frequent, careful field observations are critical.

- The chart illustrates the central role of rotation in the overall farming operation. The chart does not cover all aspects of farm management—only those that the farmers thought were most important in determining the rotation and that are linked to rotation management. Some tasks and key responsibilities relate to the entire farm and others to the rotation on a particular field. Some tasks are mental "desk tasks" (for example, B-13, "Review regulations"), and some are physical (F-10, "Plant crops"). Some relate to information processing (G-6, "Assess disease control"); others center on decision making (E-7, "Determine crop quantities").

Every responsibility listed on the chart needs consideration each year. They do not necessarily have to be addressed in the order listed, but responsibilities A through E primarily occur during the relatively quiet winter months, when production and marketing pressures are less intense and time is available to take stock and look to the growing seasons ahead; responsibility F (the actual execution and implementation of the rotation) begins in early spring and continues throughout the growing season; and responsibilities G and H intensify in fall and winter, following the most hectic portions of the field season.

Some tasks require great attention every year, while others require little effort unless the farm is undergoing major changes. Some tasks are executed only once each season (C-3, "Test soils"); some are repeatedly revisited (F-8, "Prepare work schedule"), and some carry over from one year to the next (C-9, "Categorize crops").

Key Responsibilities and Related Tasks in the Chart

This section discusses each of the key responsibilities in the "Managing a Crop Rotation System" chart (pages 12–13) and illustrates some of the important, difficult, or less obvious tasks, with examples from the operations of expert farmers (see sidebar 2.7).

Responsibility A: Identify Rotation Goals

Rotations are a means to meet overall farm goals. Expert farmers manage their field rotations in the context of their whole farm systems. Although they may not consciously review them, each farmer has a set of farming goals that guide rotation planning for each field and for the whole farm. Some goals are common to all farms (sidebar 2.8, page 14); others are unique to a particular farmer. Examples of experts' rotation goals include:

- Jack Gurley's goal is to maximize production on 100 percent of his small acreage without sacrificing soil health and tilth.
- One of Will Stevens's goals is to design rotations to keep brassicas out of fields with a history of clubroot.
- Since Jim Gerritsen produces certified seed potatoes that must be disease free, the goal of his entire rotation is to control potato diseases and increase organic matter.

Under responsibility A, the most important and most difficult task is reviewing the overall farm operation. This includes reviewing the production plan: the crops, cover crops, fallows, and livestock that need to be allocated to particular field areas in the coming year. Certain factors—including cropland available, equipment, cash flow, crop mix, and marketing strategies—define the parameters within which the rotation must be designed. Another important task is to identify which problems can be addressed by rotation.

Responsibility B: Identify Resources and Constraints

Identifying the possibilities and limits of the overall farm production plan and the rotation for each field is central to planning. At the farm scale, parameters such as market demand, available land, equipment, projected labor availability, and regulatory issues have to be reviewed

(continued on page 14)

SIDEBAR 2.7

MOST IMPORTANT AND MOST DIFFICULT TASKS

Expert farmers built the chart "Managing a Crop Rotation System" (pages 12–13) by reaching consensus on the key responsibilities and tasks involved in managing a crop rotation system. Other expert farmers reviewed the chart and indicated the ten *most important* tasks and the ten tasks they considered *most difficult* to perform. Tasks are listed in order of most to least. Codes in parentheses correspond to the number of the task on the chart.

Ten *Most Important* Tasks

1. Maintain crops. (F-12)
2. Implement production plan. (F-4)
3. Prepare soils as soon as weather permits. (F-9)
4. Plant crops. (F-10)
5. Walk fields regularly to observe crops and fields. (C-1)
6. Review overall farm operation. (A-2)
7. Draft annual [rotation] plans. (E-15)
8. Monitor soil and crop conditions. (F-6)
9. Adjust actions according to field and crop conditions. (F-13)
10. Identify problems that can be addressed through rotation. (A-3)

Ten *Most Difficult* Tasks

1. Assess profitability on a whole-farm and crop-by-crop basis. (G-5)
2. Maintain crops. (F-12)
3. Assess whether pest, disease, and weed pressures must be addressed. (D-4)
4. Investigate new market opportunities. (H-3)
5. Review overall farm operation. (A-2)
6. Review regulations. (B-13)
7. Analyze weather probabilities. (D-1)
8. Determine if successes or failures were due to on-farm or regional factors. (G-11)
9. Develop collaborations to verify successes and solve problems. (H-2)
10. Tweak the crop mix. (H-4)

The NEON "Managing a Crop Rotation System" Chart

A	**Identify Rotation Goals**	**A-1** Review overall farm & personal goals (e.g., long & short term, mission statement)	**A-2** Review overall farm operation (e.g., marketing strategies, profitability, farm family/team, production system [crop & livestock mix], length of season, equipment, raised beds or row crops, on-farm compost production)		**A-3** Identify problems that can be addressed through rotation
B	**Identify Resources & Constraints**	**B-1** Identify personal strengths, weaknesses, likes & dislikes	**B-2** Determine available land (e.g., quantity, suitability)	**B-3** Determine irrigation potential for each field (e.g., equipment, water availability)	**B-4** Identify markets for cash crops
		B-10 Inventory labor availability	**B-11** Assess labor strengths, weaknesses, likes & dislikes	**B-12** Identify input suppliers (e.g., plants & seeds, amendments, manure/compost, cropping materials, post-harvest packaging)	**B-13** Review regulations (e.g., organic certification, phosphorus regulations, other applicable relevant regulations)
C	**Gather Data**	**C-1** Walk fields regularly to observe crop growth & field conditions	**C-2** Create field maps including acreage, land, soils (including NRCS soil map data), physical characteristics, frost pockets, air drainage, microclimates; plot areas with known problems on map		**C-3** Test soils (e.g., N, P, K, secondary- & micronutrients, pH, cation exchange capacity, organic matter)
		C-8 Consult sales data & market trends	**C-9** Categorize crops (see sidebar 2.9, page 15)	**C-10** Categorize fields (see sidebar 2.9, page 15)	**C-11** Maintain records (e.g., up-to-date maps, information on crops & fields, etc.)
D	**Analyze Data**	**D-1** Assess weather probabilities	**D-2** Assess soil conditions on a bed or field basis (e.g., residue, moisture, temperature, compaction, last year's mulch; see sidebar 2.12, page 18)		**D-3** Compare crop cultural needs to field characteristics (e.g., soil test results, crop residues)
E	**Plan Crop Rotation**	**E-1** Review recent cropping history (e.g., 3 or more years; field or bed basis; by crop & sequence of botanical families, performance, production, logistical issues)		**E-2** Consider field needs & conditions (e.g., disease, fertility)	**E-3** Group crops according to maturity dates (e.g., for simultaneous or sequential harvesting)
		E-10 Schedule succession plantings of cash crops	**E-11** Determine cover crop types, field locations, & quantities	**E-12** Integrate cash & cover crops (e.g., simultaneous [overseed, interseed, undersow] or sequential [one follows another])	**E-13** Determine managed fallow field locations	**E-14** Plan crop/rotation experiments (e.g., new trials, new-to-this-farm rotations)
F	**Execute Rotation**	**F-1** Organize rotation planning & management tools (e.g., planting charts, equipment booklets, maps, reference materials)	**F-2** Review rotation & production plans	**F-3** Confirm markets for cash crops (change crops or quantities if price or demand requires)	**F-4** Implement production plan (e.g., secure labor & train labor, prepare equipment [including irrigation], order seeds & supplies)
		F-9 Prepare soils as soon as weather permits (using appropriate tillage, prepare fields when field conditions are right, avoiding compaction & allowing time for any cover crops or residue to adequately break down)		**F-10** Plant crops (follow plan & planting calendar as conditions permit; capture planting windows, "seize the moment"; adjust plan as needed based on contingency guidelines [see **E-16**])	
G	**Evaluate Rotation Execution**	**G-1** Assess soil quality (e.g., expected vs. actual)	**G-2** Assess yields (e.g., varieties, cover crops; expected vs. actual)	**G-3** Assess timing & sequencing (e.g., expected vs. actual)	**G-4** Assess costs of production (e.g., by crop, expected vs. actual)
		G-11 Determine if successes or failures were due to internal/on-farm or macro/regional issues (e.g., consult other farmers, extension agents, others)	**G-12** Analyze success & failure of rotation plan (e.g., review goals, identify factors, consult external information sources, draw conclusions)		**G-13** Maintain records (e.g., production records, experiment results, successes & failures, speculations)
H	**Adjust Rotation Plan**	**H-1** Identify successful combinations & repeat (set successful rotations on "automatic pilot")	**H-2** Develop collaborations with researchers & farmers to create solutions to problems or verify successes (e.g., trials & experiments)		**H-3** Investigate new market opportunities ("smell the niche")

The NEON "Managing a Crop Rotation System" Chart (*continued*)

A-4 Set rotation goals (e.g., manage insects, disease, weeds, soil, field logistics; see sidebar 2.8, page 14, set custom goals)	**A-5** Review annual production plan (e.g., crop & cover crop species & varieties, desired quantities)	**A-6** Balance acreage, at whole farm level, between cash crops, cover crops, livestock, and "fallow" (e.g., bare soil, stale seed-bed, sod/hay, permanent pasture, or woodlot; consider role of livestock in fertility and weed control)	**A-7** Update records (e.g., whole farm plan & farm mission, record annual production plan)

B-5 Review projected annual cash flow	**B-6** Identify neighbor issues (e.g., compost pile location, spraying, chemical drift, pollination, genetic pollution)	**B-7** Inventory farm equipment & facilities (e.g., greenhouses, tractors, post-harvest handling areas)	**B-8** Assess crop cultural needs (e.g., spacing, trellising, crop height, microclimates, irrigation)	**B-9** Identify cultural constraints based on equipment (e.g., row width, irrigation)

B-14 Determine available rotation management time	**B-15** Establish and maintain relationships with off-farm experts (e.g., extension, scouts, land grants, others; talk to laborers)

C-4 Network with farmers & others (e.g., helpers, extension, others; site-specific & practice-related)	**C-5** Study existing research data (e.g., cover crops, insects, diseases, fertility, weeds)	**C-6** Consult field records (e.g., what was planted where in previous years, successes & failures	**C-7** Consult meteorological data (e.g., frost free dates, rainfall)

D-4 Assess whether pest, disease, or weed pressures from previous season must be addressed	**D-5** Determine applicability of research data, advice, & other farmers' experience	**D-6** Assess crop mix for whole farm (e.g., market data, soil tests)	**D-7** Maintain records (e.g., record data analysis results & decisions made)

E-4 Consider harvest logistics (e.g., access to crops; field & row length, minimum walking & box-carrying distance, use of harvest equipment, plan for ease of loading onto trucks)	**E-5** Consider companion planting options	**E-6** Group crops according to botanical families	**E-7** Determine crop quantities & area (e.g., 500 row feet or 2 acres; add 10% for contingencies)	**E-8** Determine field locations of most profitable, beneficial, and "at-risk" crops	**E-9** Determine field locations of lower-priority crops

E-15 Draft annual plans (e.g., rotation plan, production plan, soil fertility plan)	**E-16** Develop guidelines for contingencies in case rotation does not go as planned (e.g., written or mental guidelines for improvisation: principles, priorities to use to make on-the-spot decisions)	**E-17** Use senses & imagination to review plan (e.g., field plans and logistics; walk fields and visualize rotation, "farm it in your head")	**E-18** Maintain records (e.g., write down plan, draw maps)

F-5 Monitor weather (e.g., short term [best day for planting]; long term [need to change plan due to drought])	**F-6** Monitor soil & crop conditions (e.g., field readiness for planting; cover crop maturity; residue incorporation)	**F-7** Monitor greenhouse conditions (e.g., observe condition of transplants relative to soil conditions; slow or accelerate growth if necessary to produce appropriate-sized transplants on-time)	**F-8** Prepare work schedule

F-11 Keep unused soil covered (e.g., cover crop, mulch, trap crops)	**F-12** Maintain crops (e.g., cultivate, spray, trellis, irrigate, harvest)	**F-13** Adjust actions according to field & crop conditions (e.g., weather, soils, weed pressure; assign crops to different fields or beds to adjust for wetness or other problems; replant if necessary, abandon crop or replace with a cover crop to cut losses)	**F-14** Maintain records (e.g., what was actually planted where, successes & failures, planting & harvest dates, compliance with regulations & organic certification)

G-5 Assess profitability on a whole farm & crop-by-crop basis (e.g., expected vs. actual)	**G-6** Assess disease control (e.g., expected vs. actual)	**G-7** Assess weed control (e.g., expected vs. actual)	**G-8** Assess insect & pest control (e.g., expected vs. actual)	**G-9** Interview work crew for suggestions; determine likes, dislikes	**G-10** Measure performance against rotation goals (positive or negative outcomes)

H-4 Tweak crop mix (e.g., based on market data & field performance; consider adding or abandoning crops or elements of rotation as necessary)	**H-5** Tweak field management (e.g., change planting or plowdown dates, crop locations; shift crop families to different fields; put poorly performing fields into hay ahead of schedule)	**H-6** Upgrade or improve equipment as necessary	**H-7** Start process over (return to A: Identify Rotation Goals)	**H-8** Maintain records (e.g., keep notes of actual changes implemented)

annually. Farmers consider complying and keeping up with regulations to be among their most difficult tasks. This responsibility also includes numerous "communication" tasks, such as establishing market relationships, making labor arrangements, accessing information, and contacting suppliers.

Constraints may include field-specific limits like whether a field is ready for planting and harvest early or late in the season and how that relates to market timing, cash flow, and profitability. Problems of specific fields in a particular year must be identified. For example, heavy weed pressure the previous season may preclude small-seeded crops. Crop cultural needs, such as spacing and trellising, also have to be accommodated. Constraints imposed by equipment, such as row width, must be figured into the rotation plan. Crops with similar irrigation, fertility, labor, and cultivation regimes or planting times are often managed as a block to simplify field operations.

Responsibility C: Gather Data

Rotation decisions, for each field and for the whole farm, are based on an impressive array of information. Some information is collected on the farm, and some is gathered from off-farm sources. Observing crops and fields is on the expert farmers' list of the ten most important tasks (sidebar 2.7, page 11). All the expert farmers agreed that regularly walking the fields is a crucial way to gather data and monitor ongoing conditions for the current and coming seasons. Will Stevens interviews his workers throughout the season, because they are able to observe many field situations he does not have the opportunity to see. Even in winter, expert farmers are observing their fields, sometimes while cross-country skiing or walking the dog. This helps them review field conditions and logistics of previous seasons and organize their thinking for the season ahead.

Production and marketing information usually needs to be updated and cross-checked annually. A new crop, research recommendations, or market arrangements may require that new data be considered. For example, seed potato grower Jim Gerritsen uses his rotation to interrupt potato disease life cycles and pest vectors. He reviews the scientific research annually, staying current to take advantage of any advances in the understanding of the ecology of his system.

Tasks C-9 and C-10, "Categorize crops" and "Categorize fields," are among the most critical steps in data gathering. Categorization of crops and fields helps guide the optimal allocation of particular crops to individual fields or beds each year. These tasks rely on the cumulative process of integrating information and experience over many growing seasons. Information about both crops and fields is necessary to effectively match them in a given year. The first task is to characterize every cash and cover crop in the farm's crop mix according to a range of important characteristics, from the number and timing of harvests to soil requirements (see sidebar 2.9). Farmers also characterize their fields, on the basis of the field's permanent characteristics (such as slope and exposure) and shorter-term conditions (such as weed pressure). Categorizations provide a reference of "interchangeable crops" if a plan needs modification. For example, it is useful to know what late crops or varieties can go into a field in a wet year. The variety of characteristics considered indicates the complexity of the issues farmers balance in crop rotation decisions.

SIDEBAR 2.9

CATEGORIZATION OF CROPS AND FIELDS

Crop Characteristics

The table below lists crop characteristics from most to least important, as ranked by expert farmers.

- Botanical family
- Market demand
- Season of planting, harvest, labor, and land use
- Susceptibility to pests and diseases
- Cash vs. cover crop
- Ability to compete with weeds
- Annual, biennial, perennial, or overwintering annual
- Direct-seeded vs. transplanted
- "Givers" vs. "takers"
- Heavy vs. light feeders
- Cultural practices (for example, spraying, cultivation, irrigation)
- Preferred seedbed conditions
- Spacing requirements
- Income per acre
- Effect on cash flow
- Harvest timing
- Costs per acre
- Tolerance of mechanical cultivation
- Ability to trap nutrients
- Root vs. leaf and fruit
- Drought tolerance
- Row vs. block planted
- Large vs. small seeded
- Deep vs. shallow rooted
- Tolerance of poor drainage
- Shade tolerant vs. intolerant
- Pollination requirements

Field Characteristics

These relatively permanent characteristics of a field are difficult to change; many affect the type of equipment that can be used and the timing of operations.

- Recent planting history (1–5 years)
- Within-field variability
- Proximity to water source
- Erosion potential
- Drainage
- Sunny or shady
- Known problems with
  ▷ weeds
  ▷ insects
  ▷ poor tilth or hardpan
  ▷ wildlife
- Slope
- Moisture-holding capacity
- pH
- Natural Resources Conservation Service (NRCS) soil type
- Aspect (north, south, east, west)
- Air drainage—frost pockets
- Size
- Cation-exchange capacity
- Proximity to barn or access roads
- Stoniness
- Shape (corners, row lengths)
- Proximity to similar fields

Responsibility D: Analyze Data

All of the decisions and information generated through previous tasks and responsibilities are pulled together for analysis at this key phase of the planning process. The data on market options, equipment, labor and seed availability, and financial constraints, along with the overall farm and rotation goals are reviewed. Information is cross-referenced and, when necessary, weighted. Possible trade-offs are considered. For example, the field crew may be able to plant two fields to high-value crops but not also harvest an early crop the same week. Crop cultural needs are compared to each field's characteristics and conditions. The experts assess soil conditions and determine how pest (animal, insect, weed) and disease pressures from the previous season should be addressed. This is among the most difficult tasks. Even weather projections are considered. Every possible crop mix is analyzed. Various possible pairings of crop to field are outlined, and options for each field are compared.

Responsibility E: Plan Crop Rotation

This responsibility is the ultimate synthesis of information and results in a production plan and a rotation plan. Expert farmers distinguish between these two types of plans. The production plan specifies what needs to be grown (the crop mix) and how it will be grown, whereas the rotation plan determines where each crop will be planted. Final decisions about the crop mix and the allocation of crops to fields and fields to crops are pivotal to this responsibility. Information such as what crops to grow, in what quantities, labor availability at various times in the season, required equipment, and desired harvest dates are integrated into the rotation plan for each field and for the entire farm.

Two questions bounce back and forth. One is what will be grown in each field? The other is where will each crop grow? These questions are answered based on observation and experience. Several steps are involved. First, the cropping history of each field or bed for the past three or more years is reviewed. This includes what crops and crop families were grown; how well they performed; any particular successes or failures; and any logistical issues relating to equipment use, irrigation, harvesting, or labor. Obviously, the size of the field and market needs (how much of each crop is required) are also considered. The allocation of crops to fields includes consideration of future cropping plans as well as the cropping history of a field. The rotation plan must be responsive to weed pressures or

other legacies from earlier years and must provide future crops with favorable conditions.

Expert farmers first assign their highest-priority crops to fields (or beds). High-priority crops include the most profitable crops, cover crops with the greatest benefits, and crops particularly vulnerable to pests, diseases, or weather. Decisions are also based on high-priority fields—for example, those that have the highest fertility, are prime locations for u-pick crops, or have current problems that need to be addressed. Remaining fields (or parts of fields) are then assigned to the remaining crops, cover crops, fallow areas, and sometimes pasturage for livestock. All these decisions are based on both business and biology. An example is provided in sidebar 2.10.

The crops and fields are tentatively matched, creating a cropping plan for the entire farm for the year. Many experts plot this information on farm maps and notebooks. They take this initial plan and, in the words of one, "Farm it in my head." That is, they work through the sequence of field operations from tillage to harvest over the entire season for each crop and field. Several expert farmers take their plans into the field and walk the farm for this task. They think through why any sequence might not work, reviewing any possible logistical or biological conflicts like

---

SIDEBAR 2.10
GROUPING CROPS BY THEIR NEED FOR ACCESSIBILITY

The logistics of harvesting affect rotations. For example, crops with frequent harvests or need for frequent care must be easily accessible. Expert farmer Jean-Paul Courtens considers road access and produce characteristics. He prefers to allocate some crops to fields with close proximity to packing sheds. Long rides on bumpy roads can bruise delicate produce like tomatoes. He locates salad greens and braising greens in the same field due to the time of day they are harvested. Crops are also grouped based on the time of the season when they are harvested.

timing of operations or spread of pests between adjacent crops. They then adjust the plan as necessary.

Responsibility F: Execute Rotation

Farmers indicated that executing the rotation involves many of the most important and difficult tasks (see sidebar 2.7, page 11). They identified maintaining crops (including activities such as weeding, thinning, and irrigation) as the most important task and the second most difficult task in crop rotation. Scheduling tillage and planting for all the fields across an entire farm every season is also a challenge for most farmers. Although they generally want to till the soil as early as possible to accelerate soil warming and residue breakdown, they must wait for workable soil moisture conditions. Other critical steps in crop production and central to executing the crop rotation are soil preparation and planting. Delays in soil preparation or planting may cause crop failures due to poor emergence, runaway weeds, or inadequately broken down cover crops and require shifts in the crop rotation (see sidebar 2.11).

Expert farmers attempt to plant priority fields or beds and their most important crops as scheduled in their plan. If they have to alter the plan, they still prioritize high-value or sensitive crops and fields. Many decisions and adjustments have to be made on the fly.

In early spring, farmers monitor the weather—sometimes hourly—as they implement and alter their rotation plan. Problems related to weather, cover crop maturity, crop emergence, and weeds may cause farmers to alter their original plan. Soil moisture conditions affect the timing of tillage and subsequent field operations (see sidebar 2.12, page 18). Cover crops are monitored to determine maturity, thickness of stands, and optimal time for incorporation. Farmers also monitor the breakdown and incorporation of crop and cover crop residues. Soil and air temperatures influence planting and transplanting decisions, as well. Any of these factors can cause crops to be reassigned to different fields or beds.

While a change necessitated by weather or the conditions in one field can cause reassignment of crops around the farm, general and farm-specific rotation goals and guidelines remain the basis of every decision; for example, cucurbit crops will never be planted in the same field two years in a row. Most expert farmers anticipate problems that might occur and have contingency plans ready (see sidebar 2.13, page 19). Expert farmer Paul Arnold suggested that this ability to make effective on-the-fly adjustments

---

SIDEBAR 2.11
CONSIDERING OPTIONS

After harvesting late snap beans, wet weather prevented expert farmer Roy Brubaker from fall-seeding a rye cover crop in a particular field. One option for the field might have been to plant oats and field peas in early spring, which would have had to be plowed down prior to planting fall brassicas. Another option would have been to plant the field to a spring crop of brassicas and then put in buckwheat or an early rye cover crop. Either decision had repercussions for the rotations on other fields because the farm's CSA needed both spring and fall brassicas.

Nonuniform cover crop growth does not change Brett Grohsgal's overall rotation, but it can change his crop mix or the selected varieties on a particular field. He may subdivide the field and plant heavy feeders where the legume cover crop was most successful. For example, beefsteak tomatoes, which are heavy feeders, would get that part of the tomato acreage that had good cover crop growth; whereas thrifty cherry tomatoes would get the remainder. Alternatively, he might plant heavy-feeding and high-value watermelons on the most fertile, weed-free areas, whereas lower-value and resilient winter squash would be assigned to the less fertile areas.

At both farms, all the options are considered before finalizing a decision.

---

is an important factor in the success of his farm. In the event of crop failure, crops may be abandoned, replanted, or replaced with a cover crop or even a different cash crop. Drew Norman, another expert farmer, described this process as finding "a profitable punt."

As the season progresses, short-season crops like salad greens are harvested, subsequent crops are planted, and cover crops are seeded or plowed under. Even as the rotation plan is implemented, the process of crop-to-field allocation and prioritization continues. The expert farmers emphasize the importance of recording actual cropping as it happens (particularly deviations from the plan) for later comparison with their initial rotation plan for the year.

Responsibility G: Evaluate Rotation Execution

Throughout the season, expert growers monitor the performance of their fields, each crop, and the farm as a whole. They record how their plans have worked and evolved. This is not just to solve problems in the current season, but also to observe, learn, and collect ideas and data for future seasons. Expert farmers do this directly and through communicating with their crews. Several said they interview their field crews at the end of the season. Workers often have suggestions, such as improving the farm layout, that enhance the efficiency of operations.

At the end of the season, growers carefully assess what actually happened relative to what they expected based on the original rotation plan. The factors they consider include yields; soil conditions; timing of events and operations; costs of crop production; disease, weed, and pest levels and their control; crop losses; labor satisfaction and efficiency; and profitability of each crop and of the whole farm. By walking around the farm and by analyzing data at their desk, they review the success of the production year. They compare the results with those of previous years to detect any trends or patterns. When attempting to analyze the causes of success or failure of various elements of the rotation, growers talk to other growers and extension agents to determine whether problems were the result of actions on their farm rather than, for example, a bad disease year for all farms in the region, regardless of rotation. Assessing whether regional conditions or on-farm mistakes were the source of problems is among the most difficult tasks, even for experts.

Rotation goals and rotation plans serve as benchmarks to measure the success of the cropping season and the rotation. Expert farmers consider how closely they followed biological principles in their rotation, whether they met their production and market objectives, and how their rotation execution supported their biological and business goals. Successes and failures are assessed, analyzed, and evaluated. The results are recorded to assist in planning and management for future seasons. Farmers note that assessing the profitability of crops, especially on a field-by-field basis, is another difficult task.

SIDEBAR 2.12

FIELD AND CROP CONDITIONS THAT EXPERT FARMERS MONITOR

Fields and crops need continual monitoring during the season. Biological and physical conditions can change relatively quickly due to management, weather, and mistakes. Experts often have contingency plans in mind to accommodate such situations, especially for their priority fields and key crops. In-season observations also inform experts' decisions for the next year's rotation. Although most farmers do not measure all these parameters directly, they are aware of, observe, and monitor conditions in their own ways. Conditions they monitor regularly include:

Pests
- Weed pressure
- Insect emergence and pressure
- Diseases

Cover crop performance
- Success of previous cover crops (e.g., production of organic matter, weed suppression)
- Ground cover
- Cover crop nodulation and nitrogen fixation

Soil fertility
- Soil test results
- Chemical balance (N, P, K, Ca, Mg, and micronutrients)

- Nutrient cycles
- "Biological health" and vitality— earthworms, etc.
- Soil organic matter

Soil tilth
- Crop residues and residue breakdown
- Composted organic matter or "humus" in the soil
- Soil aggregation
- Soil moisture
- Soil and air temperature
- Soil compaction and porosity

CONTINGENCY PLANNING

Expert farmers have enough experience to know that their best plans can sometimes be derailed. Knowing how to adapt or when to start over with a particular field or crop is essential to the success of the farm business. Expert farmers have developed many techniques to help them adapt to changing circumstances that typically influence their rotations.

- **Delayed planting due to wet fields**

A common reason to diverge from the rotation plan is wet fields in spring. This can delay the plow-down of cover crops and, consequently, of residue decomposition, field preparation, and transplanting. Many expert farmers switch key crops to other fields when this happens, causing a cascading (somewhat preplanned) shift in the allocation of many crops.

The growth of transplants in greenhouses is monitored to determine whether transplants are on schedule for planting out, relative to soil and weather conditions. Greenhouse environments are managed to speed or slow growth so that transplants are at the right developmental stage when field conditions are right for transplanting. Transplants will also be "hardened off" to prepare them for the shock of the particular season's outside environment.

- **Poor germination**

David Blyn replants crop failures with fast-growing, short-season crops like radishes. He stocks extra seed for crops like sweet corn and carrots that can be planted on multiple occasions and replants when necessary. He often finds that the reason for failed germination was a poor seedbed, and on the second try the seedbed is usually better.

Blyn also uses cover crops to "paint in" gaps caused by failed crops or early harvests.

- **Weed challenges**

Brett Grohsgal responds to heavy weed pressure by sowing cover crops at higher rates.

Crops with bad weed problems are often plowed down and planted to cover crops. Eero Ruuttila uses a cover crop of oats and field peas for this purpose, which also produces a marketable crop of pea shoots.

Growers sometimes have to decide whether a cover crop stand that has a lot of weeds is worth keeping for the fertility benefits or should be plowed under early. They weigh the potential benefits and investment in the cover crop against potential increases in the weed seed bank.

One expert farmer uses intensively cultivated crops to control bad weed infestations. For example, infestations of bindweed and Canada thistle are followed by a triple crop of lettuce, which is high value enough to justify the costs of frequent cultivation. This is followed by a weed-suppressing cover crop of rye.

- **Weather problems**

Drought can affect the germination of direct-seeded crops and shallow-rooted crops like garlic. Contingency strategies include mulching instead of cultivation for weed control, and substituting larger-seeded or transplanted crops.

In the event of drought and limited water for irrigation, Don Kretschmann irrigates only the portion of the crop destined for retail markets, allowing the wholesale portion of his crops to perish.

When an oat and pea cover crop does not winterkill, it delays planting of strawberries because of the time needed for the cover crop to break down. In that situation, Roy Brubaker plants the strawberries close together so their runners will fill in the rows more quickly for good weed control.

- **Severe pest and fertility problems**

Brett Grohsgal occasionally finds that a whole field needs to be temporarily removed from production to rebuild fertility or manage weed infestations. He chooses sequences of cover crops based on ability to add organic matter, fix nitrogen, survive drought, and compete with weeds. He often pastures livestock on these fields to disrupt weeds and add fertility.

Responsibility H: Adjust Rotation Plan

As the cropping season closes in late fall, expert farmers begin the final phase of the annual rotation cycle in which they modify their rotations and plan for the coming year. This occurs concurrently with the evaluation of the past season. They revisit the tasks associated with "Identify rotation goals" (Responsibility A). They then focus on the productivity and problems of each field and of the overall farm. They first consider altering the crop mix by adding or removing crops or changing the area planted to a crop. Such decisions are affected by the market, as well as by field and crop performance and rotation imperatives. For example, Paul and Sandy Arnold found that high-quality, disease-free beets were very important for sales at farmers' markets, so they decided to open up new acreage to break up the life cycle of soilborne beet diseases. This resulted in adjustment of their entire rotation so that their fields spend a longer time in cover crops.

Growers may also decide to change their field management by changing the order or dates of planting or plow-down of cover crops. They may decide to shift crops to alternative fields, try new crop sequences, or improve fertility of a field by planting it into a cover crop or hay ahead of schedule. They record notes for the next year's rotation plan, new guidelines for contingencies, and results of experiments. The next year's plan begins to take shape.

Adjusting the rotation plan presents three particularly challenging tasks: (1) developing collaborations to solve problems, (2) investigating markets, and (3) tweaking the crop mix. Tweaking the crop mix requires balancing market opportunities with biological needs. Growers indicated that this is a core task in managing crop rotations.

Expert growers stress the importance of experimentation, play, and a sense of adventure in managing their rotations. The art of adjusting every aspect of the rotation was discussed as the core of successfully managing rotations. While the NEON chart makes rotation planning seem linear and quantifiable, all of our farmer panelists felt that managing rotations is a continuous, integrated, intuitive, and cyclical process developed through intensive information gathering and extensive experience. They glean and incorporate new ideas into their rotations, which continue to evolve. These expert growers agreed on the importance of making new and interesting mistakes each season.

3

PHYSICAL AND BIOLOGICAL PROCESSES IN CROP ROTATION

What This Chapter Is About

Charles L. Mohler

This chapter is about the ways biologists and soil scientists view crop rotation (see inset). Unlike the farmer experts of the previous chapter, who approach rotation as a holistic process, the scientists are specialists who delve deeply into particular aspects of organic production. They study in detail how crop rotation affects a particular aspect of the farm system. Through extensive reading and discussion with others, expert farmers come to understand and practice most of the principles presented here. Understanding the concepts presented in this chapter can help resolve newly encountered problems and aid development of a rotation plan.

Researchers have studied crop rotation since the beginnings of agricultural science, in the early nineteenth century. More recently, scientists have taken a renewed interest in crop rotation due to increasing problems associated with continuous cropping of single species. In the past ten years, researchers have begun to look at crop rotation on organic farms (125). Studying multiyear crop sequences, however, requires extraordinary patience and a source of funding that lasts longer than typical government grants. Consequently, most studies have compared a two- or three-year rotation with continuous cropping. Since the organic farming community is already aware of the problems of continuous cropping, such studies often provide few data with any relevance to organic farmers. Nevertheless, some relevant studies do exist, and much can be inferred from work that did not explicitly compare different crop rotations.

The biological and physical benefits of crop rotation fall into two general, interrelated categories: improvement

All of the researchers who contributed to this chapter are knowledgeable about the organic production process and actively work to support organic agriculture. To ensure accuracy, other researchers in their respective fields who support organic agriculture reviewed their comments. To ensure relevance and a writing style that speaks to farmers rather than other researchers, organic farmers also reviewed the researchers' comments.

of soil quality and management of pests. Certain broad patterns appear in each of these.

Soil quality tends to improve with the percentage of time the land is in grass and legume sod and cover crops (figure 3.1, page 22). Legumes used as green manures supply nitrogen for succeeding crops. Many legumes also have deep taproots that loosen the subsoil and recycle leached nutrients back into the plowed horizon. Grasses produce dense systems of fine roots that secrete substances that foster aggregation of the soil into stable crumbs. Moreover, their roots decay slowly through various forms of soil organic matter that further tend to stabilize soil aggregates and supply a slow release of nutrients for crop growth. Conversely, row crops tend to have opposite effects on soil, due to (1) the relatively low average density of roots per square foot and (2) the presence of bare soil between the rows that is exposed to the impact of traffic and raindrops. Many factors can modify these contrasting trends, including the type and frequency of tillage and the degree to which the farmer uses soil amendments like compost, organic mulches, and rock powders. Nevertheless, the contrast between grass and legume sod and cover crops versus row crops makes a good starting point for understanding the relationship between crop rotation and soil quality.

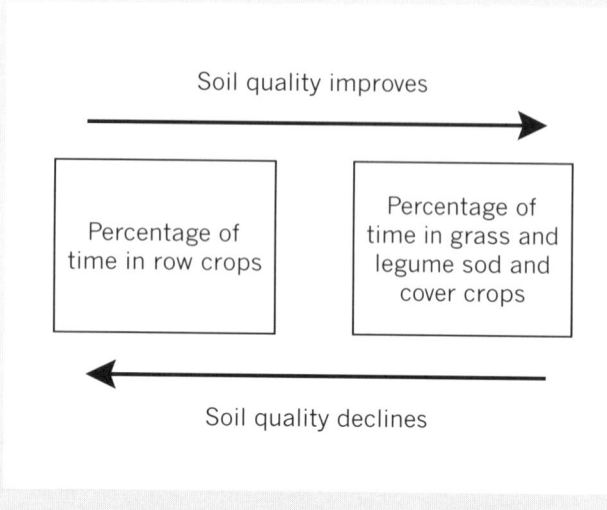

FIGURE 3.1 Relation of soil quality to the types of crops that predominate in the rotation.

Although crop rotation is a key component in the management of diseases, weeds, and many types of animal pests, it is not a panacea. Many pest problems cannot be managed by crop rotation alone, and some problems cannot be addressed by crop rotation at all. A key factor that governs the ability of crop rotation to manage pests is the host specificity of the pest (figure 3.2). Host-specific pests specialize on a particular species or family of crops, whereas generalist pests damage a wide range of crops. Additional key factors are the mobility of the pest and the persistence of dormant pest life stages (eggs, seeds, spores). Highly generalist pests can persist in the field through a variety of crops, and a grower must use management techniques in addition to rotation to keep them from reducing crop quality and productivity. Highly mobile pests can disperse into a field and cause problems even if the preceding crops have provided unsuitable habitats that caused the pest to die out. Other pests, particularly weeds and some fungi, have seeds or

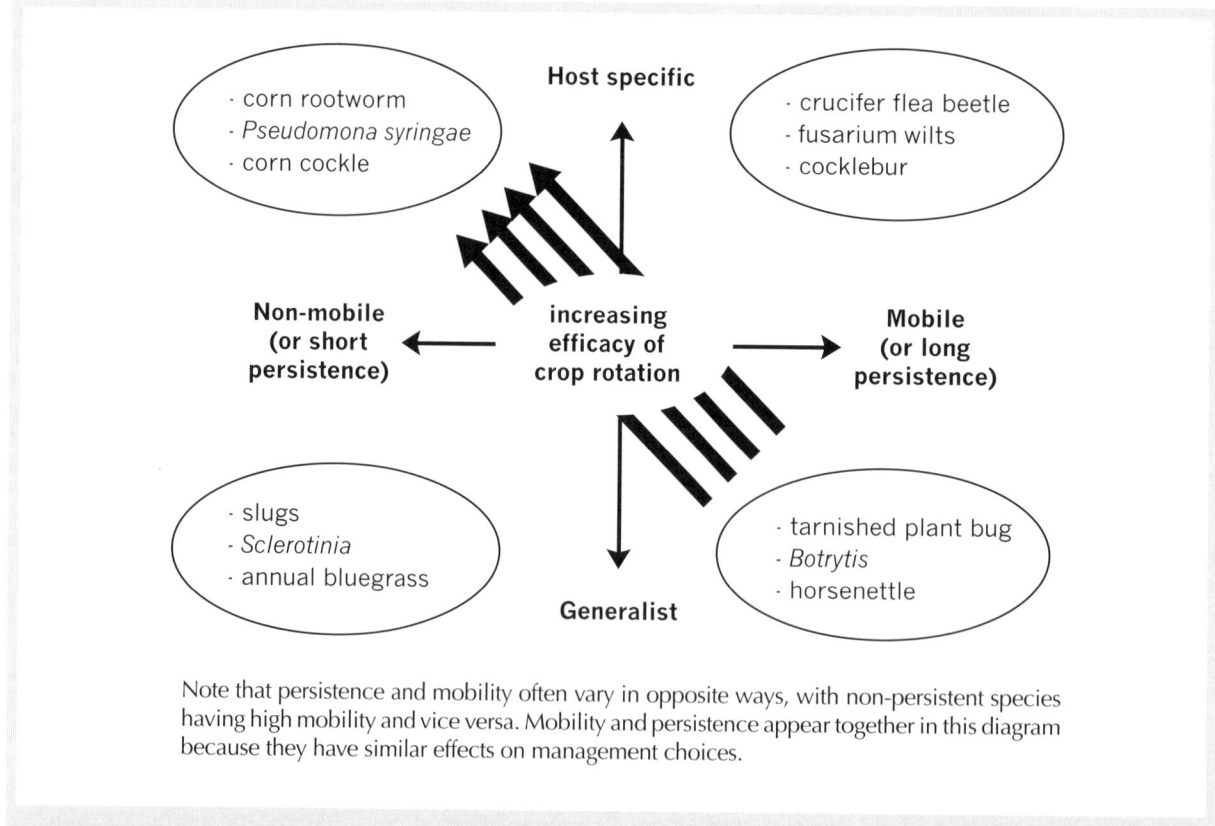

Note that persistence and mobility often vary in opposite ways, with non-persistent species having high mobility and vice versa. Mobility and persistence appear together in this diagram because they have similar effects on management choices.

Figure 3.2 The effect of host specificity, dispersal ability, and survival of dormant states (eggs, spores, seeds) on how well crop rotation controls pest organisms. Generalist pests are pest organisms that attack crops in diverse plant families or, in the case of weeds, thrive in a wide range of cropping systems. *Source*: Modified from reference 125.

spores that can remain dormant in the soil for many years. Such species are less likely to be eliminated by a short period without a suitable host crop (or for weeds, suitable cropping conditions) than are species that do not persist well in the soil. At the other extreme, nonpersistent, poorly dispersing pests that are dependent on a narrow range of crops are relatively easy to control through rotation to other types of crops. Other sections in this chapter discuss many examples of pests that are and are not effectively managed by crop rotation.

Soil management and pest management interact in many ways. For example, crop nutrition affects plant disease resistance, some cover crops can reduce certain types of soilborne diseases but promote others, and high soil physical quality improves the effectiveness of mechanical weed management. All of these interactions, and many others, are influenced by crop rotation. Some notable interactions between soil and pest management that can be managed by crop rotation are addressed in the following sections.

Crop Rotation and Soil Tilth
Harold van Es

Tilth generally refers to the physical condition of the soil as it relates to plant growth. Favorable tilth implies good conditions for seed germination and root proliferation, allowing crops to thrive. Also, a soil with good tilth facilitates other processes, such as water infiltration and aeration, which benefit both crop and environment. Good soil tilth is usually equated with *aggregation* (presence of soil crumbs), because stable aggregates promote these favorable processes. Crop rotations can have a positive impact on soil tilth, depending on the crops that are being alternated. Additional ways to improve soil tilth include reducing tillage and using cover crops. There are thus a number of approaches to improving the physical quality of the soil, and often a combined approach produces the greatest improvement.

Soil Tilth and Aggregation

Figure 3.3 shows a soil aggregate, or crumb, found in a soil of good tilth. With finer-textured soils, such aggregates may in turn be made up of smaller ones that are clumped together. The aggregates themselves are perhaps

less important than the spaces (or pores) between them, and a soil that is well aggregated also has a range of pore sizes. Each pore size plays a critical role in the physical functioning of the soil. Large pores drain rapidly and are needed for good air exchange during wet periods. This prevents oxygen deficiency in the soil, which stresses most crop types, sometimes to the point of death. Oxygen deficiency also increases pest problems. Denitrification (conversion of nitrogen to gaseous forms) is another concern with oxygen-deficient waterlogged soil. Denitrification results in rapid and significant loss of soil nitrogen and generates nitrous oxide, a potent greenhouse gas. When soil becomes degraded, either through long-term intensive cultivation and erosion or through compaction from traffic, it loses its aggregation, and the large pores are compressed into small ones. Coarse-textured sands and gravels naturally have large pores, and therefore are less dependent on aggregation to provide good tilth and aeration. Finer-textured soils, however, depend heavily on aggregates for good physical structure and tilth and, once degraded, become structureless, dense, and hard.

A mix of large and small pores is desirable. Small pores are critical for water retention and help a crop go through dry periods with minimal yield loss. Sandy and gravelly

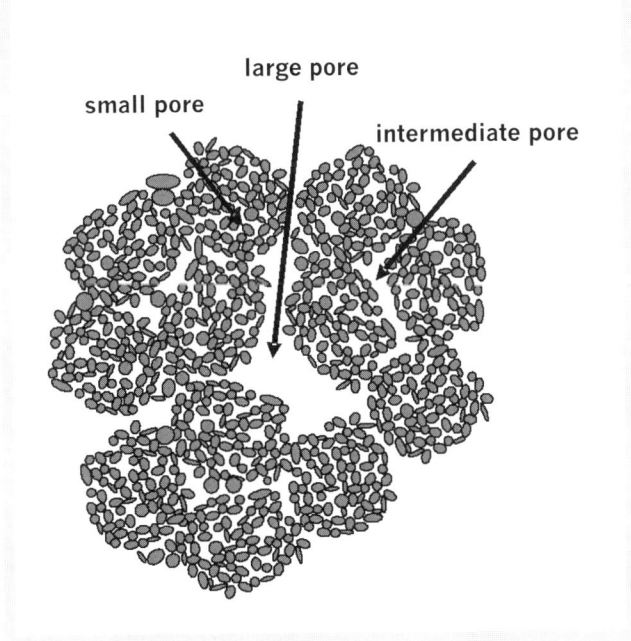

Figure 3.3 A soil aggregate or "crumb" with good tilth. *Source*: From reference 68. Used with permission.

soils are naturally deficient in small pores and are therefore drought prone, whereas loams and clays can retain and thus supply crops with more water.

Good soil management and rotations can increase crop water availability if they increase the soil's organic matter content, which is an important contributor to water retention. Coarse-textured soils can thus also benefit from good management, even though they are less dependent on aggregation.

Good soil tilth can be obtained through mechanical and biological manipulation of the soil. Mechanical soil cultivation practices, including primary tillage (moldboard or chisel plowing) followed by secondary tillage (disking, harrowing, etc.), have the aim of producing a good seedbed. When soils become degraded and compacted, such tillage practices are often deemed necessary to establish a good crop, because the soil would otherwise be too dense, hard, or cloddy. The tilth created by tillage, however, tends to be *unstable*, because the aggregation is obtained through the physical manipulation of the soil, which is short lived, especially after many years of intensive tillage. Aggregates in such soils will readily fall apart during subsequent rains, causing the soil to settle and become dense and hard. This then generates a vicious cycle in which the soil needs to be intensively tilled each year to provide good seedbed conditions, which in turn makes the problem worse. Such a soil may be considered "addicted to tillage."

The preferred scenario is for the aggregates and good tilth to be the result of natural soil building processes, such as the activity of plant roots, earthworms, and other beneficial organisms. Such *stable* aggregates will break apart during tillage or planting and therefore readily provide good tilth, as opposed to unstable, weakly aggregated soil, which tills up cloddy. Also, stable aggregates are held together by organic bonding materials that resist breakdown during soil saturation and heavy rainfall. These organic materials are themselves subject to bio-logical degradation, so there needs to be a continual effort to "feed the soil" with organic material, and to minimize organic matter breakdown from intensive tillage.

Aggregation in the Subsoil

People tend to focus on soil tilth in the plow layer, but good aggregation is also important in the subsoil, the layer below the regular depth of tillage. Such aggregates are generally not crumb-like but involve larger (2- to 6-inch) blocks of soil that are more angular and not as distinctive. These aggregates are less impacted by biological activity of microbes, earthworms, and roots than the crumbs in the surface layer. Subsurface aggregates are important for root growth deep into the profile. Deep roots allow a plant greater access to soil moisture, which helps it through drought periods. Aggregates below the surface layer can also be compacted. The main cause for this is heavy equipment loads on wet soil (figure 3.4), where the force of compaction is transferred deep into the soil, beyond the plow layer. Another significant source of subsoil compaction is the practice of plowing with a set of wheels in the open furrow. This way the subsoil is directly loaded by the tractor tires.

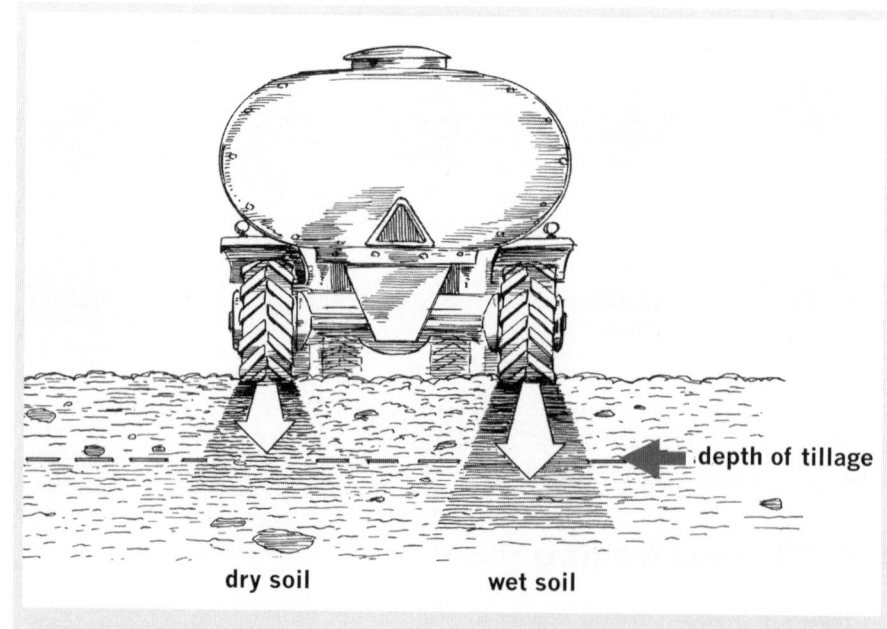

FIGURE 3.4 Compactive forces are transferred deeper in wet soils than in dry soils. *Source:* From reference 68. Used with permission.

Soil Hardness

Soils generally become harder when they dry. There is a difference, however, between well-aggregated and compacted soil, in that the latter becomes hard more readily upon drying (figure 3.5). This causes problems with crop emergence, root restriction, and reduced plant growth. A scenario that is often observed is the hardsetting of poorly aggregated (low organic matter) soil when tillage is followed by large amounts of rainfall. The aggregates forming the loose tilth after tillage are not stable and fall apart when the soil becomes saturated. The soil then settles and becomes hard. If the aggregates are stable as a result of good management and adequate organic matter, they will hold up against the rain, and good tilth will be preserved.

Similarly, compacted subsoils become hard and impenetrable to roots when they dry. Rotation with cover crops that grow aggressively in the early and late growing season are thus better able to penetrate plow pans and hard subsoil, because the soil is then moist and sufficiently soft for root penetration. In contrast, a summer annual, like corn, does not see significant root growth until the late spring, when compacted soils may already have become dry and hard.

Effects of Rotation Crops

Rotation crops can help build soils, as illustrated in figure 3.6 (page 26). Studies have shown that organic matter losses from intensively tilled row crops can be regained when the field is rotated into a perennial sod crop. There are two processes that contribute to this gain. First, the rapid rate of organic matter decomposition from tillage is stopped under the sod crop. This benefit, of course, is also gained when a no-tillage cropping system is employed. Second, grass and legume sods develop extensive root systems that continually grow and die off. The dead roots supply a source of fresh, active organic matter to the soil, which feeds soil organisms that are involved in building soil aggregation. Earthworms and many other beneficial organisms need continual supplies of organic matter to sustain themselves, and they deposit the digested materials on soil aggregates and

> *"Rotation with cover crops that grow aggressively in the early and late growing season are... able to penetrate plow pans and hard subsoil, because the soil is then moist and sufficiently soft for root penetration. "*

thereby stabilize them. Also, the living roots and symbiotic microorganisms (for example, mycorrhizal fungi) can exude organic materials that nourish soil organisms and help with aggregation. Grass and legume sod crops therefore return more organic matter to the soil than most other crops.

Sod crops appear to be the most effective in building good soil tilth in the surface layer. The dense, fibrous, rooting system of perennial grasses and shallow-rooted legumes creates a very active biological zone near the surface. If a short rotation is used, and tillage is minimized,

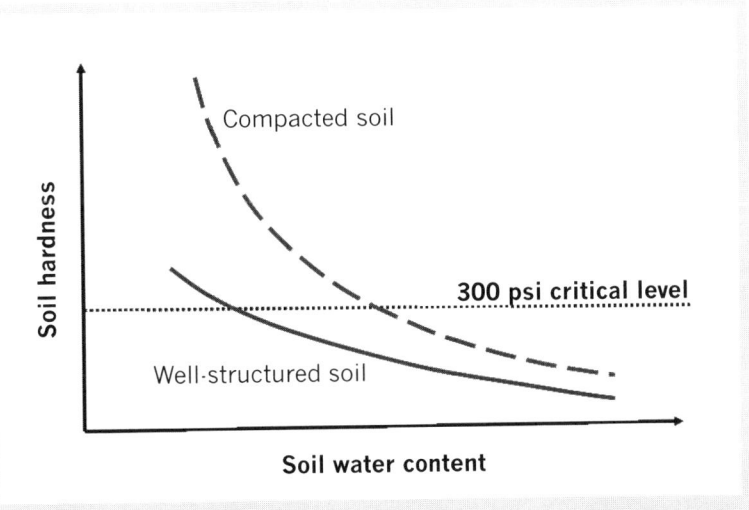

FIGURE 3.5 The effect of soil water content on soil hardness of a well-structured and a compacted soil. Compacted soils harden more rapidly than well-structured soils when drying. Hardness above 300 psi restricts root growth.

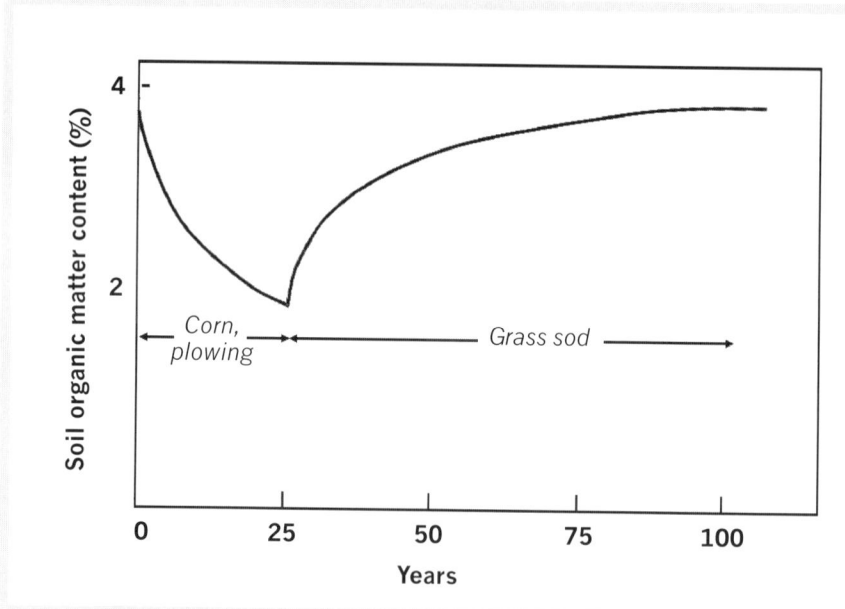

FIGURE 3.6 Loss and gain of soil organic matter under tilled corn followed by grass sod. *Source*: From reference 68. Used with permission.

72 percent (14). This provides longer periods of soil cover, thereby reducing erosion potential and loss of good topsoil. Also, it provides longer periods in which active roots feed the soil. Some crops such as rye, wheat, oat, barley, pea, and cool-season grasses grow actively in the late fall and early spring and thereby can help build stable soil tilth. They are beneficial both as rotation and cover crops, but the positive effects may be negated if intensive tillage is used to establish them.

In summary, rotations provide opportunities for improving soil physical quality, especially if the active growth period is expanded and the amount of tillage in the rotation is reduced. With careful selection, rotation crops can be targeted to help alleviate certain soil quality problems. A densely rooted sod crop helps build tilth in the plow layer, while a deep-rooted crop helps address problems with subsoil compaction. In many cases, the rotation should include a mixture of crop types to increase the diversity of organic matter that supports soil-building organisms, and to address multiple soil quality objectives.

A grower should consider a field assessment to identify problems and better tailor the rotation to the needs of the soil. This may include an assessment of soil tilth in the surface layer, rooting depth, and soil hardness in the subsoil. A soil penetrometer is a useful tool for this, but digging with a shovel is perhaps the most instructive. The Cornell Soil Health Test has recently been developed to provide an integrated assessment of soil quality through chemical, biological, and physical indicators. This includes aggregate stability, an indicator of soil tilth. For further information on the test and management practices that promote soil health, visit HTTP://SOILHEALTH.CALS. CORNELL.EDU.

For further reading, see references 14, 68, and 107.

the benefits of the sod crop are enhanced. Hay or pasture fields can be established with minimal tillage if a good no-till drill is used and weed pressure is low. Some annual rotation crops such as buckwheat also have dense, fibrous, root systems and can improve soil tilth. Sometimes, compatible mixtures of crops are beneficial because they have different rooting systems. For example, red clover seeded into winter wheat provides additional roots and a more protein-rich source of organic matter.

Other rotation crops are less effective in building tilth in the surface layer but are more valuable for improving dense subsoils. Some perennial crops, such as alfalfa, have strong, deep, penetrating tap roots that can push through hard layers, especially during wet periods when the soil is soft. These deep roots make pathways for water and future plant roots, and bring organic matter into the subsoil.

Crops can be beneficial in a rotation if they extend the period of active growth compared to conventional row crops. For example, in a corn-soybean rotation, active growth occurs only 32 percent of the time, while in a dry bean–winter wheat–corn rotation, this period is

Crop Rotation Effects on Soil Fertility and Plant Nutrition

ANUSUYA RANGARAJAN

Soil organic matter and clay particles hold large stores of plant nutrients. These reservoirs, however, are not all available to the crop. In an organic crop rotation, the grower manages soil organic matter and nutrient availability by incorporating different crop residues, cycling among crops with different nutrient needs, using cover crops, and adding organic soil amendments. Most crops deplete soil nutrients during their growth cycle. Some of these nutrients leave the farm as harvested products, and the rest return to the soil as crop residues. The nutrients in residues may or may not be available to the next crop. Crop roots and residues improve soil fertility by stimulating soil microbial communities and improving soil aggregation. This improved soil physical environment facilitates water infiltration, water holding, aeration, and, ultimately, root growth and plant nutrient foraging. This section will review different ways that crop rotations affect soil fertility.

Understanding the basics of how nutrients are added to and released from soil organic matter will help the farmer in choosing crop sequences and amendments to optimize organic crop fertility. Certain fractions of soil organic matter contribute to plant nutrition more than other fractions. To effectively plan organic crop rotations to meet crop nutrient needs, several factors should be considered. Legume crops, which capture atmospheric nitrogen and "fix" it into forms available to plants, can be used strategically in rotations to meet the needs of nitrogen-demanding crops. Cover crops used after a cash crop capture surplus plant-available nutrients and conserve these for following crops. Cash crops themselves vary in their nutrient demands (see appendix 1, pages 101–103); considering their needs helps make the most efficient use of the available soil nutrients in a rotation. Finally, other types of organic amendments, such as compost and manures or approved mineral fertilizers, can supplement nutrients at targeted times during a rotation. Each of these topics is discussed in the sections below.

The Basics: How Nutrients Are Released from Soil Organic Matter

Levels of soil organic matter range from about 0.4 percent to 10 percent in mineral soils in temperate regions. While organic matter is a relatively small fraction of the soil, it has large effects on soil structure and soil fertility. Soil organic matter contains an estimated 95 percent of soil nitrogen (N) and 40 percent of soil phosphorus (P), and with the right levels and conditions it may provide all of the N and P needs of a crop. Estimates of total nitrogen in a soil with 3 percent organic matter range from 2,000 to 4,000 pounds per acre; estimates of phosphorus range from 100 to 300 pounds per acre. Soil microorganisms release these nutrients when they consume organic matter and subsequently die. The rate of this nutrient release is affected by the availability of carbon sources (energy for the soil microbes), soil temperature, soil moisture, tillage, types and numbers of soil organisms, and quality of the soil organic matter.

A portion (10–20 percent) of the total soil organic matter has been termed the "active" fraction and is most easily decomposed by soil organisms. This active fraction is replenished primarily by additions of organic matter (cover crops, crop residues, manures, compost). Soil organisms, which make up another 10–20 percent of soil organic matter, decompose this active organic matter. Upon death, these organisms release their nutrients to plants. The remaining soil organic matter is humus. The humus is more slowly digested by soil organisms and

> "Understanding the basics of how nutrients are added to and released from soil organic matter will help the farmer in choosing crop sequences and amendments to optimize organic crop fertility."

therefore is not a large source of available nutrients. Humus is very important, however, because it provides cation exchange sites, which hold nutrients in the soil and thus maintain their availability to plants.

Organic matter amendments to soil decompose at different rates, and this affects how quickly nutrients become available to crops. Several factors affect the rate of decomposition of organic amendments, including the carbon-to-nitrogen ratio of the amendment, soil type, temperature and moisture conditions, and the crop being grown. Green manures, which are part of the more active organic matter fraction, decompose readily, liberating nutrients relatively quickly. Composts have more stable, humic organic matter, and decompose more slowly. As a result, most composts release nutrients to crops more slowly than green manures.

Organic matter decomposition is enhanced in the area immediately around roots (the rhizosphere). Roots release organic compounds, such as carbohydrates, amino acids, and vitamins, into the soil, stimulating growth of microorganisms in this zone. Many of these organisms decompose organic matter, resulting in nutrient release to the crop. Very little research has been done to determine which plant varieties or species best support these nutrient-releasing microorganisms. In the future, such information may help identify crop varieties well adapted to organic systems.

When cover crops are regularly part of a rotation, their residues increase soil organic matter. The organic matter feeds the growth of microbes, which increases the release of N as they die and decompose. Thus, integrating cover crops into a crop rotation at specific points can help enhance nutrient cycling and conservation.

Nitrogen Contributions from Legume Cover and Cash Crops

Legumes may be present in a rotation as a harvested crop (for example, alfalfa) or as a green manure (for example, vetch or clover). Legumes are of special interest in organic crop rotations because of their ability to add nitrogen to the system. Specialized bacteria (*Rhizobium* spp.) associated with the roots of legumes convert atmospheric nitrogen (N_2 gas) into plant-available nitrogen. The amount of N fixed by this association between bacteria and legumes varies with plant species and variety, soil type, climate, crop management, and length of time the crop is grown. When used strategically in a rotation,

legumes provide N to the subsequent crop. The amount of N that a legume crop contributes to following crops depends on the amount of N fixed, the maturity of the legume when it is killed or incorporated into the soil, whether the entire plant or only the root system remains in the field, and the environmental conditions that govern the rate of decomposition. As a result, estimates of the amount of N contributions by legumes to subsequent crops range from 50 to over 200 pounds per acre (see appendix 1, pages 101–103).

Nitrogen Scavenging and Conservation by Nonlegume Winter Cover Crops

Winter-hardy grains and grasses have extensive root systems that are more efficient than legumes at scavenging soil nitrates in the fall, thereby reducing late fall and winter leaching of nitrogen (75). In the northeastern US, small grains (rye and wheat) are the most common winter-hardy cover crops used by vegetable growers, since harvests of cash crops often extend into late summer and fall. Once incorporated in the following spring, these cover crops will release captured N and other nutrients to subsequent crops, but at a slower rate than from legume cover crops because of the slower decomposition of grain residues.

In some cases, such as when heavy crop or cover crop residues with high carbon-to-nitrogen ratios (30:1 or higher) are tilled into the soil, soil N may become unavailable to plants (immobilized) in the short run because it is taken up by soil microorganisms as they feed on the carbon-rich residues. Seeding a legume cover crop with small grains (for example, hairy vetch with cereal rye) can reduce N immobilization by providing additional N to microorganisms during decomposition of residues. Alternatively, delaying the planting of a cash crop for about two weeks after incorporation of residues generally allows sufficient time for the cycling of N through microorganisms and then back into the soil. Incorporating nonlegume cover crops while they are still young and leafy also reduces problems with N immobilization.

One important consideration when using overwintering cover crops is their potential to deplete soil water. Although cover crops can improve water infiltration and soil water-holding capacity, the short-term depletion of soil water in the early spring can reduce yields of subsequent cash crops in dry springs. In this situation, cover crops may need to be incorporated early to conserve soil water, or irrigation may be required. The opposite is also true—cover crops can help dry up wet fields in the spring.

Winter-killed cover crops (species vary by climate) also capture significant amounts of soil nitrogen (up to 50–90 lbs/acre) in the fall (102) prior to being killed by low temperatures. The amount of soil N captured is related to the N that is available, the time of planting, and the total growth of the cover crop prior to being killed. Researchers observed that *Brassica* cover crops grew more in the fall and, as a result, captured more N than an oat cover crop (102). Across species, however, the fall-planted, winter-killed cover crops reduced soil nitrate levels in the fall and increased levels in the spring, compared to soil left bare over the winter. Thus, excess soil nitrogen from the end of one season was captured and conserved for the following season's crop. Note that while *Brassica* cover crops are good at capturing nutrients, they may host diseases (clubroot) and insects (flea beetle) that attack other *Brassica* species in the rotation.

Differences in Crop Nutrient Uptake

Crop nutrient uptake varies due to many factors, including rooting depth and breadth; variety; and environmental factors, including soil tilth. Generally, crops may be characterized as having low, medium, or high nutrient demands based on their nutrient uptake efficiency (table 3.1). Different varieties within any crop may be more or less efficient at taking up nutrients. Those crops with a high nutrient demand (predominately N) require higher levels of those nutrients to be present in the soil solution. This high demand could be related to large vegetative plant growth prior to fruit set (in the case of corn and tomatoes) or due to poor foraging ability of the crop's roots (in the case of lettuce). Green manures and soil fertility amendments have the most benefit when they target the crops with high nutrient demands. On inherently fertile soils, crops with low nutrient requirements often achieve good yields from residual soil fertility alone.

TABLE 3.1 Ranking of annual vegetables based on relative nutrient requirements

Low	Medium	High
Beans, all	Brassica greens	Broccoli
Beet	Cucumber	Cabbage
Carrot	Eggplant	Cauliflower
Herbs	Pepper	Corn
Peas	Pumpkin	Lettuce
Radish	Spinach, chard	Potato
	Squash	Tomato
	Sweet potato	
	Watermelon	
	Winter squash	

Note: Vegetables are classified as having low, medium, or high nutrient requirements. These categories do not account for differences among varieties.

TABLE 3.2 Rooting depth and lateral spread of roots for several crops

Crop	Estimated rooting depth (inches)	Lateral root spread (inches)
Oat	60	10
Turnip	60	30
Soybean	80	20
Barley	55	10
Alfalfa	120	5
Pea	35	25
Rye	60	10
Potato	35	15
Sorghum	70	25
Wheat	60	5
Field corn	70	40

Source: Adapted from reference 42: A. A. Hanson, *Practical Handbook of Agricultural Science* (Boca Raton, FL: Taylor & Francis Group, LLC 1990).

Crop rooting depth can have important implications for nutrient availability as well as soil physical characteristics. Crop rotations that integrate deep-rooting crops with less nutrient-efficient crops can help cycle nutrients in the soil profile. The deep-rooted crops listed in table 3.2 (page 29) absorb nutrients from deep in the soil and move them to the plant's top growth. As crop residues are returned to the surface soil, these newly "mined" nutrients are potentially available to future crops. Deep-rooted crops also create channels into the soil that later can improve water infiltration. Although most of the listed crops are typical of grain rotations, the data are also relevant to vegetable producers, since grain and forage crops are integrated into vegetable rotations as cover crops.

Compost, Micronutrient, and Rock Powder Applications for Crop Nutrition

Soil tests may suggest the need for additional inputs of particular nutrients. In some cases, soils are naturally low in nutrients; in other cases, export of nutrients in crops has led to soil depletion. Organic soil amendments such as composts, trace element mixes, plant and animal meals, and rock powders can be used to meet some of these needs. Many organic soil amendments become available only slowly; in some cases application to the previous cover crop improves availability to the cash crop. Since some of these amendments can be expensive, they should be applied strategically within a rotation. Prior to

TABLE 3.3 A sample nutrient budget for nitrogen and phosphorus from a dairy farm rotation

Year	Crop	Yield[1]	Nitrogen Budget (lbs N/acre)				Phosphorus Budget (lbs P/acre)			
			N export	N input source	N input	Cumulative N balance	P export	P input source	P input	Cumulative P balance
1	Alfalfa	4 t/ac	224	Alfalfa, manure	234	10	21	Manure	18	-3
2	Alfalfa	5 t/ac	280	Alfalfa	269	-1	26		0	-29
3	Alfalfa	6 t/ac	336	Alfalfa, manure	414	77	31	Manure	18	-42
4	Corn	110 bu/ac	92	Alfalfa, starter fertilizer	45	30	24	Starter fertilizer	15	-51
5	Barley	50 bu/ac	38	Manure	100	92	9	Manure	18	-42
6	Alfalfa	4 t/ac	224	Alfalfa	224	92	21		0	-63
7	Alfalfa	5 t/ac	280	Alfalfa, manure	369	181	26	Manure	18	-71
8	Alfalfa	5 t/ac	280	Alfalfa	269	170	26		0	-97
9	Corn	90 bu/ac	84	Alfalfa, manure, starter fertilizer	145	231	22	Manure, starter fertilizer	33	-86
10	Barley	60 bu/ac	46		0	185	12		0	-98

Note: Ten tons of manure were applied every other year. The cumulative balances are based on the difference between the export and the input of nutrients. Not all of the nutrient inputs are available in the first year.

[1] t= tons, bu = bushels, and ac = acres

the application of any of these materials, adjust soil pH to the desired range for the majority of crops within the rotation (generally 6.2 to 6.8). High or low pH will reduce the availability of phosphorus and many micronutrients.

Most composts contain relatively stable forms of organic matter and low levels of readily available nutrients. Some types, such as poultry compost, may contain high levels of nutrients compared to other organic fertility amendments, but not compared to commercial fertilizers. Good composts applied at specific points in a rotation can improve soil fertility in the long term by enhancing soil structure and tilth, improving soil water movement, and providing a slow-release fertility source. Usually, meeting the complete nitrogen needs of a crop by using only compost is difficult without also adding excessive phosphorus. Build-up of excessively high phosphorus levels can occur when composts based on animal manures are used at high rates (greater than 10 tons/acre) once or twice per year. Accumulation of excess P can damage neighboring bodies of water and stimulate weed growth (see "The Role of Crop Rotation in Weed Management," page 44).

Micronutrients can be supplemented using foliar-type fertilizers, including seaweed extracts and borax (consult the Organic Materials Research Institute's approved materials list for organically acceptable formulations, HTTP://WWW.OMRI.ORG/OMRI_PRODUCTS_LIST.PHP). These can provide low levels of nitrogen, calcium, magnesium, boron, zinc, and iron. Foliar fertilizing must be managed carefully, since effectiveness depends on uptake of the micronutrients through the plant cuticle. Depending on application rates, environmental conditions, and plant maturity, foliar feeding can sometimes result in burning of leaves.

Rock powders (ground limestone, gypsum, granite dust, rock phosphate) and trace element mixes slowly release nutrients to plants. The more finely ground the powder, the sooner the minerals will be available to the crop due to a greater surface area of the powder available for microbial digestion and physical weathering. Like composts, rock powders cannot be used to provide immediate crop needs. They should be used as long-term sources of crop nutrients.

Putting It All Together: Nutrient Budgets During Crop Rotation

One strategy for reviewing the effects of a crop rotation on soil nutrients is to construct a nutrient budget. A nutrient budget can be complex or fairly simple, depending

TABLE 3.4 A sample nutrient budget for nitrogen and phosphorus from an organic vegetable rotation

Year	Crop	Yield[1] (lb/ac)	Nitrogen Budget (lbs N/acre)				Phosphorus Budget (lbs P/acre)			
			N export	N input source	N input	Cumulative N balance	P export	P input source	P input	Cumulative P balance
1	Tomato	45,000	49	Compost	300	251	17	Compost	80	63
2	Lettuce, spinach	8,000, 5,000	28	Compost	150	373	4	Compost	40	99
3	Winter squash	20,000	37	Compost	300	636	16	Compost	80	163
4	Lettuce, pepper	8,000, 30,000	60	Compost	150	726	8	Compost	40	195
5	Cabbage	40,000	69	Compost	300	957	12	Compost	80	263

Note: The grower applied 20 or 10 tons of mushroom compost each year. The cumulative balances are based on the difference between the export and the input of nutrients. Nutrients from the compost are not all available in the first year.

[1] t= tons, bu = bushels, and ac = acres

> **"Generally, the technique of using crop rotation for disease management is to grow non-host plants until the pathogen in the soil dies or its population is reduced to a level that will result in negligible crop damage."**

on its purpose. For simplicity, consider just soil N and P. Think of them as deposits in a soil fertility bank account. Most of these nutrients are tied up in long-term investments, in the form of organic matter. But a portion of the account is available for withdrawal. Assuming a soil is relatively fertile, the long-term goal is to maintain an approximately constant balance in the account, rather than to increase or decrease nutrient storage. As crops are removed, nutrients are withdrawn or exported from the system. As legumes, manures, composts, or other amendments are added to the soil, the nutrient bank balance increases. By examining rotations through time, a farmer can make general estimates of the increase or decrease in potentially available nutrients and change his or her management accordingly.

Consider the examples in tables 3.3 and 3.4 (pages 30 and 31). In the first example (table 3.3), periodic applications of manure to a long-term rotation resulted in moderate increases in soil nitrogen but did not help maintain soil phosphorous levels. Through each cycle of the five-year rotation, about 50 pounds of P was exported off the farm. Future crops may require an additional source of P. In the vegetable rotation (table 3.4), yearly compost additions led to a rapid buildup of soil nitrogen and phosphorous. Such high levels are not environmentally sound and may be prohibited in some states, depending on nutrient management regulations. Also notable in the vegetable rotation is the low level of nutrient export via these crops, compared with the agronomic crops (table 3.3). Excess nutrients in the vegetable rotation may leach out of or run off from the system eventually, even if cover crops or other cultural practices are used to minimize losses.

By reviewing the inputs and outputs of a rotation, general trends of nutrient accumulation or depletion can be detected. Although nutrient exports by crops or nutrient inputs via cover crops and other amendments can only be estimated (appendix 1, pages 101–103), these values and budgets will still point to potential problems in nutrient management within a crop rotation. This approach will not account for losses through leaching or soil erosion. It also does not include an estimate of the "starting" reserves of soil nutrients. History of management, inputs, and native soil organic matter levels in each field will all contribute to the starting reserve. With this information on the general trends of nutrient accumulation within a field, alternative rotations or different crops (including cover crops and green manures) may be considered to strategically capture, export, or contribute essential plant nutrients.

For further reading, see references 24, 42, 75, 92, 102, and 107.

Managing Plant Diseases with Crop Rotation
Margaret Tuttle McGrath

Rotating land out of susceptible crops can be an effective and relatively inexpensive means for managing some diseases. To successfully use crop rotation for disease management, however, requires understanding the life cycle of the disease-causing organism (pathogen). Generally, the technique of using crop rotation for disease management is to grow non-host plants until the pathogen in the soil dies or its population is reduced to a level that will result in negligible crop damage. To manage a disease successfully with rotation, one needs to know (1) how long the pathogen can survive in the soil, (2) which additional plant species (including weeds and cover crops) it can infect or survive on, (3) other ways it can survive between susceptible crops, (4) how it can be spread or reintroduced into a field, and (5) methods for managing other pathogen sources. For example, a pathogen that can survive in the soil but can also disperse by wind may not be successfully managed by rotation if an infected planting occurs nearby or the spores can disperse long distances.

Appendix 3 (pages 124–137) lists sources of pathogen inoculum and recommended rotation periods for diseases of vegetable and field crops in the greater northeastern US (including the mid-Atlantic region). The number of years needed to suppress a disease cannot be stated precisely for many diseases because of the impact of other factors and lack of extensive research, but general guidelines have been developed from research and farm observations, as well as knowledge of pathogen biology. While these periods are based on research and observations from conventional production systems, they are generally applicable to organic systems because pathogen biology doesn't change. However, if the activity of beneficial soil microorganisms that suppress a pathogen is much higher in an organic field than in a conventional field, the required rotation period might be shorter. On the other hand, if

more organic matter, such as an incorporated cover crop, is present in an organic system, those pathogens that can survive on decomposing organic matter may be more difficult to manage. Knowing which weeds can host a disease is important, as these weeds will need to be controlled during the rotation (see appendices 3 and 5, pages 124–137 and pages 142–147). Avoiding reintroduction of the pathogen when the crop is planted again is also critical. For example, infested seed, transplants, or soil on farm machinery can reintroduce a pathogen to a clean field.

The sections below describe the biological basis for managing plant diseases with crop rotation. First, several critical aspects of pathogen biology are discussed. These dictate whether rotation is a potentially viable option for managing a particular pathogen and the disease it causes. Second, how the characteristics of certain rotation crops affect pathogens is considered: Good rotations do more than simply provide an unsuitable host. Third, the impact of cover crops and incorporated green manures on diseases is considered. Fourth, various environmental and management factors that affect the success of crop rotation for disease suppression are discussed. Finally, some selected diseases that can be managed successfully with rotation are discussed, followed by some examples of diseases that cannot be controlled by rotation. These examples help explain the factors that affect rotation success. Although the focus here is on diseases of vegetable and field crops in the northeastern US, the principles are broadly applicable, and many of the specific diseases discussed occur in other regions as well. Because the same disease name is often applied to diseases caused by several different pathogens, scientific names are used frequently in the following sections to avoid ambiguity (see sidebar 3.1).

Pathogen Characteristics that Determine the Success of Rotation and Length of the Rotation Period

Rotation can effectively suppress a crop disease when the target pathogen is capable of surviving in the soil or on crop debris for no more than a few years. Some fungal and bacterial pathogens can survive in soil only in crop debris, and these are the most suitable pathogens to target for management with crop rotation because they cannot survive once the debris has decomposed. Pathogens that survive on soil organic matter but for only a few years can also be managed with crop rotation. These short-term residents of the soil are called *soil invaders* or *soil transients*.

SIDEBAR 3.1

IMPORTANCE OF SCIENTIFIC NAMES IN DISEASE MANAGEMENT

When designing a rotational sequence for managing a particular disease, focus should be on the pathogen's scientific name, because common names can be misleading. For example, powdery mildew, downy mildew, bacterial blight, and fusarium wilt are usually caused by different pathogens in different crops. On the other hand, white mold, which occurs in several crops, is caused by the same fungus that causes lettuce drop.

Knowing whether the pathogen exists as specialized strains that limit the host range is critical for designing disease-controlling rotations. For example, all grasses get anthracnose; however, host specialization was recently found to occur in the fungal pathogen causing this disease. Consequently, grass weeds do not play as important a role as alternate hosts for anthracnose in corn as was originally thought. Strains of some fungi are called *formae speciales* (f. sp.); others are called pathovar (pv.). These abbreviations occur in some of the pathogen scientific names listed in appendix 3 (pages 124–137).

> ## "Wind, irrigation water, or insects can spread the pathogen from infected crops and re-infest the field after rotation."

Pathogens in this group vary in the length of time they can survive, and thus in the length of rotation needed.

Survival time partly reflects the type of plant host tissue infected. For example, the barley scald pathogen primarily infects leaves and leaf sheaths, which decompose fairly rapidly. In contrast, the net blotch pathogen also infects barley stems, including the nodes, which are more resistant to decay. Consequently, a longer rotation is needed to manage net blotch than to manage scald. Infected seed, and also wind-dispersed spores for the net blotch pathogen, are additional sources of these pathogens that need to be managed to ensure successful control through rotation.

Similarly, managing the bacterial canker disease that affects tomatoes requires a longer rotation than is needed to manage bacterial speck and bacterial spot. The canker-causing bacteria get inside tomato stems, whereas speck and spot are restricted to rapidly decomposing leaves and fruit. All three pathogens can be seed-borne. Rotation is only one aspect of a good control program. Managing other sources of bacterial pathogens is critical for success. This is covered in detail in the section on specific diseases below.

A few fungal and bacterial pathogens are true soil inhabitants, able to grow on organic matter in the soil. Such organisms are referred to as *saprophytes*. These are hard to manage with rotation. Examples of soil inhabitants are the fungi *Pythium*, *Rhizoctonia*, and *Fusarium* and the bacteria *Erwinia*, *Rhizomonas*, and *Streptomyces*.

Several species of *Pythium* and *Rhizoctonia* are commonly found in most soils as part of the normal soil flora. These fungi attack seeds and the roots and stems of tender seedlings, causing seed decay and damping-off. *Pythium* species also cause fruit rot in cucurbits, and *Rhizoctonia solani* causes wirestem, bottom rot, and head rot in crucifers. Although crop rotations will not completely control these fungi, reducing the pathogen population by rotating with small grains can reduce losses in subsequent crops. Since these saprophytes can also use fresh plant residues, incorporating large amounts of organic matter will stimulate their growth. Thus, crops planted too soon after incorporating a cover crop could be severely affected by these fungi. Other types of organic matter, such as leaves or incompletely decomposed compost, could have a similar effect. Some fungi that cause fusarium wilts can survive in or on roots of plants that do not develop symptoms ("symptomless carriers"), and they can also grow as saprophytes on plant debris and other partly decomposed organic matter.

Some fungal pathogens produce specialized structures that, like seeds, enable them to persist in a state of dormancy. These structures help the pathogen survive periods when host plants are absent, as well as cold winter temperatures and other adverse conditions. The maximum survival time varies among types of structures and species of pathogen. Fungal structures capable of dormancy include oospores, sclerotia, chlamydospores, and cleistothecia. Similarly, some pathogenic nematodes produce cysts. Recognizing that these terms refer to resting structures is helpful when reading about plant diseases because they indicate that a pathogen can potentially persist in soil.

Some pathogens are *heterothallic*, which means they produce the dormant structure only when individuals of opposite mating types (the fungal equivalent of male and female) interact. This is important because presence or absence of the different mating types can determine whether the pathogen persists in the soil. For example, although the cucurbit downy mildew fungus, *Pseudoperonospora cubensis*, is potentially capable of producing oospores, only one mating type occurs in the US; thus, it cannot produce oospores, and that prevents it from surviving winter in the northeast US. In contrast, the onion downy mildew fungus, *Peronospora destructor*, does produce oospores in the northeast US, and they can survive four to five years in soil. The situation can change, however: Until recently only one mating type of the late blight fungus, *Phytophthora infestans*, existed in the US. Now two mating types are present, and the pathogen can persist in soil as oospores. *Phytophthora erythroseptica*, which causes pink rot in potato, is *homothallic*. Thus, it can produce oospores when just one mating type is present.

Sclerotia and chlamydospores are structures that can be produced without interaction between fungi of opposite mating types. Sclerotia produced by *Colletotrichum coccodes*, which causes anthracnose and black dot in tomato, survive at least eight years. Those formed by *Sclerotinia sclerotiorum*, the white mold fungus, can survive up to ten years. *Rhizoctonia* spp. also produce sclerotia. *Verticillium dahliae*, which causes verticillium wilt, produces tiny sclerotia (microsclerotia) that can survive up to 13 years. Fungi causing fusarium wilts can persist for many years as chlamydospores.

The target pathogen should have a narrow host range for rotation to be successful. *Peronospora farinose* f. sp. *spinacia* causes downy mildew only in spinach. Another spinach pathogen, *Albugo occidentalis*, causes white rust in spinach and in some species of lambsquarters and goosefoot. However, the strains of fungi that attack the different species are specialists, and this host specificity can prevent cross infection. Thus, white rust may occur only on spinach or only on weeds in a field. In contrast, the fungus *Sclerotinia sclerotiorum*, which causes white mold, can infect more than 360 plant species. Corn and cereals are among the few non-host crops that can be used in rotation to decrease abundance of this pathogen. Weeds must be managed carefully, however, for this rotation to be successful. In addition, rotation out of susceptible crops for at least five years is needed because this fungus produces long-lived sclerotia. Effectiveness of a rotation can be compromised when nearby plantings have white mold. Wind, irrigation water, or insects can spread the pathogen from infected crops and re-infest the field after rotation.

When considering rotation to manage a fungal pathogen that produces wind-dispersed spores, it is critical to know how far the spores can travel. Powdery mildew and downy mildew fungi produce spores that can disperse great distances. These cucurbit pathogens can move up the entire eastern coast of the US each year, helped by the sequential planting of these crops from south Florida to Maine as conditions become favorable. Clearly, pathogens like these would be difficult to control with rotation. In contrast, downy mildew of onion can be controlled with rotation, partly because the crop is not grown as extensively. Several other fungal pathogens that attack leaves, including *Alternaria, Cercospora, Septoria,* and *Stemphylium*, are more effectively controlled by rotation because they produce large spores. They disperse only short distances by wind, although they can leave the field on equipment. Other fungal pathogens, such as *Colletotrichum*, produce spores on leaves and fruit that disperse by splashing water. Bacteria are also dispersed by splashing water and in windblown water droplets.

New findings or changes in the pathogen can affect rotation guidelines. For example, a short rotation was initially thought to be adequate for *Phytophthora capsici*, which causes blight in cucurbits, pepper, tomato, and eggplant. Recently this pathogen was found on new hosts (lima bean, snap bean, purslane, and a few other weeds), which may explain why short rotations have not been effective. Additionally, it may be able to move between fields more easily than anticipated, possibly accounting for its occurrence in fields where susceptible crops had not been grown. Recently, most cases of early blight in tomatoes have been shown to be caused by a different species of *Alternaria* than the species causing early blight in potato. Consequently, early blight may not be more severe in tomatoes that follow early blight–affected potatoes than in tomatoes that follow other crops.

As a group, plant-pathogenic nematodes are more difficult to manage with rotation than fungi and bacteria because almost all exist for part of their lives in the soil. Only a few nematodes attack just leaves, rarely entering soil, and none of these infect vegetable or grain crops.

None of the few soilborne viruses that affect vegetable or grain crops occur in the northeastern US. Most viruses cannot persist in soil between crops because they survive only in living host tissue or vectors, and few viruses are vectored by nematodes or soilborne fungi. However, some viruses can persist between crops in weeds—for example, cucumber mosaic in chickweed and potato virus Y in dandelion (appendix 5, pages 142–147).

"Corn, small grains, and other grasses are usually good crops to rotate with vegetable crops."

Beneficial Plants to Include in Rotations

The typical focus in designing a rotation for disease management is to alternate among crops that are susceptible to different pathogens. Alternating crops in different families is a good starting point, but some pathogens attack crops in two or more families. For example, *Phytophthora capsici* causes blight in cucurbits, peppers, and lima beans. Corn, small grains, and other grasses are usually good crops to rotate with vegetable crops. Fusarium fruit rot, however, has been more common in pumpkin following corn.

Some plants suppress pathogens in addition to being unsuitable hosts. These include some cover and green manure crops, as well as cash crops. Including disease-suppressive species in a rotation sometimes reduces the time needed before a particular cash crop can again be produced successfully. Examples include some legumes and crucifers. These plants suppress pathogens by stimulating beneficial organisms in the soil and by producing toxic chemicals. The specific mechanisms involved appear to vary with the crop and the pathogen. Depending on the mechanism, the beneficial effect can disappear shortly after incorporation or last for years. Suppression can vary with how well the pathogen is established in a field. Also, to achieve success, beneficial crops may need to be grown more than once before a susceptible cash crop is replanted. It is important to remember that incorporating large quantities of biomass in the form of green manure stimulates general microbial activity, which can include pathogens like *Pythium,* as described earlier.

Including legumes such as clover, pea, bean, vetch, and lupine in crop rotations has been recognized as beneficial for disease management since ancient times. Legumes stimulate the growth and activity of soil microbes, in addition to increasing soil nitrogen and organic matter. Hairy vetch residue incorporated into soil reduces fusarium wilt in watermelon and enhances crop growth. On the other hand, hairy vetch is a good host for root-knot nematodes.

Members of the mustard plant family (crucifers) release substances while decomposing that are toxic to some fungi, nematodes, and even weeds; and they also stimulate beneficial microorganisms. One group of chemical breakdown by-products from these plants is the volatile isothiocyanates. These originate from glucosinolates, which are themselves harmless. Glucosinolate content varies among plants of the mustard family. White mustard, brown mustard, and rapeseed have especially high concentrations. IdaGold is a yellow mustard variety bred for high glucosinolate content. Glucoraphanin is a glucosinolate found at much higher levels in broccoli than in other cruciferous plants. Using these plants to manage pests is called *biofumigation*. Research has been done in California with mustard seeded in fall and incorporated in spring. In the northeast US, mustard would be seeded in early spring, then incorporated several weeks later when it is in full flower and organic matter is at a maximum. Soil temperature should be 59° to 77°F. Amending the soil with crucifer seed meal can similarly suppress disease. Isothiocyanates are thought to be less damaging to beneficial soil organisms than conventional chemical fumigants. These compounds can also be toxic to crops; thus, planting should be delayed about a month after incorporation. Quantity of isothiocyanates produced can vary with soil type, as well as variety of crucifer. The degree of disease control has been related to the quantity of isothiocyanates in some systems, but in other systems disease suppression evidently is due to another mechanism. Beneficial microorganisms stimulated include myxobacteria and *Streptomyces*.

Note that although a mustard or legume crop can suppress some pathogens, such crops may also promote pathogens that attack plants in those families.

"The degree of control was better than that achieved by fumigating with chloropicrin, a product used by conventional farmers."

Examples of Specific Diseases Influenced by Crop Rotation

- **Carrot root dieback.**

  The soilborne fungi *Pythium* spp. and *Rhizoctonia solani* can infect and kill the tip of carrot tap roots, causing them to become forked or stubby. In severe cases, they kill the plants. A study in California showed that when carrots were grown after alfalfa, populations of *Pythium* and *Rhizoctonia* were larger, and fewer marketable carrots were produced. The study also revealed more misshapen carrots and a higher population of *Pythium* when barley preceded carrots, but the barley residue may not have decomposed sufficiently before the carrots were planted. Carrots and pathogen populations were normal when onions or a fallow period preceded the carrot crop. Another reason not to grow alfalfa before carrots is that alfalfa is a host for the fungus causing cavity spot of carrot, *Pythium violae*.

- **Clubroot.**

  The roots of mustard family crops that are attacked by the slime mold fungus *Plasmodiophora brassicae* become greatly swollen. This pathogen can survive in soil for seven years in the absence of mustard family crops or weeds. Clubroot has declined more quickly when tomato, cucumber, snap bean, and buckwheat were grown. Clubroot was effectively controlled by growing summer savory, peppermint, garden thyme, or other aromatic perennial herb crops for two or three consecutive years.

- **Verticillium wilt.**

  Rotating among crop families is generally recommended, because crops within a family are typically susceptible to the same diseases; however, growing broccoli immediately before cauliflower resulted in a reduction in verticillium wilt, even though these plants are closely related. Broccoli produces more of a specific glucosinolate and stimulates myxobacteria that reduce survival of *Verticillium* microsclerotia. The degree of control was better than that achieved by fumigating with chloropicrin, a product used by conventional farmers. Fresh broccoli residue is more effective than dry residue. The greatest reductions in pathogen microsclerotia occurred when soil temperatures were above 68°F. Verticillium wilt diseases of other crops in California were also suppressed by broccoli.

- **Verticillium wilt and scab of potato.**

  Both these diseases were reduced when corn or

> **"Rotation that includes a fallow period can be the key for controlling some pathogens that have a wide host range."**

alfalfa was grown the previous year rather than potato. Verticillium wilt severity also was lower when a buckwheat green manure preceded potato than when canola or a fallow preceded potato.

- **Lettuce drop and white mold.**

  Broccoli is also a good crop to grow in rotation with lettuce and crops susceptible to white mold. The number of sclerotia of the lettuce drop fungus, *Sclerotinia sclerotiorum*, decreased after residue from a spring broccoli crop was incorporated during the summer. This resulted in reduced incidence of lettuce drop in a fall lettuce crop. Similar results were obtained in California when two consecutive crops of broccoli in one year were followed by two consecutive crops of lettuce the next year.

  Density of sclerotia of *Sclerotinia minor* was lower following broccoli than where broccoli was not grown, and broccoli was associated with lower incidence of white mold in subsequent crops. In contrast, cover crops of Lana woollypod vetch, phacelia, and Austrian winter pea in California hosted *S. minor*, and incidence of drop was higher where lettuce was grown after these cover crops were incorporated than in plots that had been left fallow. This pathogen also caused disease on purple vetch but not on oilseed radish, barley, or fava bean. Oilseed radish, however, is a host of the clubroot pathogen and root-knot nematodes. Phacelia and purple vetch are also hosts of root-knot nematodes.

Other Factors Affecting Success of Rotation in Managing Disease

Rotation is more likely to be effective if the entire field is rotated out of susceptible crops rather than just the section previously planted to the crop. When farm equipment is used throughout the field, infested soil or crop debris

> **"Rotations of at least five or seven years often prevent the pathogen population from building up to a level that can cause economic damage."**

can be moved from the contaminated section to other parts of the field. If a field is divided into management units, rotation can be effective within a unit if cultivators and other farm equipment are cleaned before working in another unit and water does not flow between units during heavy rainstorms.

Time required for rotation to be effective can vary with disease severity and environmental conditions. When a disease has been severe, a longer rotation may be needed to reduce the pathogen's inoculum level sufficiently to avoid economic loss. A two-year period between wheat crops is generally needed to reduce Septoria leaf spot; however, just one year without wheat resulted in a similar reduction in disease severity when environmental conditions were less favorable for this disease. Sclerotia can be sensitive to drying. Some pathogens, such as *Sclerotium rolfsii*, which causes southern blight, are adapted to warm conditions and do not survive low soil temperatures. That is why southern blight does not occur in most of the northeastern US.

Using other cultural practices with rotation can be the key to successfully controlling some pathogens. For example, after rotating land out of tomatoes to reduce pathogen populations, staking and mulching the subsequent tomato crop minimizes the potential for pathogen propagules remaining in the soil to disperse up onto the tomato plants. For a similar reason, deeply burying infested crop debris and pathogen survival structures by moldboard plowing reduces disease incidence. For this to work, the residue must be buried deeply enough that it is not pulled back up during seedbed preparation and cultivation. Burying diseased material is especially useful against pathogens that produce sclerotia and those that infect only aboveground plant tissue. However, deep, full inversion plowing decreases soil health by burying beneficial organisms that live in the top few inches of the soil profile. The value of incorporating debris is illustrated by

corn diseases, in particular gray leaf spot, that are more common and more severe under no-till production. Breaking up infested crop debris immediately after harvest—for example, with flail chopping or repeated disking—can hasten decomposition of the debris, thereby reducing survival time for those pathogens that cannot survive in soil without debris.

While several pathogens are more likely to cause disease in subsequent crops when infested crop debris is left on the soil surface, there are exceptions. An in-depth study on survival of *Colletotrichum coccodes*, which causes anthracnose and black dot in tomato, revealed that its sclerotia survive longer when buried shallowly in the soil than when on the soil surface, probably because temperature and moisture vary more on the surface. The sclerotia of this species also appear to survive longer when *not* associated with plant tissue, likely because the skin tissue of tomato fruits becomes colonized by beneficial fungi that can parasitize the sclerotia. Roots are an important, overlooked source of this pathogen. Tomato roots in several fields were found to be infected and to have sclerotia when there were no symptoms on aboveground parts of the plants. Additionally, this fungus is pathogenic on roots of other plants in the nightshade and cucurbit families, including several weeds (see appendix 3, pages 124–137). It can also survive on the roots of numerous other non-host plants (symptomless carriers), including chrysanthemum, white mustard, cress, cabbage, and lettuce. This could account for *C. coccodes* occurring on tomato roots in fields with no previous history of tomato or other crops in the nightshade family.

Rotation that includes a fallow period can be the key for controlling some pathogens that have a wide host range. Bacteria causing soft rot are generally not considered amenable to management by rotation because they are common soil inhabitants with a wide host range. However, one of the common bacteria causing soft rot, *Erwinia*, does not survive well in a field that is fallow and repeatedly tilled.

Some cultural practices can also negate the benefit of rotation. Incidence of scurf (*Monilochaetes infuscans*) in sweet potato can be increased when animal manure is applied. Diseases caused by the fungus *Rhizoctonia solani* can be enhanced when undecomposed crop residue is present at planting. Potato and onion cull piles can be sources of pathogen inoculum and thus need to be destroyed before planting the next crop. Tillage can spread disease throughout a field from an initial few infested areas.

Some Diseases That Can Be Managed with Crop Rotation

Understanding the mechanisms that allow or prevent management of specific diseases by rotation can improve success and avoid wasted effort. This section discusses some diseases that can be successfully managed by crop rotation; the next section discusses some diseases that cannot. Other diseases for which rotation is or is not effective are listed in appendix 3 (pages 124–137).

- ***Bacterial spot of pepper and tomato***.

The bacterium causing spot (*Xanthomonas campestris* pv. *vesicatoria*) can be effectively controlled with rotation because this pathogen cannot survive in the soil once diseased plant debris decomposes. A minimum of two years without a host crop is recommended.

- ***Bacterial speck of tomato***.

This disease is more difficult to control with rotation than bacterial spot because the pathogen (*Pseudomonas syringae* pv. *tomato*) can survive on roots and leaves of taxonomically diverse weeds. Therefore, success requires good control of weeds and volunteer tomatoes during the rotation period. A study on survival of this bacterium showed that it lived up to 30 weeks on crop debris but less than 30 days just in soil.

Bacteria causing spot and speck, as well as *Clavibacter michiganensis* subs. *michiganensis*, which causes bacterial canker in tomato, can occur on seeds. Thus, subsequent crops should be planted with seed lots that have been tested and shown to have no detectable pathogen to avoid reintroducing the pathogen into the field. The seed should also be hot water treated, because bacteria could be present at a low, undetectable level. A description of how to treat seed with hot water is at HTTP://VEGETABLEMDONLINE.PPATH. CORNELL.EDU/NEWSARTICLES/PEPPERLEAFSPOT.HTM. These tomato diseases also affect peppers, but resistant pepper varieties are available.

Volunteer tomato and pepper plants could grow from infested seed left in the field from a previous crop. Thus, volunteers need to be destroyed during rotation to ensure successful suppression of bacterial diseases. Destroying volunteer crop plants is also important for other seed-borne bacterial diseases, in particular, bacterial fruit blotch of watermelon. Bacterial pathogens of tomato can also survive on tomato stakes and planting supplies, so these materials need to be replaced or disinfected before reuse.

- ***Root-knot nematodes***.

Northern root-knot nematode (*Meloidogyne hapla*) is the most common species of root-knot nematode in the northeastern US and the only one found during a recent study of vegetable soils in New York. The predominant species in the mid-Atlantic region is southern root-knot nematode (*M. incognita*), although northern root-knot nematode also occurs there. These nematodes have a large range of hosts that includes most vegetables. Growing sorghum, small grains, or grasses or leaving a clean summer fallow between crops can reduce the nematode population to a tolerable level. The effect of these crops on root-knot nematodes is short lived, so they should be routinely incorporated into the cropping sequence. Weeds need to be controlled during the rotation to grasses, because some, notably nutsedges, are good hosts for these nematodes. Varieties of alfalfa, common bean, soybean, cowpea, peppers, and tomato are available with resistance to certain root-knot nematode species.

Some commonly used cover crops, notably hairy vetch, are good hosts of root-knot nematodes.

Some Diseases That Cannot Be Easily Managed with Crop Rotation

- ***Fusarium wilts of crucifers, cucurbits, pea, spinach, and tomato***.

These diseases are difficult to manage with rotation because the pathogens can persist for many years in soil in the absence of their crop host. They persist as dormant chlamydospores and on roots of some non-host plants (symptomless carriers). Rotations of at least five or seven years often prevent the pathogen population from building up to a level that can cause economic damage. However, if the disease has been severe in a field, even seven years may not be enough. Selecting resistant varieties is a more effective and practical means of controlling fusarium wilt. Multiple races have been identified for many of its host-specific forms. Therefore, knowing what races have occurred in an area is important when selecting resistant varieties. Fusarium wilt fungi also can be seed-borne and are easily moved on infected transplants. They can also be easily moved between fields in soil on equipment. These are the major ways they are brought onto a farm. Drought, mechanical damage, low soil pH, soil compaction, and other stress factors can predispose plants to infection by fusarium wilt fungi. Fortunately, the fusarium wilts in various crops are caused by different strains of the fungus

TABLE 3.5 Insect pests managed by crop rotation

Insect Pest	Practice to be avoided	Overwintering stage and location	Notes on biology and cultural management
Corn rootworms (*Diabrotica* spp.)	Corn following corn	Eggs in soil in the field	In the northeast US, a single-year rotation with a non-host should be adequate, but rootworms in the Midwest are adapting to defeat repeated corn-soybean rotations. Western corn rootworm strains have adapted by laying more eggs in soybean fields, and a small percentage of northern corn rootworms have adapted by extending egg diapause to two years.
Wireworms (*Melanotus communis, Limonius* spp.)	Highly wireworm-susceptible crops (e.g., root crops, corn, melons) following grassy sod or small grain crops	Larvae in soil in the field	Wireworms can continue to be damaging in a particular field for many years, since some species remain in the larval stage for 3–6 years. Plowing in late summer or fall exposes the larvae to predation. Baiting can be used to detect wireworm infestations before planting.
White grubs (*Phyllophaga* spp.)	Highly grub-susceptible crops (e.g., corn, potatoes, strawberries) following grassy sod	Larvae in soil in the field	*Phyllophaga* grubs remain in soil as larvae for 3–4 years. Late summer or early fall plowing kills grubs through physical damage and by exposing them to predation. Annual white grub species, such as European chafer, oriental beetles, Japanese beetles, and Asiatic garden beetles, all of which are pests of turf, also spend the winter as larvae and may be confused with *Phyllophaga*. Because the annual species are short lived and highly mobile as adults, crop rotation is not an effective control for them.
Colorado potato beetle (*Leptinotarsa decemlineata*)	Potatoes, tomatoes, or eggplant following potatoes, tomatoes, eggplant, or high densities of horse nettle	Adult beetles in soil or on the edges of the field	Planting as little as 200 meters (~650 feet) from previous solanaceous host crops delays infestation by 1–2 weeks, reduces initial population density, and causes emergence of most summer adults to be too late to produce a 2nd generation in Massachusetts. However, a distance of 0.8 km (½ mile) or major barriers to movement may be needed for adequate control. Barriers include plastic-lined trenches; reusable plastic troughs; or dense plantings of wheat, rye, or other cover crops. Straw mulch can also delay host finding by the beetles and reduce their survival.

Fusarium oxysporum (see sidebar 3.1, page 33). Thus, for example, healthy muskmelons can be grown in a field where fusarium wilt previously affected watermelon.

- ***Rhizoctonia diseases.***

When environmental conditions are favorable (warm and wet), *Rhizoctonia solani*, a common fungus in most soils worldwide, can become a serious pathogen on susceptible crops. This fungus is subdivided into several strains, which further complicates management. It has a wide host range. Potatoes, beans, lettuce, and cabbage are among the most important hosts. Other hosts include broccoli, kale, radish, turnip, carrot, cress, cucumber, eggplant, pepper, tomato, and sweet potato. Symptoms produced on a host can vary with the time of infection. For example, in crucifers it causes damping-off of seedlings, wirestem in young plants, bottom rot in midseason, and head rot as heads mature. Although difficult to manage, rotating away from the most susceptible crops for at least three years can be helpful; cereals are an especially good choice for rotation crops. Incorporating residue of host plants can help.

Summary

Crop rotation can be an effective and relatively inexpensive means to manage some diseases, but achieving success can be challenging, and some diseases cannot be managed with rotation. The challenge can be met by knowing which diseases can be managed with rotation and understanding the aspects of a pathogen's biology that make it amenable to such control. Effectiveness can be improved by designing a rotation with crops that, in addition to not being a host, decrease pathogen survival by producing chemicals toxic to pathogens or stimulating beneficial organisms in the soil. Length of time needed in rotation to decrease disease occurrence may be shorter where beneficial organisms that affect the pathogen are more active. Understanding the reasons that some pathogens are not affected by rotation can allow a farmer to focus on more appropriate measures for managing these diseases, including use of resistant varieties and preventing introduction of the pathogen to a farm.

For further general reading on this topic, see references 20, 98, and 114; for further reading on field crops, see 3 and 118; for further reading on vegetables, see 4, 18, 21, 23, 43, 53, 66, 72, 94, 97, 105, 115, and 124.

Management of Insect Pests with Crop Rotation and Field Layout

Kimberly A. Stoner

The effectiveness of crop rotation as a tool for insect management depends on the life cycle of the target insect. For crop rotation to control an insect pest well, the insect must spend the period from the end of one crop to the beginning of the next in a stage with low mobility and must have a restricted range of host plants. Not many insect pests fit this pattern. Most have a period during the adult stage when they can travel easily across at least a single farm. Often this highly mobile stage comes when insects are emerging from their overwintering stage in the spring, so crop rotation from one year to the next will not affect them. Many pests, including corn earworms, cabbage loopers, and potato leafhoppers, do not even overwinter in the northeast US. Rather, they travel hundreds of miles to re-infest host crops each year.

However, some key pests can be managed through crop rotation (table 3.5). Western corn rootworm and northern corn rootworm are important examples. The adult beetles feed on corn silks (and on many flowers, including cucurbit flowers) in August and September and lay their eggs in soil at the base of corn plants. The eggs overwinter, and then newly hatched larvae feed on corn roots in the spring. They do not survive on small grains, sorghum, or broadleaf crops or weeds, and survive only at a very low level on grassy weeds. Thus, these two beetle species have relied on widespread planting of continuous corn for their survival and became major pests only when continuous planting of corn became a common practice in the Midwest.

In the same way, Colorado potato beetle became a major pest of potatoes because of the practice of continuous potato planting, particularly in the northeast US. The beetles emerge in late summer (August in Massachusetts) and spend the winter as adults, mainly along the field edges but also in the soil, in the same field where they developed. When they emerge from overwintering the following spring, they prefer to walk to hosts, if any are in the area, and there is a delay before they can regenerate their flight muscles. Spring infestations can be delayed or reduced by moving potatoes to a new field distant from the previous year's potatoes, and by using various kinds of barriers (plastic-lined trenches, dense plantings of grain crops, etc.) to interfere with their ability to walk to the new field. The life cycle includes a long-distance flying stage—in first-generation adults, which emerge in mid-summer—that can hit fields far from the previous year's potatoes, but rotation is an effective way to avoid early-season damage.

Wireworms (larvae of click beetles, Elateridae) and *Phyllophaga* grubs tend to be localized pests that can build up in a field following sod or small grains and then remain for multiple years, because the larvae are long lived. When monitoring indicates a problem, root crops and corn should not be planted in the field.

> "For many specialist pests with multiple generations per year (such as crucifer flea beetles), successive plantings of the same crop within a field increase the opportunity for building up high populations."

No-Till Farming, Early-Season Weeds, and Crop Residue Effects on Insect Pests

As explained in chapter 2 (pages 3–20), crop rotation planning must account for the whole range of field requirements and operations. Field management practices can influence insect pest problems, and the overall rotation plan should take this into account. The scientific literature, mostly written about corn and other field crops, indicates that no-till farming has a mixed effect on various species of insect pests within a single field. Some pests with low mobility, notably black cutworms, armyworms, slugs, white grubs, and wireworms, are favored by the presence of crop residue, cooler and wetter soil conditions, and the lack of soil disturbance in no-till farming. However, many predators of soil pests, including ground beetles, spiders, and predatory mites, are also favored by the same conditions within a field. In landscapes consisting of large fields tilled at least annually, strips of undisturbed vegetation around field edges are critical refuges for these predators, and also for the overwintering stages of parasitoids of insect pests such as European corn borer, true armyworm, and cereal leaf beetle.

Mobile insect pests may overwinter in crop residue in the field, and thus plowing and breaking down this residue will reduce their survival. European corn borer, squash vine borer, onion maggot, and spinach leaf miner are examples of insects whose overwintering stages, and the crop residues in which they reside, can be destroyed by plowing. Because these species are all mobile adults when they emerge in the spring, the effect of increased mortality may not be apparent in a single field or farm, but

timely plowing across a region could reduce the size of the local population.

Plowing also destroys winter annual or biennial weeds that can have a role in drawing insect pests to a field at the beginning of the season. Black cutworm moths lay their eggs early in the spring and prefer low-lying, poorly drained, weedy fields. The caterpillars begin development on the weeds or on a cover crop. When those host plants are plowed and replaced with a cash crop, the caterpillars attack the stems of the new crop, unless enough time (10–14 days) has been allowed to starve them out before planting.

Cruciferous weeds, especially yellow rocket, also attract crucifer flea beetles (*Phyllotreta cruciferae*) into the field early in the season, before other host plants are present. The flea beetles overwinter as adults and are active and feeding from the first warm days in early spring.

Freshly plowed residues, still breaking down at the time of planting, attract seedcorn maggot flies to lay eggs. The larvae hatch out and feed on germinating corn, bean, or cucurbit seeds or tunnel into stems of new transplants.

Planting Time and Insect Pests

Some pests, including corn flea beetles, crucifer flea beetles, striped flea beetles, and cabbage maggots, do most of their damage early in the season on small seedlings. Damage can be avoided by delaying planting or protecting early plantings with row covers. A rule developed from research in New York State to avoid cabbage maggot damage is to wait to transplant seedlings of cole crops until after the peak bloom of yellow rocket. Timing to avoid flea beetle damage in cole crops may push the planting even later—until mid-June in Connecticut.

Other pests, such as Mexican bean beetle, come out of their overwintering sites later (late June in Connecticut) but prefer to lay eggs on the largest and most vigorous plantings, which are often the earliest plantings. Biological control programs using the parasite *Pediobius foveolatus*, a small beneficial wasp, have taken advantage of this preference by planting early trap crops of attractive host plants (snap beans) and releasing the wasps in these heavily infested early plantings.

Movement between Crops during the Growing Season

A good crop rotation plan includes not only the crop-to-crop sequences but also how the crops will be laid out on the farm over the entire season. For many specialist pests with multiple generations per year (such as crucifer flea beetles), successive plantings of the same crop within a field increase the opportunity for building up high populations. While adult insects generally have a dispersal stage that easily travels long distances, having multiple plantings adjacent to each other helps the insects to find new food plants even in life stages that normally travel only a few yards.

Other pest insects feed on many different host plants and may build up in large numbers on one host, then move to another. An awareness of these possibilities can help a grower avoid a potential problem. For example, tarnished plant bugs feed on hundreds of different species of broadleaf host plants, preferring to feed on flowers and developing seeds. The nymphs may develop on cover crops such as hairy vetch, weeds such as pigweed or lambsquarters, or roadside vegetation. The new adults then move out when the plants are mowed or when the seeds become more mature and less suitable. Strawberry growers trying to reduce damage can substitute straight rye (a poor host for tarnished plant bug) for a mixture of rye with hairy vetch (a favorable host) adjacent to and upwind from strawberry fields. Strawberry growers who include alfalfa or clovers in their crop rotations can also avoid mowing these legumes during the time the strawberries are flowering and developing fruit to avoid mass movement of tarnished plant bug adults.

Summary

A few major insect pests can be managed directly by crop rotation on a single farm, but many more are influenced by farm management choices of whether and when to till, when to plant, how to manage spring weeds, and whether to put successive plantings of a crop in the same field. Because insects are so diverse in their overwintering, dispersal, and host-finding strategies, it is hard to identify cultural practices that will prevent problems across a range of crops and pests. The best approach is to identify the most important pests that have historically damaged major crops on a particular farm, and find cultural methods that interrupt the life cycle, interfere with movement, or otherwise limit the numbers of pests or damage from those pests.

For further reading, see references 33, 34, 47, 50, 55, 57, 71, 86, 93, 101, 103, 104, 122, and 127.

TABLE 3.6 Organic weed management practices

Practice	Effect
Tillage	Kills growing weeds; damages perennial roots and rhizomes; buries seeds too deeply to emerge; brings weed seeds to surface.
Post-planting cultivation	Removes weeds from the crop.
Stale seedbed	Flushes weeds from the soil before planting.
Organic fertility sources	Favor crops over faster-growing weeds due to slow release of nutrients.
Drip irrigation	Directs water to the crop rather than to weeds.
Mulch (plastic, straw)	Smothers weeds; delays those that do emerge.
Transplanting small-seeded crops	Increases the competitive ability of the crop; allows earlier cultivation.
Planting competitive cultivars	Improves competitive ability of the crop against weeds.
Increased density and more uniform arrangement of crop plants	Tend to suppress weeds by early shading.
Rapid cleanup after harvest	Prevents seed set by residual weeds.
Planting cover crops	Suppresses weeds by competition when cash crops are not present; improves soil tilth, which increases effectiveness of cultivation.

Note: Stale seedbed is the practice of preparing a seedbed, allowing the weeds to germinate and killing them without further soil disturbance. In organic systems killing the weeds is usually accomplished with a flame weeder. The crop is then planted into the weed free bed with as little disturbance as possible.

> **"Experimenting on small areas to find the right balance between seed cost of cover crops and weed control is often worthwhile."**

The Role of Crop Rotation in Weed Management

CHARLES L. MOHLER

Ideally, weed management in an organic cropping system involves the integration of a broad range of cultural practices. Although cultivation after planting is usually a key component, a variety of other factors make important contributions to weed control on organic farms (table 3.6, page 43). All of these practices occur within the context of a sequence of crops that are planted on a field—the crop rotation. The identities of the crops are critical for disease and insect management, but for weed management the identity of the crop species is less critical than the type of soil preparation and cultural weed control practices used with each crop. In general, crop sequences that take advantage of multiple opportunities to suppress and remove weeds from the field will improve weed management on the farm (61).

Few studies have examined the role of crop rotation in weed suppression, and most have looked at crop rotation in conventional agricultural systems with herbicides. Such studies primarily indicate the impact of varying the type of herbicide used rather than other factors associated with crop rotation. The few rotation studies without herbicides have generally found that more diverse systems had a lower density of problem weeds but a greater diversity of weed species (60, 62). This is reasonable, since the variation in cultural practices during the rotation will tend to disrupt the life cycle of each particular weed species but create niches for a greater variety of species.

Although the sparse literature offers only general insights into the design of weed suppressive crop rotations, the ecology of weeds offers clues to the sort of crop sequences that are most likely to minimize weed problems.

The usefulness of the principles outlined below has been documented by practicing farmers in many cases.

- ***Include clean fallow periods in the rotation to deplete perennial roots and rhizomes and to flush out and destroy annual weeds.***
  Most perennial weed species will resprout after their roots and rhizomes have been cut into small pieces by tillage implements (40). Thus, many new shoots are produced, but each shoot is weakened due to less belowground food storage. If these plants are again cultivated into the soil, they are further weakened. A few such cycles once every two to three years can greatly suppress or eliminate most perennial weeds whose roots are within the plow layer and help keep deeper-rooted perennials in check.

  Similarly, tillage tends to stimulate the germination of seeds of most weed species (73), and subsequent cultivation will kill the seedlings so they will not compete with future crops. This is an important approach to reducing the density of weed seeds stored in the soil. In northern Pennsylvania, Eric and Anne Nordell have nearly eliminated weeds from their vegetable farm by alternating between a year with a cash crop and a year with weed-suppressing cover crops and a cultivated summer fallow (39). Over the years, they have greatly shortened the fallow periods as weeds have become less problematic.

- ***Follow weed-prone crops with crops in which weeds can easily be prevented from going to seed.***
  Weed control is inherently more difficult in some crops than others. For example, unless mulches are used, winter squash and pumpkins tend to become weedy because cultivation and hand weeding are essentially impossible after the vines have run out of the row. Moreover, weeds have usually set seed by the time these full-season crops have matured. Following such crops with a rapid

succession of short-season crops like spinach and lettuce that are harvested before weeds can set seed will kill off many of the seeds produced in the vine crop. This reduces weed problems in subsequent crops. Similarly, small grains cannot be effectively harrowed after the stems begin to elongate, and, especially in spring-sown grain, weeds often go to seed before harvest. The long-term consequences of this seed production can be reduced by following the small grain with an easily cultivated, highly competitive crop like soybean or potato.

Weed control is often more difficult in direct-seeded vegetables than transplanted vegetables because the direct-seeded crops have a prolonged early period when the crop competes poorly and cultivation is difficult. Direct-seeded species like carrot and spinach that have small seeds are more of a problem in this regard than are large-seeded crops like snap beans and sweet corn. If weeds proliferate in the direct-seeded crop, it is usually advisable to follow it with an easily cultivated species that is transplanted or has a large seed.

- **Plant crops in which weed seed production can be prevented before crops that are poor competitors.**

Weed control is often difficult in crops like onion and carrot because they are slow growing and cast relatively little shade. Although some weeds establish from the long-term seed bank in the soil, many of the weeds encountered in a given year establish from seeds shed in the previous year or two. Consequently, growing a crop in which weed seed production can be prevented before planting a poor competitor can reduce the amount of precision cultivation and hand weeding required for successful production of the poor competitor. Cropping strategies in which management prevents weed seed production include successive plantings of short-season crops, short-cycle cover crops alternating with clean fallow periods, crops grown with weed-suppressing mulch, and highly competitive crops that are intensively cultivated (for example, potato).

The crop types that prevent seed production will vary depending on the practices of the farmer. For example, mulched vine crops may be used as a weed "cleaning" crop because the combination of mulch and a dense canopy effectively suppresses weeds, whereas without mulch, vine crops often contribute to the weed seed bank because they become difficult to cultivate or hand weed late in the season.

If weeds become a serious barrier to the production of noncompetitive crops, growing poor competitors in a special crop rotation in which they alternate only with cleaning crops may prove worthwhile. When weed populations have declined substantially, the rotation can be broadened to include occasional crops in which seed production is more difficult to prevent.

- **Rotate between crops that are planted in different seasons.**

Weed species have characteristic times of the year during which they emerge. Common ragweed emerges most readily in early spring and is often a problem in spring-sown organic small grains like barley and oat. In contrast, henbit and shepherd's purse are typically fall-germinating species and are likely to be found in winter wheat and spelt. Rotations that include both spring-planted and fall-planted crops tend to suppress both sorts of species. The spring-germinating weeds tend to be competitively suppressed by fall-sown grain because it is already well established and growing vigorously by the time they germinate. Conversely, fall-germinating species tend to be destroyed before they can set seed when soil is tilled for a spring crop.

Similarly, competitive spring-planted crops tend to suppress midsummer germinating species like purslane, whereas summer tillage for midseason planted vegetables will kill most spring-germinating weed species before they can set seeds.

- **Work cover crops into the rotation between cash crops at times when the soil would otherwise be bare.**

Weeds establish most easily when the ground is bare. Plant canopies suppress seed germination of many weed species by reducing the amount of light and the relative amount of red-wavelength light reaching the soil surface (5). In addition, cover crops compete with any weeds that do emerge. Thus, for example, planting winter rye or mustard cover crops following plow-down of pasture reduced spring weed cover from 52 percent to 9 percent with rye and to 4 percent with mustard (70).

Many studies have shown that grain and legume crops are more competitive against weeds when planted at high density and uniformity (74, 121), and the same principle applies when these species are used as cover crops. Increasing seeding rates by 50 to 100 percent relative to recommended rates for grain or forage production usually produces noticeably improved weed control, particularly if the cover crop is broadcast. Very high-density sowings of competitive cover crops like buckwheat, soybean, and grain rye can completely smother even many perennial weeds. Experimenting on small areas to find the right balance between seed cost of cover crops and weed control is often worthwhile.

Cover crops interseeded into standing cash crops during the last cultivation can help suppress late-emerging weeds but may also compete with the crop (9). Interseeding of cover crops is discussed more fully in chapter 7 (pages 95–100).

- *Avoid cover crop species and cover crop management that promote weeds.*

Many cover crops can behave as weeds if allowed to go to seed due to a delay in mowing or incorporation. Buckwheat and winter grains are particularly prone to cause problems if allowed to seed, because they are fast-growing, competitive species.

Hairy vetch should be avoided on any farm that grows winter grain. Some portion of any hairy vetch seed lot will be "hard" seeds (seeds that are dormant due to a seed coat that does not allow absorption of water). Even if the hairy vetch cover crop is not allowed to go to seed, some of the hard seeds from the original sowing will germinate in subsequent winter grain crops and can severely reduce both yield and grain quality.

Long-season cover crops like red clover and sweet clover are useful for supplying nitrogen and improving soil structure, but they are relatively uncompetitive early in their development and can become weed infested. Because they remain in the ground most of a year or more, annual weeds have time to set seeds, and perennials have plenty of time to increase by growth of roots and rhizomes (underground stems). Such cover crops thus work best when sown with or interseeded into a grain "nurse" crop that can suppress weeds while the legume cover crop develops. Even with a nurse crop, however, weeds can be a problem in the following crop, and many growers choose to avoid red clover and sweet clover before most vegetable crops.

Even hairy vetch or a winter grain like rye may allow seed production by winter annuals like chickweed and shepherd's purse if the cover crop is not incorporated promptly in the spring. The problem is greatest when the cover crop stand is light or spotty. The problem can be avoided, however, by incorporating the cover crop at the first sign of capsule formation on the weeds.

- *Rotate between annual crops and perennial sod crops.*

Although weed seed populations decline more rapidly when the soil is tilled, substantial decreases in populations of most annual weeds occur when sod crops are left in the ground for a few years (79). This occurs by natural die-off of seeds in the soil and because annuals that germinate in a perennial sod are competitively suppressed by the already well-established perennial legumes and grasses. The few annuals that do establish are usually prevented from setting seeds by repeated mowing or grazing. One study found that 83 percent of farmers surveyed in Saskatchewan and Manitoba noticed decreased weed problems following sod crops, and most indicated that the effect lasted more than one year (27). In addition to reducing annual weeds, many of these farmers indicated a reduction in Canada thistle, probably because mowing several times each year depleted food storage in the thistle's roots.

Precautions are required, however, when alternating sod crops with annual crops. Perennial grass weeds like quackgrass should be well controlled prior to planting the sod, or they will likely increase during the sod phase of the rotation. Also, annual weeds may set many seeds during establishment of the sod crop, thereby negating the expected decline in the weed seed bank. Weed seed production can be minimized by using a grain nurse crop that competes with the annual weeds, early harvest of the nurse crop for forage or straw before annuals go to seed, and subsequent mowing of the sod during the establishment year. Another strategy to reduce weed seed production during sod establishment is to plant the sod crop in late summer or early fall.

Although the impact of crop rotation on weeds will not be seen as quickly as the impact of tillage or cultivation, the cumulative affect of a well-planned rotation strategy can, over several years, greatly decrease weed density. Rotation planning is a key way organic growers can substitute brain power for labor and purchased inputs. This principle applies not just to weeds, but also to diseases, insects, soil nutrients, and soil health, as discussed in previous sections of this chapter.

For further reading, see references 5, 9, 27, 39, 40, 60, 61, 62, 70, 73, 74, 79, 96, and 121.

4

CROP SEQUENCES FROM EXPERT FARMERS' FIELDS

SUE ELLEN JOHNSON

Most experienced organic farmers have a good grasp of the biological principles of crop rotation (see sidebar 4.1). Considering an organic farm field with a healthy, high-yielding crop, the natural question is, what cropping history (or crop rotation) contributed to its vigor and productivity?

Chapter 2 (pages 3–20) reviewed the multiple interacting factors that experts balance as they manage crop rotations. This chapter presents crop sequences for actual fields, as implemented by expert organic farmers on their own farms. Twelve expert farmers each recounted the four- or five-year cropping history of one real field on their own farms at a 2002 workshop (see chapter 2, pages 3–20). Cropping sequences used by four additional expert farmers are also included to better represent the range of crops and farm types in the northeastern US. All of the farms whose field sequences are presented in this chapter were nominated as exemplary by organic certifiers or other organizations that work with organic farmers. (The farmers are described in sidebar 4.2, page 48.)

The examples in this chapter are illustrations, not recommendations. The farmers emphasized that these sample sequences may not be (and probably are not) directly transferable to other farms.

These cropping histories illustrate the use of rules-of-thumb (sidebar 4.3, page 55) and the prevalence of crop couplets and short sequences. The farmers developed these couplets and short sequences using observation, cumulative knowledge, judgment, and trial and error under real farm, field, and seasonal conditions. Many sequences continue to evolve as the farms themselves do.

Although whole-farm requirements of cash flow, market demands, equipment, and labor availability set the priorities that guided the development of these sequences, the rationale underlying each sequence is based on the needs of each particular field. Another major element influencing each rotation is the total land area that the farm has available for cropping (see sidebar 2.4, page 6). Although a few sequences may occur on multiple farms, the market goals and farm logistics guiding them may be different in each case. Several farms achieve similar biological goals with different sequences of crop families.

Reading the "Real Fields on Real Farms" Tables

On the next several pages of tables, the year and season are noted in the left-hand columns, and the sequence of crops is presented in one column for each farm's sample field. These tables are color coded to show each crop's

(continued on page 55)

SIDEBAR 4.1

EXAMPLES OF CONVENTIONAL ROTATION WISDOM

- Avoid planting the same crop family in the same field too often.
- Alternate cover crops with cash crops.
- Alternate deep-rooted crops with shallow, fine-rooted crops.
- Precede heavy feeders with nitrogen-fixing cover crops.
- Avoid following a root crop with another root crop.

SIDEBAR 4.2
EXPERT FARMER PROFILES

These profiles reflect the status of the farms and farmers in 2002, when the information on the sample sequences was collected. Of course, farms (and faces) have evolved since the 2002 workshop, but the general character of the sequences and the farmers remains unchanged:

- On Four Winds Farm in Gardiner, New York, **Polly Armour** has been growing vegetables with her husband, Jay, on three acres for 15 years. They use the rest of their land for grazing poultry and cattle. They run a small CSA and also market to restaurants, wholesalers, and at farmers' markets.

- In Argyle, New York, **Paul Arnold** owns Pleasant Valley Farm. For 14 years, he and his wife, Sandy, have raised vegetable crops on five acres. They market almost exclusively through local farmers' markets. The Arnolds have graciously hosted many organic farming events, including the NEON rotation workshop.

- **David Blyn** farms on 12 acres in Roxbury, Connecticut. For 13 years, his operation has sold vegetables at farmers' markets, wholesale outlets, and through a CSA.

- Village Acres Farm in Miflintown, Pennsylvania, is a 30-acre farm owned by **Roy Brubaker**. Farming with his family, he has marketed vegetables, berries, and flowers for 20 years through farmers' markets, the Tuscarora Organic Growers Cooperative, and, more recently, through a CSA.

- **Jean-Paul Courtens** farmed 150 acres with 30 acres in cash crops in Kinderhook, New York, for 13 years. He runs a 650-member CSA.

- In Bridgewater, Maine, **Jim Gerritsen** has been raising seed potatoes that are available by mail order and through wholesale markets. Wood Prairie Farm spans 45 acres and has been in business for 26 years. Jim understands the challenges of rotation on a farm with only one important cash crop.

- Even Star Organic Farm in Lexington, Maryland, is farmed by **Brett Grohsgal**. He cultivates 10 acres and manages 100. A former chef, Brett sells to ten restaurants, four grocery stores, a university, and at two farmers' markets.

- **Jack Gurley** has been farming on five acres in Spark, Maryland, for nine years. His farm, Calvert's Gift Farm, sells vegetables through its CSA to restaurants, at farmers' markets, on the farm, and with other organic growers through a cooperative.

- Kretschmann Farm is a 650-member CSA in Rochester, Pennsylvania. **Don Kretschmann** has been farming for 28 years and sells his produce wholesale, as well as running the CSA.

- On One Straw Farm in Maryland, **Drew Norman** has been growing vegetables for 18 years. One hundred acres are in vegetables and another hundred in hay at any given time. One Straw Farm supplies vegetables for a CSA, farmers' markets, and wholesale outlets.

- **Eero Ruuttila** of Nesenkeag Farm in Litchfield, New Hampshire, has been growing vegetables on 40 acres for 16 years. He markets to restaurants, restaurant wholesalers, food banks, and a newly formed multi-farm CSA.

- Golden Russet Farm in Shoreham, Vermont, spans 82 acres and has 10 acres in vegetables in any given year. **Will Stevens** has been farming for 21 years and sells his crops through a CSA, on-farm sales, farmers' markets, food cooperatives, and local restaurants.

- **Anne and Eric Nordell** grow vegetables on seven acres of Beech Grove Farm in northern Pennsylvania. For over 22 years, they have relied on horses and their own labor to supply several farmers' markets.

- In Penn-Yan, New York, **Klaas and Mary-Howell Martens** farm approximately 1,200 acres, raising grain, soybeans, and processing vegetables. In addition, they operate an organic feed mill and seed processing facility for local producers. They began farming organically in 1992.

- **John Myer** is one of the pioneers of certified organic grain production in New York. He has been farming organically since 1982 and raises soybeans, wheat, spelt, corn, alfalfa, dry beans, and clover seed, along with beef cattle, on 880 acres in Ovid, New York.

- **Ed Fry** operates Fair Hills Farm in Chestertown, New Jersey, on 550 rented acres. A dairy farmer for 42 years, he began organic grain and hay production in 1997. He sells organic feed in addition to operating a 150-cow dairy.

Real Fields on Real Farms:
Sample Four- and Five-Year Vegetable Crop Rotations

		Calvert's Gift Farm Jack Gurley, Md.	**Even Star Organic Farm** Brett Grohsgal, Md.	**Four Winds Farm** Polly & Jay Armour, N.Y.
Y1	Winter	Garlic	Crimson Clover	Oats
	Spring	Winter Squash	Tomatoes **OR** Peppers	Potatoes **OR** Tomatoes[a]
	Summer			
	Fall		Red Clover / Winter Brassicas / Lettuce (strip crop)	Straw mulch / Garlic (in alternate beds)[b]
Y2	Winter	Spinach	Red Clover	
	Spring		Okra – Flowers – Basil	Winter Squash (in alternate beds) / Straw mulch
	Summer	Soybeans		
	Fall		Winter Brassicas / Vetch / Lettuce (strip crop)	
Y3	Winter	Oats	Vetch	Straw mulch
	Spring	Fava Beans		Beans
	Summer		Cucurbits	
	Fall	Brassicas	Crimson Clover / Lettuce (strip crop) / Winter Brassicas	Compost
Y4	Winter	Vetch	Red Clover	Direct-Seeded Quick Crops / Small-Seeded Greens / Radishes
	Spring			
	Summer	Tomatoes		Cucumbers (mulched with straw) / Lettuce
	Fall	Garlic	Red Clover / Winter Brassicas / Lettuce (strip crop)	
Y5	Winter	*Return to Year One*	*Return to Year One*	*Return to Year One*
	Spring			
	Summer			
	Fall			

[a] This rotation switches between potatoes and tomatoes in alternate cycles.
[b] This rotation is designed around alternate beds.

KEY
- "Fallow" indicates a deliberate period of bare soil, often with frequent cultivation to kill weeds.
- Split boxes indicate strip crops or split beds.
- Intercrops with crops from more than one family are represented by a dark gray background.
- Cash crops are indicated by black text, cover crops and fallows by white text.

The boxes below show the color codes for plant families in the rotation diagrams.

Grasses– Poaceae	Legumes – Fabaceae	Brassicas – Brassicaceae	Nightshades– Solanaceae	Cucurbits – Cucurbitaceae	Beets, spinach – Chenopodiaceae	Mulch	Cash Crop
Lettuce – Asteraceae	Alliums – Liliaceae	Carrot– Apiaceae	Miscellaneous	Fallow	Grass-legume mix	Intercrop	Cover Crop

		Golden Russet Farm Will Stevens, Vt.	**Kretschmann Farm** Don Kretschmann, Pa.	**Nesenkeag Farm** Eero Ruuttila, N.H.
Y1	Winter	Wheat **OR** Oats	Alfalfa	Rye – Vetch
	Spring	Brassicas	Tomatoes	Winter Squash
	Summer			
	Fall		Rye – Vetch	Rye – Vetch
Y2	Winter	Oats		
	Spring	Potatoes	Lettuce (triple crop)	Potatoes
	Summer		Spinach / Turnips	
	Fall			
Y3	Winter	Wheat (overseed)	Rye – Vetch	Rye – Vetch
	Spring		Beets	
	Summer	Winter Squash Summer Vetch	Late Brassicas with Underseeded Rye **OR** Oats	Sudangrass
	Fall			Oats – Field Peas
Y4	Winter	Wheat		Lettuce / Spinach / Chard / Beet Greens
	Spring			
	Summer	Sweet Corn / Summer "Smalls"ᶜ		Arugula / Mustard / Brassicas / Lettuce
	Fall		Alfalfa	Rye – Vetch
Y5	Winter	Oats (and compost)		
	Spring	Spring "Smalls"ᶜ		*Return to Year One*
	Summer	Summer Fallow		
	Fall	Wheat **OR** Oats		

KEY • "Fallow" indicates a deliberate period of bare soil, often with frequent cultivation to kill weeds.
• Split boxes indicate strip crops or split beds.
• Intercrops with crops from more than one family are represented by a dark gray background.
• Cash crops are indicated by black text, cover crops and fallows by white text.
The boxes below show the color codes for plant families in the rotation diagrams.

ᶜ "Smalls" indicates any crop grown in small quantities, such as scallions, green beans, and other "oddballs."

Grasses – Poaceae	Legumes – Fabaceae	Brassicas – Brassicaceae	Nightshades– Solanaceae	Cucurbits – Cucurbitaceae	Beets, spinach – Chenopodiaceae	Mulch	Cash Crop
Lettuce – Asteraceae	Alliums – Liliaceae	Carrot– Apiaceae	Miscellaneous	Fallow	Grass-legume mix	Intercrop	Cover Crop

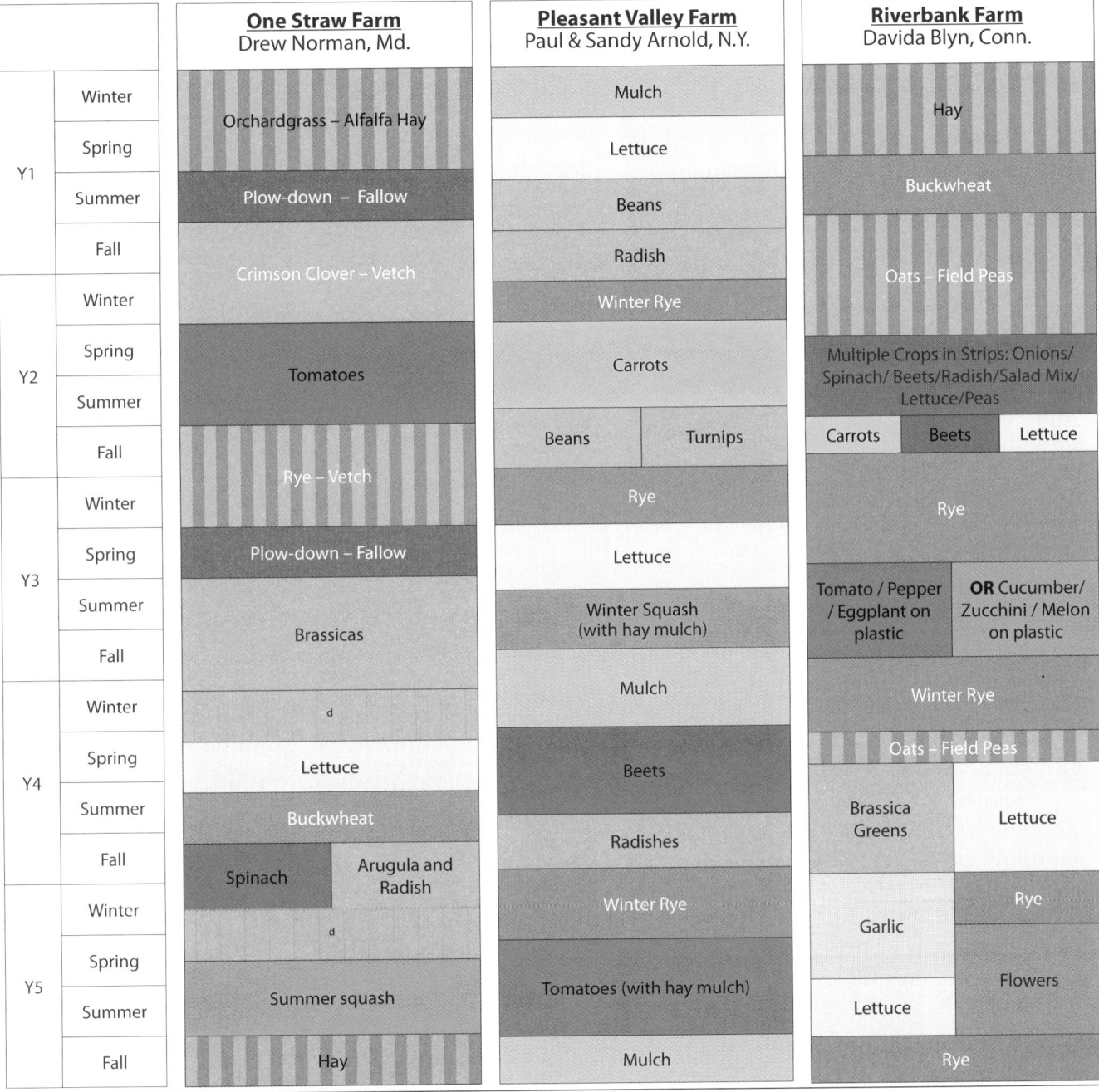

		One Straw Farm Drew Norman, Md.	**Pleasant Valley Farm** Paul & Sandy Arnold, N.Y.	**Riverbank Farm** Davida Blyn, Conn.
Y1	Winter	Orchardgrass – Alfalfa Hay	Mulch	Hay
	Spring		Lettuce	
	Summer	Plow-down – Fallow	Beans	Buckwheat
	Fall	Crimson Clover – Vetch	Radish	Oats – Field Peas
Y2	Winter		Winter Rye	
	Spring	Tomatoes	Carrots	Multiple Crops in Strips: Onions/ Spinach/ Beets/Radish/Salad Mix/ Lettuce/Peas
	Summer			
	Fall	Rye – Vetch	Beans | Turnips	Carrots | Beets | Lettuce
Y3	Winter		Rye	Rye
	Spring	Plow-down – Fallow	Lettuce	
	Summer	Brassicas	Winter Squash (with hay mulch)	Tomato / Pepper / Eggplant on plastic | **OR** Cucumber/ Zucchini / Melon on plastic
	Fall			
Y4	Winter	d	Mulch	Winter Rye
	Spring	Lettuce	Beets	Oats – Field Peas
	Summer	Buckwheat		Brassica Greens | Lettuce
	Fall	Spinach | Arugula and Radish	Radishes	
Y5	Winter	d	Winter Rye	Garlic | Rye
	Spring	Summer squash	Tomatoes (with hay mulch)	| Flowers
	Summer			Lettuce |
	Fall	Hay	Mulch	Rye

KEY • "Fallow" indicates a deliberate period of bare soil, often with frequent cultivation to kill weeds.
• Split boxes indicate strip crops or split beds.
• Intercrops with crops from more than one family are represented by a dark gray background.
• Cash crops are indicated by black text, cover crops and fallows by white text.
The boxes below show the color codes for plant families in the rotation diagrams.

[d] Harvest of brassica and fall cool-season crops extends into winter. Clovers may be inter-seeded at the last cultivation.

Grasses – Poaceae	Legumes – Fabaceae	Brassicas – Brassicaceae	Nightshades– Solanaceae	Cucurbits – Cucurbitaceae	Beets, spinach – Chenopodiaceae	Mulch	Cash Crop
Lettuce – Asteraceae	Alliums – Liliaceae	Carrot– Apiaceae	Miscellaneous	Fallow	Grass-legume mix	Intercrop	Cover Crop

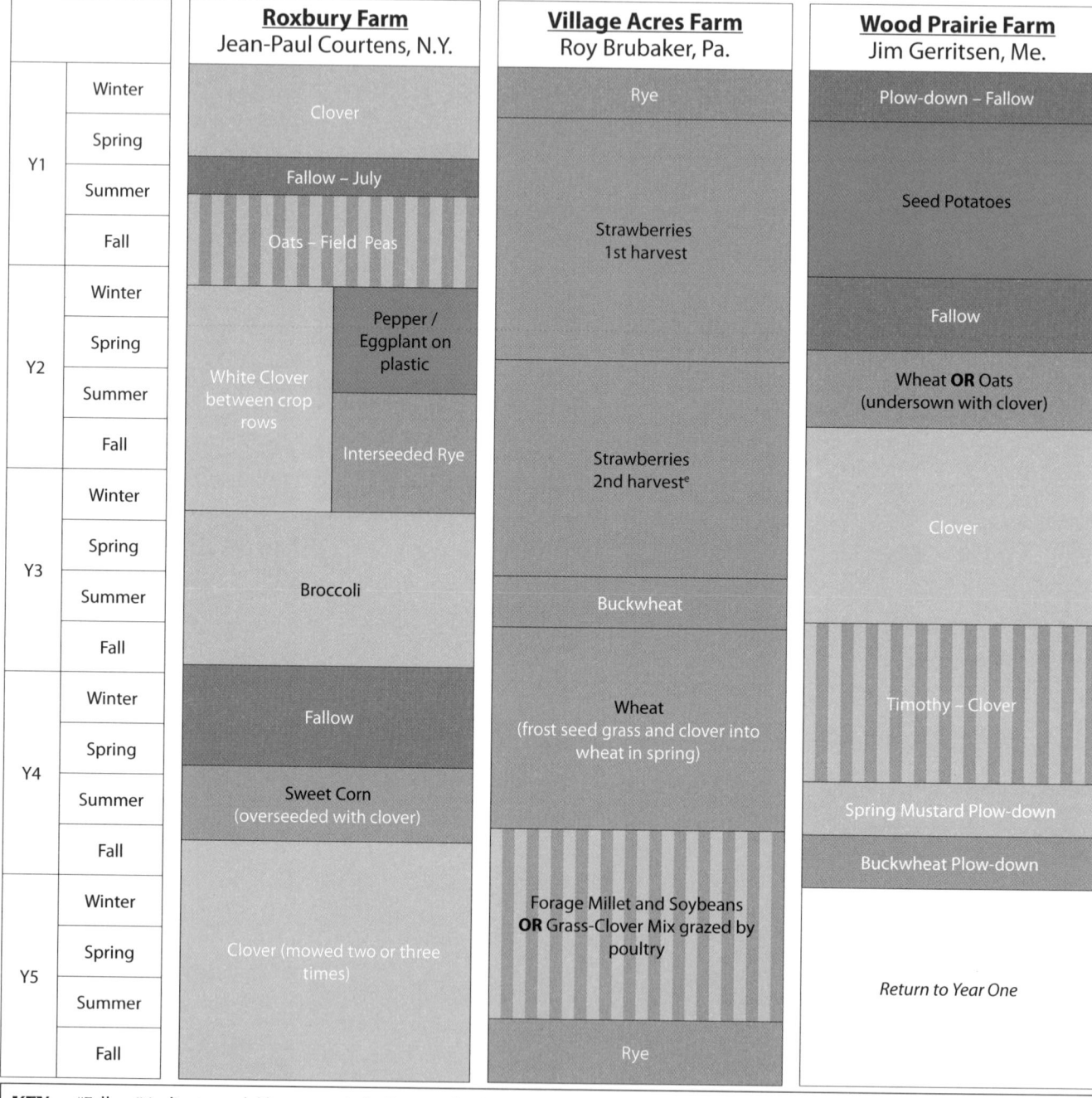

		Roxbury Farm Jean-Paul Courtens, N.Y.	**Village Acres Farm** Roy Brubaker, Pa.	**Wood Prairie Farm** Jim Gerritsen, Me.
Y1	Winter	Clover	Rye	Plow-down – Fallow
	Spring		Strawberries 1st harvest	Seed Potatoes
	Summer	Fallow – July		
	Fall	Oats – Field Peas		
Y2	Winter	White Clover between crop rows		Fallow
	Spring			Wheat **OR** Oats (undersown with clover)
	Summer	Pepper / Eggplant on plastic	Strawberries 2nd harvest[e]	
	Fall	Interseeded Rye		Clover
Y3	Winter	Broccoli		
	Spring			
	Summer		Buckwheat	
	Fall		Wheat (frost seed grass and clover into wheat in spring)	Timothy – Clover
Y4	Winter	Fallow		
	Spring			
	Summer	Sweet Corn (overseeded with clover)		Spring Mustard Plow-down
	Fall		Forage Millet and Soybeans **OR** Grass-Clover Mix grazed by poultry	Buckwheat Plow-down
Y5	Winter	Clover (mowed two or three times)		Return to Year One
	Spring			
	Summer			
	Fall		Rye	

KEY
- "Fallow" indicates a deliberate period of bare soil, often with frequent cultivation to kill weeds.
- Split boxes indicate strip crops or split beds.
- Intercrops with crops from more than one family are represented by a dark gray background.
- Cash crops are indicated by black text, cover crops and fallows by white text.

[e] This strawberry rotation is followed by cycling into a vegetable rotation sequence.

The boxes below show the color codes for plant families in the rotation diagrams.

Grasses – Poaceae	Legumes – Fabaceae	Brassicas – Brassicaceae	Nightshades– Solanaceae	Cucurbits – Cucurbitaceae	Beets, spinach – Chenopodiaceae	Mulch	Cash Crop
Lettuce – Asteraceae	Alliums – Liliaceae	Carrot– Apiaceae	Miscellaneous	Fallow	Grass-legume mix	Intercrop	Cover Crop

		Beech Grove Farm Anne and Eric Nordell, Pa.			
Y1	Winter	Fallow			
	Spring	Oats			
	Summer	Cultivated Fallow			
	Fall	Field Peas			
Y2	Winter				
	Spring	Onion			
	Summer				
	Fall				
Y3	Winter	Rye			
	Spring				
	Summer	Cultivated Fallow			
	Fall	Rye – Vetch			
Y4	Winter				
	Spring				
	Summer	Lettuce	Carrot	Spinach	
	Fall	Lettuce	Carrot	Spinach	Rye (interseeded)
Y5	Winter	*Return to Year One*			
	Spring				
	Summer				
	Fall				

KEY • "Fallow" indicates a deliberate period of bare soil, often with frequent cultivation to kill weeds.
• Split boxes indicate strip crops or split beds.
• Intercrops with crops from more than one family are represented by a dark gray background.
• Cash crops are indicated by black text, cover crops and fallows by white text.

The boxes below show the color codes for plant families in the rotation diagrams.

Grasses – Poaceae	Legumes – Fabaceae	Brassicas – Brassicaceae	Nightshades– Solanaceae	Cucurbits – Cucurbitaceae	Beets, spinach – Chenopodiaceae	Mulch	Cash Crop
Lettuce – Asteraceae	Alliums – Liliaceae	Carrot– Apiaceae	Miscellaneous	Fallow	Grass-legume mix	Intercrop	Cover Crop

Real Fields on Real Farms:
Sample Four- and Five-Year Grain Crop Rotations

		Martens Farm Klaas & Mary-H Martens, NY	**Myer Farm** John Myer, NY	**Fair Hills Farm** Ed Fry, MD
Y1	Winter	Red clover (plowdown)	Alfalfa (fourth year)	Rye (silage)
	Spring	Corn		Corn (grain) Rye (overseeded)
	Summer			
	Fall			
Y2	Winter	Fallow		Rye (silage)
	Spring		Corn	
	Summer	Soybean		Corn (silage)
	Fall			
Y3	Winter	Winter wheat	Fallow	Rye (silage)
	Spring	Winter wheat Red clover (overseeded)		
	Summer		Soybean	Corn (silage)
	Fall	Red clover		
Y4	Winter	Return to Year One	Winter wheat	Fallow
	Spring		Winter wheat Red clover (overseeded)	
	Summer			Alfalfa
	Fall			
Y5	Winter		Red clover	
	Spring			
	Summer			
	Fall			

KEY
- "Fallow" indicates a deliberate period of bare soil, often with frequent cultivation to kill weeds.
- Split boxes indicate strip crops or split beds.
- Intercrops with crops from more than one family are represented by a dark gray background.
- Cash crops are indicated by black text, cover crops and fallows by white text.

The boxes below show the color codes for plant families in the rotation diagrams.

Grasses – Poaceae	Legumes – Fabaceae	Brassicas – Brassicaceae	Nightshades– Solanaceae	Cucurbits – Cucurbitaceae	Beets, spinach – Chenopodiaceae	Mulch	Cash Crop
Lettuce – Asteraceae	Alliums – Liliaceae	Carrot– Apiaceae	Miscellaneous	Fallow	Grass-legume mix	Intercrop	Cover Crop

botanical family. A few of the sequences include mulch applications, but most of the plans do not indicate other aspects of production such as compost applications and tillage operations, which many of the farmers indicated were integral to their rotation management. The differences between the rotations are striking. Note that no one pattern characterizes the rotations on these successful, expertly managed organic vegetable and field crop farms. Also notice that some fields or beds are subdivided among different crops at certain points in the rotation sequence. At the next planting they are cycled back and managed as single field units.

SIDEBAR 4.3

NORTHEAST GROWERS' RULES OF THUMB

We asked numerous organic growers to share their crop sequencing "rules of thumb." These illustrate the common practices of many organic growers. Some sequences have been scientifically tested, and others have not.

Below is a sampling of some of their recommended crop "couplets." These are simply rules of thumb that individual farmers use in their own rotation planning. All farmers do not use the same couplets because of variation between farms in cropping practices, pest and weed pressures, marketing strategies, climate, length of season, and other factors. Growers' rationales for these couplets include (1) disease and pest management, (2) fertility management, (3) weed management, (4) double cropping, and (5) seedbed preparation. Many rules relate to the nightshade family, perhaps because it is prone to problems that can be managed by crop rotation.

General Rules:
- Grow winter cover crops *before* late-planted crops to accumulate organic matter and nitrogen.
- Grow winter-killed cover crops (oat-pea) *before* early-season crops, so the seedbed will be easy to prepare.
- *Never* grow any crop after itself.

Nightshades (tomatoes, potatoes, peppers, eggplants):
- Grow tomatoes *after* peas, lettuce, or spinach, because tomatoes take a lot out of the soil.
- Grow lettuce *before* potatoes, because it is a light feeder and an aboveground crop.
- Grow legume cover crops *before* potatoes or corn, so that they can feed the crops.
- Grow potatoes *before* crops that are poor competitors, because potato production involves aggressive cultivation and further working of the soil during harvest, both of which reduce weed pressure.
- *Avoid* growing potatoes before corn, because both are heavy feeders.

- *Be cautious* when growing bell pepper before another vegetable crop, because of diseases.
- *Avoid* planting potatoes after corn, because of wireworm problems.

Grasses, Corn, and Grains:
- Grow beans *after* corn to rebuild nitrogen.
- *Avoid* growing legumes before small grains to prevent lodging.

Alliums:
- Use a summer fallow *after* onions, because usually there are many weeds.

Lettuce and Crops in the Beet and Spinach Family:
- Grow peas *before* fall greens, because there is time for double cropping, and fall greens benefit from the nitrogen fixed by the peas.
- Grow a root crop like beets *after* lettuce or cabbage.

Observations on the Sample Sequences

The sample rotation sequences vary from farm to farm. The farmers explained that some cropping practices relate to the immediately preceding or following cash crop, and some relate to crops two or three seasons apart. Couplets of cover crops and cash crops are common. Careful examination of the crop sequences reveals several interesting points.

- For some fields, five years was inadequate to capture the full sequence of crops. For example, fields on Village Acres, Wood Prairie Farm, and Myers Farm are cycling through a longer period of cropping and have longer rotations due to the inclusion of perennial crops like hay and strawberries. In these cases, the crop sequences may show only two or three crops.

- Most of the farms rarely repeat a planting of the same crop family in the same field from one season to the next. When they do, they try to move the crops from bed to bed to avoid repeating on the same area of the field. This limits the buildup of soilborne pests and diseases.

- Most of the farms use a diversity of cover crops and plant a cover crop in most years. Some farms are exceptions, however. Notably, the two farms with the smallest acreage rely on compost to supply nitrogen and soil-building organic matter.

- A series of cover crops is grown in sequence on Nesenkeag Farm (rye-vetch intercrop, sudan grass, oat-pea intercrop). Riverbank Farm also follows rye with an oat-pea intercrop. In both cases, the sequence of cover crops is used to prepare the seedbed for high-value small-seeded crops.

- On those farms and on Golden Russet Farm, a winter-killed cover crop of oats and field peas tends to precede spring plantings of high-value direct-seeded crops with small seeds.

- Both cultivated fallows and mulching are important steps in sequences on some farms. Both are used for weed control.

- At Beech Grove Farm, crop rotation follows a fixed four-year cycle with prescheduled cultivated fallows and cover crops. The system is designed to minimize weeding and distribute labor. The vegetable production field is divided into 12 half-acre strips. In any particular year, only 6 of the strips are planted with vegetables.

Each growing season, 3 strips are used for spring-planted vegetables and 3 strips for summer-planted vegetables. The remaining 6 strips are taken out of production. The strips that are out of production are cover cropped over the winter and produce substantial biomass. For six weeks during midsummer they are shallowly tilled several times, then planted to another cover crop in early August. Winter-killed covers like oats and field pea are used in strips that will be planted to early vegetable crops. Winter-hardy cover crops like rye and hairy vetch are used in strips where vegetable crops will be planted the following summer. This creates a four-year rotation cycle of (1) cover crops and fallow, (2) early vegetables followed by cover crops, (3) cover crops and fallow, and (4) summer vegetables. Alternating cash crops with bare fallow and cover crops appears to have exhausted the weed seed bank and built high soil quality. As a result, weed control needs and weed competition are minimal even when weather interferes with timely cultivation. Harvest and planting efforts are spread across the season.

- Brassicas are often followed by a grass cover crop (with or without a legume). Farmers indicated that this is because brassicas are nutrient-demanding crops, and a cover crop is needed to rebuild the soil and provide quick soil cover.

- Cucurbits tend to follow a cover crop or an early salad crop—spinach, lettuce, or brassica greens. Planting cucurbits is delayed until early summer, to allow double cropping of the same ground in a single season.

- Tomatoes, potatoes, and peppers (nightshades) are often preceded by a legume like clover, vetch, or hay. On two farms nightshades are preceded by fallow, in part to improve weed control and in part to increase available soil nitrogen through breakdown of a cover crop.

- Fair Hills Farm operations are based around its dairy and feed sales to organic dairies. As on many dairies in the northeast US, grasses are grown continuously (corn-rye-corn) for several years before rotation into alfalfa or mixed hay. Predominance of grasses in the rotation seems to cause few problems, possibly because the application of manure supplies nutrients and harvest and removal of the entire aboveground portion of the rye and corn plants for silage keeps pest populations in check.

Summary

Keep in mind that these sequences describe the cropping history of only one field or bed on farms that have many fields and beds (sometimes several hundred). Since the sequences were described, several farmers have reported that they continue to modify the sequences on the fields depicted as new lessons are learned or to deal with changing conditions and opportunities (see chapter 2, pages 3–20).

Note that cash crops rotate among members of different crop families. A diversified cropping approach produces both resilience and flexibility, for optimal ecological and business management of a farming system.

Expert farmers' crop sequences make sense for individual fields, but also for their farm businesses. Several farmers offered specific reasons particular crop sequences work for them. Jack Gurley believes he needs to maximize use of cover crops without losing growing space. Consequently, he looks for opportunities to interseed cover crops into cash crops (for example, hairy vetch into broccoli, white clover into tomatoes). In her no-till bed system, Polly Armour follows potatoes with winter squash that she mulches heavily, thereby controlling weeds arising from seeds that get stirred to the soil surface during potato harvest.

Cover crops fulfill diverse and multiple roles on these fields. The farmers stressed the importance of matching the cover crop to the following crop. For example, since crops differ in their ability to tolerate cover crop residues, some farmers plant winter-killed cover crops where early spring crops will be planted.

5

A CROP ROTATION PLANNING PROCEDURE

Charles L. Mohler

This chapter provides a step-by-step procedure for planning crop rotations on an individual farm. The procedure is based on methods used by the panel of expert farmers (chapter 2, pages 3–20), supplemented with other sources. It distills what experienced growers do, based on experience, knowledge, and intuition, into a systematic method. For the sake of simplicity, the instructions are written as if the person doing the planning is the manager of the farm.

The crop rotation planning procedure works through a series of steps. You will (1) organize your information, (2) develop a general rotation plan (optional), (3) construct a crop rotation planning map, (4) plan future crop sequences for each section of the farm, and (5) refine your crop sequence plan.

The procedure is *easiest* for a farm that produces only a few crops and has uniform field conditions, but it is *most useful* for farms with complex operations. Examples of farms with relatively simple rotation problems include most grain farms and some wholesale vegetable operations, where all of the crops can be grown on all of the fields. The procedure can be used to plan rotations with more crops and multiple soil types, but the process is time consuming. The rewards of systematic crop rotation planning increase, however, with the number of crops and the complexity of the fields. On farms that grow only a few crops, reasonable rotations can be maintained using a few rules of thumb. With a complex operation, however, a long-term problem can develop without the farmer realizing that the rotation practices are suboptimal. Although the planning procedure described below is divided into many steps, it is not complicated. Simply proceed one step at a time, and you will end up with a plan. Besides helping you develop a plan, working through the procedure will likely give you new insights into your farm and

> **"The rewards of systematic crop rotation planning increase, however, with the number of crops and the complexity of the fields."**

how you manage it. It can also serve as a new baseline and record system for your farm.

The crop rotation planning process becomes more complex if the crop mix is highly diverse, if you plant the same crop multiple times each season, if you double or triple crop fields, or if the fields vary in their ability to grow various crops. For farms that require a complex cropping plan, using Microsoft Excel spreadsheets instead of paper worktables is advised. These can be downloaded from HTTP://WWW.NEON.CORNELL.EDU/CROPROTATION. The site also contains a modified version of this chapter in which the instructions are adapted to worksheets rather than paper tables. For any farm, the computer worksheets will simplify data entry and sorting.

The procedure described here is not a cookbook recipe. It will not tell you which crop should follow another— for example, to precede a crop with hairy vetch or follow it with potato. Rather, the procedure will help you organize diverse data on the management and biology of the crops you want to grow to define rotations that work for your particular farm. You need to know your fields and your crop mix to use this planner. Only you know the particular goals, problems, and opportunities of your farm operation. The procedure can help you recognize the critical decisions that need to be made, however, and prompt you to make them in a logical order. The worksheets (tables 5.1, 5.2, and 5.3, pages 61–67) will help you enter, compare, and sort the information you need to plan a good crop rotation, for each field and for the entire farm.

> **"Expert growers simplify their planning by building their rotations around short sequences of two or three crops or cover crops."**

Tips for Sequencing Crops

Because the planning procedure presented below is lengthy and detailed, some of the most useful steps are summarized briefly in this section. Growers who do not wish to go through the detailed planning procedure will still find this summary useful in planning crop sequences. Note that the simplified steps presented here do not cover development of a flexible generalized rotation plan (see sidebar 5.1) but rather summarize the ad hoc sequencing introduced in chapter 2 (pages 3–20). To avoid confusion, the steps in this simple summary section are labeled A, B, C to distinguish them from the numbered steps in the systematic planning procedure.

A. *Identify and prioritize goals.*

Write down what you want your crop rotation to accomplish (see sidebar 2.8, page 14 for rotation goals of expert farmers). Decide which goals take precedence this year if not all goals can be met simultaneously.

B. *Write down your crop mix.*

List the crops you plan to grow next season and the amount of land you will devote to each crop. For crops grown in succession plantings, list each planting as a separate crop (for example, spring broccoli, fall broccoli). This will help with planning, since the crops and cover crops that precede and follow will differ with the season of the planting.

SIDEBAR 5.1
ROTATION PLANNING VS. CROP SEQUENCING

Cropping plans have two aspects: the development of a general rotation plan and the sequencing of particular crops. The general rotation plan might specify, for example, that nightshade crops will be followed by mustard family crops, then salad greens other than mustards, and finally cucurbits; or that full-season crops will be followed by a year of cover crops and then early-planted short-season crops. The rotation plan provides the framework; the sequencing plan provides the details of what crop goes where in succeeding years. The rotation plan needs to be general enough to allow flexibility in sequencing. The sequencing plan is necessarily tentative and ideally leaves room for alternative crops in case weather or markets force last-minute changes.

The relative importance of rotation planning versus crop sequencing in overall crop planning depends on the farm. In general, as the complexity of the farm operation increases, rotation planning becomes less possible and careful crop sequencing becomes more critical (figure 5.1, page 60). If your farm operation is suited to rotation planning, developing a plan will greatly simplify your crop sequencing. If, however, your operation is highly complex, following a general plan is likely to prove futile. In that case, detailed record keeping and careful placement of crops become the keys to avoiding rotation problems.

C. *Check for excessive acreage of one family.*

Write the family name next to each crop and add up the acreage of each family (family names of crops are given in appendix 1, pages 101–103). If you find that any one family (other than grasses) would be grown on more than 25 percent of your land, consider increasing the diversity or balance of your crop mix. A high proportion of land in one family necessarily means that most locations will rotate back to that family quickly. This can lead to problems with soilborne diseases (see "Managing Plant Diseases with Crop Rotation," page 32, and appendix 3, pages 124–137).

D. *Identify crop couplets and short sequences that work well on your farm.*

Expert growers simplify their planning by building their rotations around short sequences of two or three crops or cover crops. Think about what has worked on your farm in the past. Many additional short sequences can be gathered by talking with other farmers or gleaned from the sample rotations in chapter 4 (pages 49–54) and from appendix 2 (pages 104–123).

E. *Make a crop rotation planning map.*

Thoughtfully dividing your farm into relatively small management units of approximately equal size greatly simplifies planning and record keeping. The management units should be no larger than the area you ever manage as an independent unit. On grain farms, management units are often long strips across the field. On vegetable farms, they may be individual beds. Having the farm divided into relatively small units allows you to keep track of exactly what you planted on a particular piece of ground one, two, or five years later. In addition, if soil conditions, weed problems, or other factors that affect management vary across a field, managing the farm in small units allows systematic matching of crops to conditions for site-specific management. A single crop will often be planted on several adjacent management units if that is convenient.

Make a map of your farm showing every management unit. Make the map large enough so that information can be written in each management unit (this may take more than one sheet of paper). Give each unit a number. When you are satisfied with your map, make multiple (six or more) copies. Creating a computer version of your map reduces the labor of writing crop names onto management units, simplifies revising plans, and makes producing copies of the map easy (see appendix 6, pages 148–149).

F. *Identify conditions that affect what crops can be grown on each management unit.*

On one copy of the map, note any difficult or desirable characteristics that influence what crops you may want to plant there. Some locations may be wet; others may warm earlier in the spring. Sidebar 2.9 (page 15) lists field properties that expert growers take into account when placing crops, and table 5.5 (page 74–75) provides abbreviations that fit easily onto a map. Although these lists are long, note that many of the field characteristics probably do not vary across your farm and thus are of no interest to you.

G. *Plan next summer.*

On another copy of your map, assign each crop to as many management units as you need to meet the area specified by your crop mix (see step B above). If a management unit will be double or triple cropped, separate the crop names with slashes (for example, May lettuce / buckwheat cover / fall spinach). Placing crops in the following order often works well:

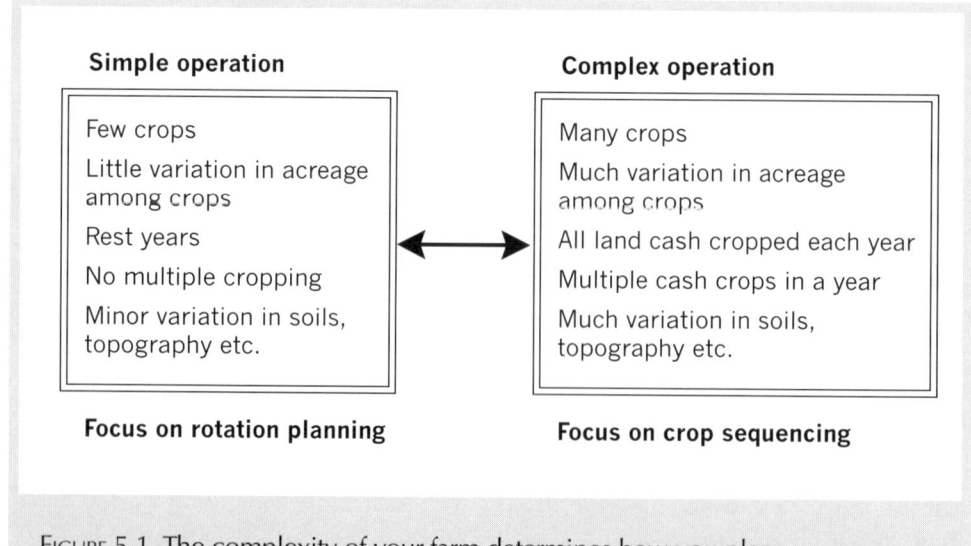

Simple operation	Complex operation
Few crops	Many crops
Little variation in acreage among crops	Much variation in acreage among crops
Rest years	All land cash cropped each year
No multiple cropping	Multiple cash crops in a year
Minor variation in soils, topography etc.	Much variation in soils, topography etc.
Focus on rotation planning	**Focus on crop sequencing**

FIGURE 5.1 The complexity of your farm determines how you plan.

(continued on page 68)

TABLE 5.1 Crop characteristics worktable

Crop	Area/ Year	MUs/ Year	Family	Planting Time	Harvest Ends	Net $/ Acre											

TABLE 5.2 Field conditions worktable — Part A

Field Name	Field Type	Mgmt Unit	Crop Three Summers Ago	Crop Two Winters Ago	Crop Two Summers Ago	Crop Last Winter	Crop Last Summer

TABLE 5.2 Field conditions worktable — Part B

Field Type	Mgmt Unit	Current Winter												
		Crop	Plant	Harv										

TABLE 5.3 Field futures worktable — Part A

Field name	Field Type	Mgmt Unit	Next Summer Crop	Plant	Harv	Next Winter Crop	Plant	Harv	Two Summers from Now Crop	Plant	Harv

TABLE 5.3 Field futures worktable — Part B

Field Type	Mgmt Unit	Two Winters from Now			Three Summers from Now			Three Winters from Now			Four Summers from Now		
		Crop	Plant	Harv	Crop	Plant	Harv	Crop	Plant	Harv	Crop	Plant	Harv

TABLE 5.3 Field futures worktable — Part C

Field Type	Mgmt Unit	Four Winters from Now			Five Summers from Now			Five Winters from Now			Six Summers from Now		
		Crop	Plant	Harv	Crop	Plant	Harv	Crop	Plant	Harv	Crop	Plant	Harv

TABLE 5.3 Field futures worktable — Part D

Field Type	Mgmt Unit	Crop	Plant	Harv	Crop	Plant	Harv	Crop	Plant	Harv	Crop	Plant	Harv

1. Crops that are already planted. (You do not want to plow them up!)
2. Crops in your major crop family, especially if one family will cover more than a fourth of your acreage. Do these early in the process so that you can avoid locations that have had that family recently. This does not apply to grasses, since they rarely foster soilborne diseases.
3. High-value crops that do best in particular field conditions.
4. Other high-value crops.
5. Lower-value crops that do best in particular locations.
6. Lower-value crops that can be grown anywhere.

When placing a crop onto a management unit, refer to your list of crop couplets, avoid units that have had the same family in the past few years, and check appendix 2 (pages 104–123) for potential problems. To limit buildup of pests and disease, avoid placing succession plantings of a crop species in adjacent management units.

H. *Plan the following year.*

To plan the next seasons, repeat the same process you used in step G. For the moment, ignore winter cover crops.

I. *Plan fall-planted crops and cover crops.*

Place your fall cover crops and overwintering cash crops on another copy of the map by the same process used for G and H. Note that the cover crop on each management unit needs to work well with both the preceding and the following crops.

J. *Take your plans to the field.*

Take your maps with the crops written on them and walk your fields. For each group of management units assigned to a crop, imagine farming that piece of land through the coming years. Consider tillage, planting, maintenance, and harvest of the crops to see if the proposed crop sequence makes sense for that location. Note any changes you decide to make.

K. *Develop contingency plans.*

Think ahead to see what problems might arise with growing the proposed crops in the planned management units. How might the plans need to shift if the spring is too wet for early-planted crops, if labor for transplanting is unavailable at a critical time, or if you experience some other problem that could affect where various crops can be planted? Write action plans for coping with various potential problems and make provisions for possible problems (for example, by obtaining extra crop or cover crop seed to fill in locations that could not be planted as planned).

The steps above capture the essence of the planning procedure. The following sections include a method for developing a general rotation plan, examples, additional hints, an explanation of why these steps are sensible, and a means of checking for errors to ensure that your plans do not contain contradictions.

SIDEBAR 5.2

SMALL VALLEY FARM: AN EXAMPLE TO ILLUSTRATE THE PROCEDURES

Small Valley Farm is a cash grain and beef operation (figure 5.2, page 72). The farmers grow grain and soybeans for human consumption and alfalfa-grass hay for winter feed for their herd of beef cattle. The farm has 720 tillable acres. Although the farmers can grow all crops successfully on all of the tillable land, 240 acres are sufficiently steep that erosion is a potential problem when they grow row crops. A desire to avoid row crops on their steep land has motivated them to undertake rotation planning.

In the past, they have followed a six-year rotation: oat/clover/spelt → spelt/hay → hay → hay → corn → soybean and then back to oat/clover/spelt. Their crop mix is summarized in table 5.4 (page 70). They establish alfalfa-grass hay by overseeding it into spelt in the spring. They plow hay in the fall before corn to allow the sod to break down, and they sow an oat cover crop to protect the soil over the winter. They plant red clover with oat to provide a boost of N for the following spelt crop.

A Complete, Step-by-Step Rotation Planning Guide

Before You Begin . . .

Before you begin, please read through the instructions to see where you are headed with each step. This will also tell you whether the effort involved is worthwhile for your farm. Earlier chapters in this manual provide many suggestions as to how to think about the problem of developing general crop rotation plans and specific crop sequences. Tables in the appendices provide a wealth of factual information to help you avoid problems and take advantage of opportunities related to particular cropping sequences. Becoming familiar and consulting with that information will help you work through the steps that follow. The procedure may prompt you to rethink your farming operation and crop mix, as you order the sequence of crops on particular fields.

Initial Steps

1. **Copy tables from this manual.**

   If you are using the Excel worksheets mentioned above, skip this step.

   Otherwise, make several copies of table 5.1 (Crop Characteristics Worktable, page 61). You will need enough copies so that each planting of every crop during a typical year can have one line. You may find a few extra copies useful, as well.

   Make several copies of table 5.2 (Field Conditions Worktable, pages 62–63). Note that the table consists of two separate sheets (parts A and B), and you will need multiple copies of each sheet. How many copies you make to start with depends on how accessible the nearest copier is. The exact number of copies you will need cannot be determined at the outset, but you can determine the approximate number of copies as follows: Divide the cropped area of the farm by the acreage of your smallest-acreage crop. You probably will not need more than that number of copies. You probably will need at least a fourth of that number.

   Make copies of table 5.3 (Field Futures Worktable, pages 64–67). Make as many copies of this table as you made of table 5.2. Note that the Field Futures Worktable consists of four sheets (parts A–D), and you will need multiple copies of at least the first two sheets. Whether you need to copy the third and fourth sheets depends on

how far forward you want to plan.

Cut your copies of the Field Conditions Worktable, part B, along the vertical line between "Manage unit" and "Current winter." Now tape each part B sheet to each part A sheet to make one extra-wide sheet. "Current winter" should now be next to "Crop last summer" on Part A. Discard the scrap with "Zone" and "Manage unit." Place a long piece of tape on the back where the two sheets meet, as eventually you will need to cut the sheets lengthwise to sort the lines.

Repeat the cutting and taping for the Field Futures Worktable. The column for "Two winters from now" on part B should end up adjacent to "Two summers from now" on part A. Again, discard the scrap. Depending on how far forward you are planning, add parts C and D to the strip.

2. **Set rotation goals.**

   Identify what you would like your crop rotation to accomplish. Sidebar 2.8 (page 14) provides a list of potential rotation goals developed by experienced organic farmers. The fictional example of Small Valley Farm will be used to illustrate various steps in the planning process (sidebar 5.2). Their rotation goals are as follows:

   - Avoid growing the same crop in the same location two years in a row (except hay, of course).
   - Ensure that all crops have sufficient nitrogen, especially corn.
   - Avoid planting row crops and spring grains on sloping land.

3. **Prioritize your goals.**

   Order your goals. This is particularly useful if you have a long list of goals, since you may find it impossible to meet all of the goals completely every year. Some goals may be so easily met that, although they are critical, they need little attention in the rotation planning process. For Small Valley Farm, providing N for the crops is economically important, but since one third of the land is in nitrogen-building grass-alfalfa hay each year and a clover cover crop can be interseeded into either oat or spelt, providing sufficient N is easy to accomplish. Consequently, the farm's goals are prioritized as follows:

   a) Avoid growing the same crop in the same location two years in a row.
   b) Avoid planting row crops and spring grains on sloping land.
   c) Ensure that all crops have sufficient nitrogen, especially corn.

Filling Out Your Crop Characteristics Worktable

4. ***Write down your desired crop mix for the coming year.***

Make a list of the crops you grow and how many acres, beds, or square feet you want to grow of each crop to meet your market requirements. Use your copy of the Crop Characteristics Worktable to organize the list by families. (Look up the family of your crops in appendix 1, pages 101–103, if necessary.)

Next, for each crop family, group crops that you grow using similar practices and planting and harvest times. Members of these crop groups are functionally equivalent with respect to many aspects of crop rotation.

Fill in the name of each crop you plant down the left-hand column. If you plan to make multiple plantings of a crop, enter each planting on a separate line with a unique name (for example, lettuce 1, lettuce 2, etc.). Separating plantings is useful because each has different planting and harvest times and therefore has different cash and cover crops that can precede or follow it. For crops that remain in the ground for several years, you may find listing each crop year useful (for example, strawberry yr 1, strawberry yr 2, etc.). Table 5.4 shows the crop mix for Small Valley Farm.

5. ***Add crop characteristics to the Crop Characteristics Worktable.***

Now look at your Crop Characteristics Worktable, and going across the page add column titles in spaces to the right of "Net $/acre" that you think will be useful in deciding either the sequence in which you order crops or where the crops will be placed on the farm. Crop

TABLE 5.4 Crop mix for Small Valley Farm

Crop	Acres/year
Tofu soybean	120
Corn	120
Oat/clover/spelt	120
Spelt/hay (1st year)	120
Hay (2nd year)	120
Hay (3rd year)/oat cc	120

characteristics that expert farmers take into account when planning their rotations are listed in sidebar 2.9 (page 15). Including columns for target planting and harvest times will be useful if you plant some crops multiple times during the season or if you grow many different crops. Next, fill in the appropriate information for each crop in the various columns. For now, ignore the column headed MUs/year—you will use that later. For crops that are harvested repeatedly, the final harvest is the critical time relative to crop rotation, since that is when the field becomes available for planting the next cash or cover crop. Sidebar 5.3 provides codes for planting and harvest times that fit easily on the worksheet. Enter the net income per acre (or other unit of land area). This information will be used to help prioritize where crops go. Approximate numbers are good enough—you just need to be able to tell the ranking of values for the various crops. Copy from appendix 1 (pages 101–103) any information you think is useful for sequencing crops on your farm.

6. **Check for lack of diversity in your crop mix.**

Scan your worktable and determine which plant family will have the greatest area. For this computation, ignore the grass family (see sidebar 5.4). Add up the area for the most widely planted, non-grass family. Now divide the total cropped area of the farm by the area of that family. This number represents the *average rotation return time* for the most common non-grass crop family you grow. For example, if the average rotation return time is 4, the most prevalent non-grass plant family will occur on a given location once in every four years, provided you are careful to ensure a maximum lag between planting members of that family throughout the farm. Of course, many factors, including field-to-field variation in soil conditions, production of perennial crops, and changes in cropping plans due to weather will lead to shorter return times at some locations. *If the average rotation return time for the most prevalent family is less than 4, check appendix 3 (pages 124–137), and consider renting additional land or changing your crop mix so that a smaller percentage of the farm is planted with that family.* Sidebar 5.5 shows an example of return time calculation.

SIDEBAR 5.5

COMPUTATION OF AVERAGE RETURN TIME FOR THE MOST PREVALENT CROP FAMILY: AN EXAMPLE

Suppose a farm has the crop mix shown below:

Crop	Family	Number of Beds
Lettuce	Lettuce	6
Onion	Lily	6
Leek	Lily	3
Garlic	Lily	3
Tomato	Nightshade	6
Potato	Nightshade	6
Pepper	Nightshade	4
Green bean	Legume	4
Pea	Legume	4
Carrot	Carrot	2
Summer squash	Cucurbit	4
Total		48

The most prevalent crop family is the nightshades, with 16 of the 48 beds. Average return time for nightshades is 48/16 = 3 years. That is, a given piece of ground will have a nightshade crop every third year, even if the sequencing is ideal. This may be too frequent for long-term prevention of soilborne diseases of nightshade crops (see appendix 3, page 124–137). The second-most prevalent group are the alliums in the lily family, with an average return time of 48/12 = 4 years. Consequently, shifting from nightshades to an increase in alliums will not help diversify the crop mix appreciably. With such rapid return times for two major families, the farmer should consider either expanding his land base or developing markets for crops in other families.

Identifying Good Sequences in Your Planning

7. **Identify crop sequences that you use repeatedly.**

Look at your planting records and list all the 2- and 3-year crop sequences that you have found work well on your farm. These form the backbone around which you will build your rotation plan. You will probably find that these reliable sequences meet certain rotation goals or make your operation run smoothly. Note what each sequence is doing to facilitate your operation. This will allow you to explore alternative sequences that provide the same benefits. For Small Valley Farm, sequences and notes might look like this:

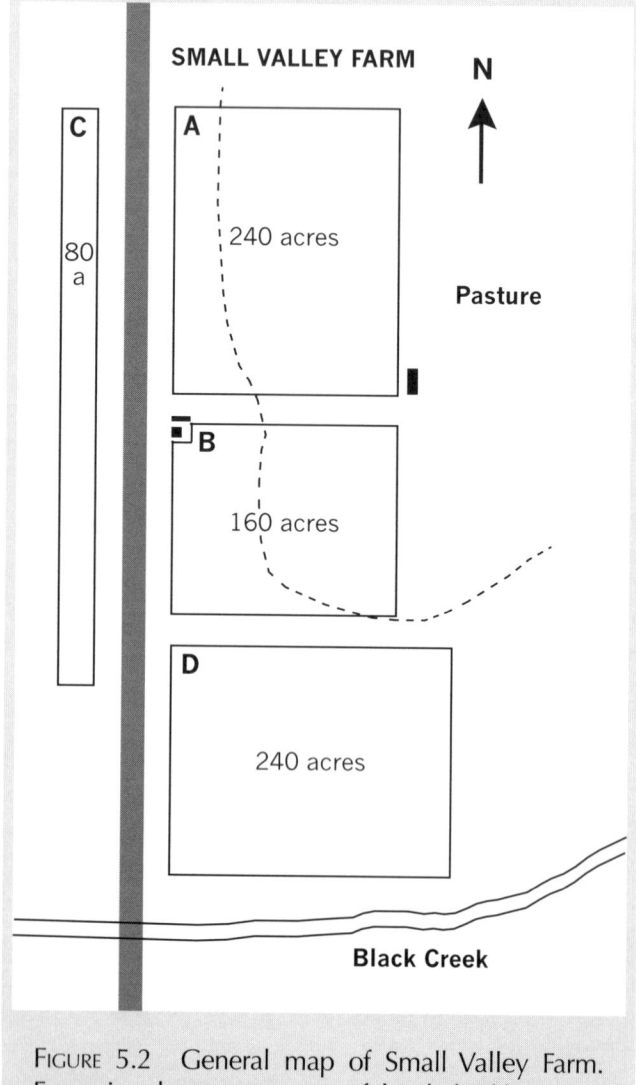

FIGURE 5.2 General map of Small Valley Farm. Excessive slopes occur east of the dashed line.

- spelt/hay—hay—hay: Hay can be established by overseeding into spelt. The spelt provides a good nurse crop and can be harvested before most spring-germinating weeds go to seed.
- hay/oat cover crop—corn: Alfalfa in the hay provides a source of nitrogen for the corn, and the decomposing roots maintain good soil structure during the row crop portion of the rotation. The oat cover crop protects the soil after incorporation of the hay sod but winter-kills so that corn can be planted as soon as the weather permits.
- oat/clover/spelt: There is plenty of time for planting spelt after oat harvest, whereas the window of opportunity is narrow after soybean and nonexistent after corn. Sowing red clover with oat provides N for the spelt.

The "Real Fields on Real Farms" color plates in chapter 4 (pages 49–54) provides many examples of sequences that farmers use successfully. Appendix 2 (pages 104–123) shows problems and opportunities associated with various crop sequences.

Identifying Critical Variations in Field Conditions

8. **Identify areas of your land that offer special opportunities or pose problems.**

Identify fields and parts of fields that grow certain of your crops particularly well or pose production problems for particular crops. Note these areas on a map of your farm. Table 5.5 (page 74–75) provides a list of field characteristics that experienced growers take into account when planning crop rotations.

For Small Valley Farm, the main problem area is the east side of fields A and B, which slopes too steeply for safe production of row crops (figure 5.2). Field D is flat, fertile bottomland that can support intensive row crop production.

Choose a few of these field characteristics that you think are most critical for planning your rotations, and based on them, categorize the fields into a few basic types. Realize that you will probably need a separate rotation plan for each type of field. Consequently, choose the most important field characteristics on which to focus. Meshing many separate rotations to get your desired crop mix each year will become hopelessly complex, particularly if you are producing many crops. **Therefore, if you have** *many critically different types of fields or if you grow many crops and all land is cash-cropped each year, do not bother developing a general rotation plan. Instead, skip to step 11.* On the other hand, if you grow fewer than eight types of cash crops (the crop groups discussed in step 4) and have only one to three types of fields, you will probably benefit from development of a general rotation plan. Similarly, if you rest at least a third of your land each year without planting cash crops on it, consider developing a general rotation plan. See figure 5.1 (page 60).

Developing a General Rotation Plan (optional)

9. *Divide the farm into field types.*

Based on your map and notes from the previous step, block the farm into field types. All land with a particular field type should be suitable for growing the same set of crops. Note that if all areas of the farm are reasonably suitable for all crops, you are lucky to have only a single field type to deal with. Areas of a particular field type do not have to be adjacent, and field types do not have to cover equal areas of the farm (in the Small Valley Farm example (table 5.6, page 77), the areas in the three field types were made equal to simplify the illustration).

Small Valley Farm has the following field types:

I. Field C and the west sides of fields A and B—suitable for all crops.
II. East side of fields A and B—unsuitable for row crops and spring grains due to excessive slope.
III. Field D—particularly good land suitable for intensive row crop production.

10. *Propose reasonable crop rotations for each field type.*

Using your short, 2- or 3-year sequences and other short sequences you think might work, develop a preliminary rotation for each of the field types on your farm. Make the crop rotations in each of the field types have the same number of years (cycle length) in the rotation or an exact multiple of the shortest rotation length. Otherwise, meshing the rotations to achieve your desired crop mix each year will be difficult.

Although the Small Valley rotation plan discussed below focuses on particular crops, many farmers prefer to focus on crop types. These crop types could be botanical families or relate to the season when the crop is in the ground. For example, the Nordells' rotation plan, presented in chapter 4's "Real Fields" chart (pages 49–54),

alternates spring-planted crops with a year of fallow and cover crops and then summer-planted crops. Basing the rotation plan on planting time can simplify field operations by synchronizing them over substantial blocks of land. However, if your rotation plan is based on crops grouped by planting time, you may need to make additional provisions to ensure that botanically similar crops are not grown too closely in the sequence. This could be accomplished, for example, by repeating the basic planting time sequence with different families in each repetition.

The Small Valley farmers decided on the following rotations:

- Field type I. Spelt/hay—hay—hay/oat cover crop—corn—soybean—oat/clover/spelt. This is the six-year rotation they have used previously.
- Field type II. Spelt/hay—hay—hay/spelt—spelt/hay—hay—hay/spelt. This is a three-year rotation, repeated twice in a six-year period. It avoids row crops and spring tillage on the steep land.
- Field type III. Oat/clover—corn—soybean—oat/clover—corn—soybean. This is an intensive rotation with row crops two years out of three.

Essentially, the Small Valley farmers moved the row crops and spring grain from field type II to field type III, leaving only erosion-resistant sod and winter grain crops on the erosion-prone land of field type II. Over the course of the six-year cycle, the mix of cash crops has not changed at all. Placing these crop sequences on particular plots of land to achieve the desired crop mix in each year, however, still requires some additional planning.

Making and Using a Crop Rotation Planning Map

11. *Draw a crop rotation planning map.*

This map may need to be more detailed than the map you use for organic certification. Begin by noting the dimensions of each field on the map. In this step you will subdivide fields into small management units (MUs) of approximately equal size across the whole farm. Only one crop will be grown on any particular MU at a time, and usually several MUs will be required to grow the full acreage of a crop in any given season. Crops will move from one block of MUs to another between years. Dividing the farm into management units allows accurate record keeping and helps you to stay organized when moving crops between fields that vary in size, shape, and other important characteristics.

Experienced growers have identified the factors listed here as factors they note when planning crop sequences. The table is laid out to show column title codes and abbreviations that are useful when filling out the Field Conditions Worktable (table 5.2, pages 62–63) in steps 17 through 19. Management units (MUs) are pieces of land of uniform size, each of which is farmed as a block. The usefulness of dividing the farm into uniformly sized management units is discussed in step 11.

Column title	Explanation
Field name	Your name for the field—e.g., SW, upper creek.
Field type	Parts of the farm that share a common rotation plan—I, II, III, IV, etc. See optional steps 9–10.
Mgmt. unit	Number of this MU. Each unit should have a unique number. Number adjacent units sequentially.
Field history	
Crop 3 summers ago	Names of crops (and cover crops) three summers ago.
Crop 2 winters ago	Name of cover crop or crop two winters ago.
Crop 2 summers ago	Names of crops (and cover crops) two summers ago.
Crop last winter	Name of last winter's cover crop or crop.
Crop last summer	Names of last summer's crops (and cover crops).
Current winter—crop	Name of the current cover crop or crop.
Current winter—plant	Planting time of the current cover crop or crop.
Current winter—harv.	Expected harvest or incorporation time of the current cash crop or cover crop.
Field Characteristics that can be entered in the blank columns of the Field Conditions Worktable	
Soil series	Name of the soil series from your county soil survey.
Texture	SaL (sandy loam), SiL (silt loam), CL (clay loam), etc. Obtain this from your county soil survey but temper it with your judgment.
Drainage	E (excessive—droughty), W (well), MW (moderately well), SP (somewhat poor), P (poor).
Slope	Percent slope of the MU. Enter range if it varies.
Aspect	Direction the land slopes: N, NE, E, etc. C for complex slopes, F for flat.
Irrig?	Is irrigation available? Y (yes), N (no).
Shaded?	Is the MU shaded by trees or steep hills? Y (yes), N (no).
Air drain.	Air drainage. G (good), I (intermediate), P (poor). Air drainage affects tendency toward late spring and early fall frosts.
Air circ.	E (exposed), I (intermediate), S (sheltered). Exposed fields may be susceptible to wind damage; sheltered fields may be more susceptible to spread of disease.
Access	G (good—e.g., near farmstead), I (intermediate), P (poor—e.g., the other side of the woodlot).
Visibility	VV (very visible) , V (visible), H (hidden). You may prefer to put crops that attract customers near the road, and experiments that may fail where they cannot be seen.
Neighbors	Note issues with neighbors—e.g., may not want to spray next to homes; pollen drift from conventional growers.
Moist. hold. cap.	Moisture holding capacity. G (good), I (intermediate), P (poor).
Org. matter	Enter range of recent percent organic matter values.

Column title	Explanation
Org. mat. qual.	Your judgment of the quality of the organic matter. Is it well decomposed to humus, or is a lot of coarse fiber and wood present? G (good), I (intermediate), P (poor).
Tilth	Your judgment of the tilth of the soil. G (good—tilled soil is loose, with little tendency to crust), I (intermediate), P (poor—tilled soil is cloddy, compacted, tends to crust).
Aggregation	G (good—soil has good crumb structure), I (intermediate), P (poor—soil is massive and blocky or loose sand with few crumbs).
Nut. release	Ability of soil to release nutrients to the crop. G (good), I (intermediate), P (poor).
Nut. imbal?	Note any nutrient imbalances—e.g., poor Ca:Mg or Ca:K ratios.
Erosion	Tendency toward erosion if soil is left uncovered. H (high), I (intermediate), L (low).
Deer pres.	Deer or other animal pressure. H (high), I (intermediate), L (low).
Dis. crops	List crops that in this MU have had a recent history of soilborne diseases.
Diseases	Names of the diseases of the crops just listed.
Ann. weeds	Annual weed pressure. H (high—many annual weeds if not controlled), I (intermediate), L (low—little history of annual weed problems).
Worst ann. spp.	List the worst annual weed species.
Peren. weeds	Perennial weed pressure. H (high—perennial weeds have posed problems recently), I (intermediate), L (low—little history of perennial weed problems).
Worst peren. spp.	List the worst perennial weed species.

Figure 5.3 (page 76) shows how Small Valley Farm laid out its 40-acre MUs across the farm. Since the farm has a total of 720 tillable acres, it has a total of 18 MUs.

Appendix 6 (pages 148–149) provides easy instructions for making rotation planning maps using Microsoft Excel.

Consider the following points when determining the size and arrangement of your management units:

- MUs should be no larger than the area planted to your smallest acreage crop. If some crops that are grown on small acreage (for example, annual herbs) are rotated as a block, the several species could be considered as one "crop" for rotation purposes.
- Choose an MU size that allows areas of each crop on your Crop Characteristics Worktable to convert to a whole number of MUs. On Small Valley Farm, since 1 MU = 40 acres, they thus grow three MUs of each crop per year.
- If you did steps 8 and 9 (rotation planning), the number of MUs in a field type should be some multiple of the number of years in the longest rotation sequence for any field type. For example, on Small Valley Farm, each field type should have six MUs, or some multiple of six, since the longest rotation sequence is six years (in field type I). They chose to keep things simple and use six MUs per field type (figure 5.3, page 76). If you skipped steps 8 and 9 due to high farm complexity, you can ignore this consideration.
- If you use permanent beds, each bed should be a separate MU. If fields vary in length, subdivide long beds at cross alleys as necessary to ensure that the MUs are approximately equal in area.
- On grain farms and large wholesale vegetable farms, vary the length and width of management strips for your convenience, and keep the MUs large enough so that you can perform field operations like tillage or cultivation on a single unit.
- Make the map at a scale that allows writing information onto the area representing each MU. If necessary, use separate pages for various fields or groups of fields.

Now divide the fields into management units on your map. Note that small variations in the size of MUs due to irregularities in field shape are unavoidable but probably will not matter much since most crops will be grown on several to many MUs.

12. *Record your crop mix in terms of management units.*

On your Crop Characteristics Worktable, record how many management units you want to grow of each crop. You already have the amount of each crop recorded in acres, square feet, or some other unit, but converting these to MUs will simplify thinking about how you sequence the crops on particular MUs. If you made an error in the previous step, the conversion of area to MUs may result in some crops being grown on fractions of an MU. In this case, adjust your crop mix slightly, so that all crops will be grown on a round number of MUs.

13. *Number each management unit.*

Put the number of each MU in the upper left corner of each management unit on the map. Make the numbers sufficiently large and legible that they will photocopy well. Blocks of land that you commonly manage together should be numbered sequentially.

14. *Make several copies of the maps.*

You will need at least eight copies of the maps, and a few more may be useful later. Be sure to save the original map in a safe place for making future copies. And be sure to label each map as you complete steps 15–16.

15. *Record especially valuable MUs on one copy of the map.*

You noted the most important field characteristics in a general way in step 8. Now it is time to characterize each MU in detail. Note MUs that have especially useful properties on one copy of the map. Favorable properties may include proximity to the farmstead, access to irrigation if irrigation is limited, slope or drainage characteristics that allow early planting, and many others (see table 5.5, page 74). Note only exceptional properties on the map. Writing something for each MU would be time consuming and is not necessary. Use the abbreviations in table 5.5 if you are cramped for space.

16. *Record problem MUs on another copy of the map.*

Label another copy of the map, and note on that copy management units with problems that restrict the types

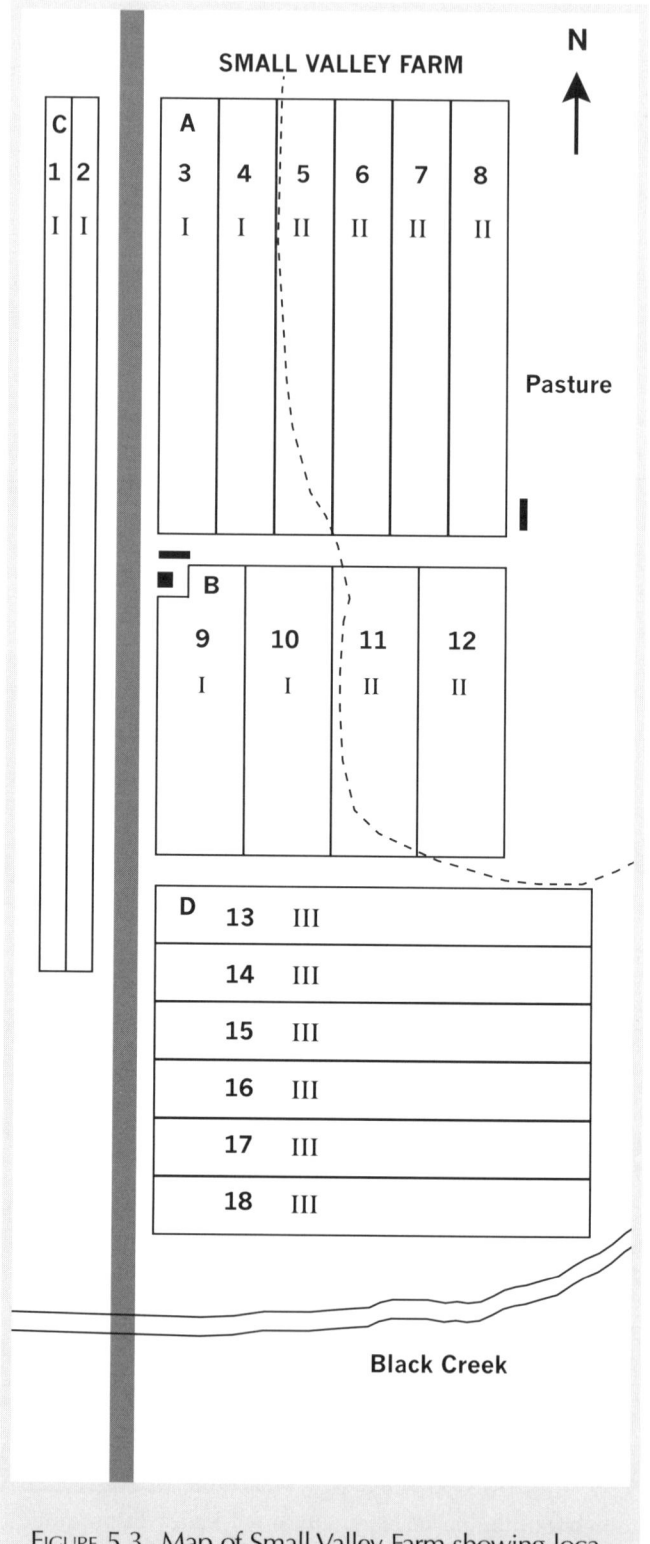

FIGURE 5.3 Map of Small Valley Farm showing location of management units. Excessive slopes occur east of the dashed line. Management units are numbered and field type is indicated by Roman numerals.

of crops you can grow. Such problems include poor soil drainage, severe animal pressure, shadiness, frost pockets, and slope characteristics that lead to slow warming in the spring. See table 5.5 (pages 74–75) for a list of characteristics assembled by experienced growers.

Filling Out the Field Conditions Worktable

17. *Number MUs on your Field Conditions Worktable.*

Put the field name and number of each MU on a line in the Field Conditions Worktable (your copy of tabl e 5.2, pages 62–63). Number the MUs sequentially. If you did steps 9 and 10 above (general rotation planning), fill in the column titled "Field type," also; otherwise, leave this column blank. See the first three columns of table 5.6 for an example. (Hint: If you commonly plant several crops and cover crops on individual MUs within a single season, leave a blank line between units so you will have enough room to include them all when you fill in the crops later.)

18. *Fill in your map data.*

Copy the information you noted on the maps into the blank columns of the Field Conditions Worktable. This puts the map data in a form that allows you to sort management units on the basis of their characteristics. Using your maps of valuable fields and problem fields, label a blank column for each different type of characteristic you noted (for example, "erosion potential," "soil quality"; see table 5.6). Then record information about each MU in the appropriate box.

19. *Record your recent cropping history.*

Fill out the columns in the Field Conditions Worktable describing the cropping history for each management unit for the past three years. Write the actual year above "Crop 3 summers ago." This planning procedure assumes that you are doing your planning in the winter and thus begins with the current winter's cover or cash crops. Write in the names of current crops and their planting and expected harvest times. Now work backward from the present to preceding years as you go from right to left. If more than one cash or cover crop was grown during a given period, enter both names into the cell in the order they will be grown using a slash (/) as a separator (for example, spelt/hay). If two crops were grown on different parts of an MU in some past year, for the sake of simplicity, just enter the name of the crop that covered the largest portion of the MU.

Table 5.7 (page 78) shows the cropping history of Small Valley Farm.

20. *Sort the management units.*

Cut your completed Field Conditions Worktable into strips to separate the management units. Management units with similar histories often do not need to be separated. *If you did steps 9 and 10*, group the strips by field type. Arrange the strips so that, within each field type, (1) units with similar crop histories are together; and (2) within those groups, adjacent management units are in numerical order. *If you skipped steps 9 and 10*, arrange the strips so that (1) MUs with similar critical field conditions are together; (2) within those groups, MUs with similar crop

TABLE 5.6 Example of the field characteristics portion of the Field Conditions worktable (table 5.2, pages 62–63) for Small Valley Farm

Field name	Field type	Mgmt. unit	Erosion potential	Soil quality
C	I	1	low	good
C	I	2	low	good
A	I	3	low	good
A	I	4	low	good
A	II	5	high	fair
A	II	6	high	fair
A	II	7	high	fair
A	II	8	high	fair
B	I	9	low	good
B	I	10	low	good
B	II	11	high	fair
B	II	12	high	fair
D	III	13	very low	very good
D	III	14	very low	very good
D	III	15	very low	very good
D	III	16	very low	very good
D	III	17	very low	very good
D	III	18	very low	very good

histories are together; and (3) within each crop history group, adjacent management units are in numerical order.

Everyone: For this purpose "similar crop histories" means similar in how the history affects what crops you will grow in the future. For example, if one management unit had broccoli and another had cauliflower two summers ago but otherwise their histories do not differ, you may decide that they are not sufficiently different to warrant separating them into different groups for planning future crop sequences. Use coins or other weights to hold the strips in place while you sort them. When you are satisfied with your sorting, tape the strips to a piece of paper with clear tape, so that you have a permanent record of the cropping history of the farm in terms of your newly defined management units.

After the Small Valley farmers sorted their MUs, units 9 and 10 were grouped with the other flat, ordinary MUs (units 1–4). Similarly, the steep MUs (units 5–8, 11, and 12) were grouped together (table 5.8, page 80).

Planning Future Crop Sequences

21. ***Number the management units on the Field Futures Worktable.***

Number the MUs on the Field Futures Worktable (your copy of table 5.3, pages 64–65) in the sequence in which they appear on your sorted Field Conditions Worktable. Also fill in the field name and, if you did steps 9 and 10, the zone. For example, MU 9 appears on line 5 of both the sorted Field Conditions Worktable and the Field Futures Worktable for Small Valley (table 5.8, page 80).

22. ***Plan the next growing season.***

Look at your completed crop worktable (your version of table 5.1, page 61) and note how many management units of each crop you plan to grow. Fill in the names of the crops you will grow on each MU next summer. If more than one crop will be grown on an MU, write them all in the cell in the sequence they will be grown (for example, "lettuce/buckwheat cc/fall broccoli"). Place crops in the following order, referring to your field conditions maps as needed:

a) Begin by writing in cash crops that are already planted but will not be harvested until next summer or later. Examples include garlic, strawberries, winter grains, and hay.

TABLE 5.7 Cropping history of Small Valley Farm (part of their Field Conditions worktable)

Field name	Field type	Mgmt. unit	3 years ago	2 years ago	Last year
C	I	1	corn	soybean	oat/clover/spelt
C	I	2	corn	soybean	oat/clover/spelt
A	I	3	soybean	oat/clover/spelt	spelt/hay
A	I	4	soybean	oat/clover/spelt	spelt/hay
A	II	5	soybean	oat/clover/spelt	spelt/hay
A	II	6	oat/clover/spelt	spelt/hay	hay2
A	II	7	oat/clover/spelt	spelt/hay	hay2
A	II	8	oat/clover/spelt	spelt/hay	hay2
B	I	9	corn	soybean	oat/clover/spelt
B	I	10	spelt/hay	hay2	hay3/oat cc
B	II	11	spelt/hay	hay2	hay3/oat cc
B	II	12	spelt/hay	hay2	hay3/oat cc
D	III	13	hay2	hay3/oat cc	corn
D	III	14	hay2	hay3/oat cc	corn
D	III	15	hay2	hay3/oat cc	corn
D	III	16	hay3/oat cc	corn	soybean
D	III	17	hay3/oat cc	corn	soybean
D	III	18	hay3/oat cc	corn	soybean

b) Now place high-value crops that require special field conditions. For example, melons may produce a large net income per acre, but you can grow them well on only one field. So place melons or other high-value crops with special needs onto MUs first.

c) Next, place crops that have the shortest family return times, as computed in step 6 (but ignore grass-family crops). Begin with the most valuable crop in the family with the shortest average rotation return time. Work through all crops in families (other than grasses) with average return times of less than four years.

d) Next, place other crops that produce a large net income per acre but can be grown almost anywhere.

e) Place less profitable and low-acreage crops that require special MU characteristics.

f) Place any remaining crops.

Points to take into account when placing crops:

- When possible, use the proven crop sequences you identified in step 7. Be careful not to repeat crops of the same family too soon. This is especially important if you have noticed symptoms of soilborne disease. If you have noticed such disease in the past, check appendix 3 (pages 124–137) to see how many years to wait before repeating a crop with similar susceptibility. If you have not noticed soilborne diseases, try to use a minimum separation of at least one year between similar crops, and remember that a longer separation is a good preventative measure. Growing the same crop in close succession may be an acceptable practice if you then rotate the MU into other crops for many years. Even then, however, growing at least one cash or cover crop in between will help minimize direct transmission of diseases on crop residue (see "Managing Plant Diseases with Crop Rotation," page 32). Note that most of the sample rotations used by experienced farmers shown in chapter 4 (pages 49–54) have return times for crops in a family of four years or longer.

- Refer to appendix 2 (pages 104–123) as you work to check for problems and opportunities in the crop sequences you are choosing.

- If an MU has special characteristics, try to plant it with a crop that takes advantage of them, but remember that that may not be possible every year.

- Separate the locations of early and later plantings of the same crop to avoid disease buildup through the season. Alternating strips of different crop types with similar planting and harvest times (for example, lettuce and mustard greens) is a way to stay organized while still separating succession plantings of a given crop type. To be effective, however, the intervening strips must be wide enough to act as an effective barrier to dispersal of diseases and insects. Consult appendix 3 (pages 124–137) to see how particular diseases are spread.

For those developing a general rotation plan (you did steps 9 and 10 above); others skip to step 23: Most of the considerations discussed above are essentially covered by your general rotation plan. The key for placing crops next season is to begin converting from the previous cropping history to the general rotation plan. This requires looking forward more than just one year. Getting each MU on track requires some imagination and a lot of trial and error (on paper). Remember, however, that once you have the desired crop mix within a field type, future crops can follow more or less automatically. If your general rotation plan is based on crop categories (for example, early-season greens, full-season nightshades) rather than specific crops, place the crop categories on the MUs first. Then go back through and place the specific crops within each category.

Consider the example of Small Valley Farm in table 5.8 (page 80). In field type I last year they planted three management units of oat/clover/spelt. Ultimately, they would like to get one MU of field type I into each of the six crop-years of the six-year rotation. The spelt, however, is already planted, and they are loath to plow it under. This results in three MUs of spelt in field type I next spring and none in field type II, where they would ultimately like to have it.

In MUs 1, 3, and 10 they simply proceed into the planned next crop. Instead of overseeding hay into the spelt in MU 2, they overseed with clover next spring and then plant oat followed by spelt two years from now. Similarly, instead of overseeding hay into the spelt in MU 9 they overseed red clover, and then plant corn the following year. To get MU 4 on track, they treat the overseeded hay as a cover crop and plant oat followed by spelt next summer. Thus, by two years from now, they have one of each of the six crop-years on one MU of field type I, and the rotation plan is in place for that field type of the farm.

Similar slight departures from their desired sequences are necessary in the other two field types. Most notably, in field type II they grow oat as a hay crop on MU 11 next year and on MU 12 two years from now to make up for the shortage of grass-alfalfa hay. Except for the substitution of oat hay for their usual grass-alfalfa hay, note that they grow the desired crop mix in each future year. Note also that they meet their explicit goal of avoiding the same crop immediately in succession. Three years from their planning exercise, the rotation plan has been implemented for the whole farm.

23. *Check next growing season's crop mix.*

After you have assigned crops to all MUs, add the number of MUs of each crop. Compare these with the number of MUs you intended to grow, as indicated on your Crop Characteristics Worktable. If the two numbers do not agree, either assign some MUs to other crops or change the planned number of units on the Crop Characteristics Worktable.

If you think it will be helpful, enter the planting and harvest times for next summer's crops. The planting and harvest times are most useful when you plant the same

crop multiple times during the season (for example, succession plantings of lettuce or spring and fall broccoli crops). See sidebar 5.3 (page 70) for a simple system of codes for recording planting and harvest times.

24. *Plan next winter and two growing seasons from now.*

Fill in any cash crops that will be present next winter (for example, garlic, spelt). Do not assign winter cover crops yet.

Fill in cash and cover crops for two summers from now as you did for next summer (see step 22). When making decisions, always look back over the whole cropping history of the management unit up to this point, as well as the special properties of the MU. Refer to appendix 2 (pages 104–123) to check for potential problems and opportunities.

TABLE 5.8 Recent crop history and future crop sequences for Small Valley Farm (*continues on next page*)

Field name	Field type	MU	3 years ago	2 years ago	Last year	Next year	2 years from now
A	I	1	corn	soybean	oat/clover/spelt	spelt/hay	hay2
A	I	2	corn	soybean	oat/clover/spelt	spelt/clover cc	oat/clover/spelt
B	I	3	soybean	oat/clover/spelt	spelt/hay	hay2	hay3/oat cc
B	I	4	soybean	oat/clover/spelt	spelt/hay	oat/clover/spelt	spelt/hay
C	I	9	corn	soybean	oat/clover/spelt	spelt/clover	corn
C	I	10	spelt/hay	hay2	hay3/oat cc	corn	soybean
B	II	5	soybean	oat/clover/spelt	spelt/hay	hay2	hay3/spelt
B	II	6	oat/clover/spelt	spelt/hay	hay2	hay3	hay4/spelt
B	II	7	oat/clover/spelt	spelt/hay	hay2	hay3/spelt	spelt/hay
B	II	8	oat/clover/spelt	spelt/hay	hay2	hay3/spelt	spelt/hay
C	II	11	spelt/hay	hay2	hay3/oat cc	oat hay/hay	hay2
C	II	12	spelt/hay	hay2	hay3/oat cc	soybean	oat hay/hay
D	III	13	hay2	hay3/oat cc	corn	soybean	oat/clover cc
D	III	14	hay2	hay3/oat cc	corn	soybean	oat/clover cc
D	III	15	hay2	hay3/oat cc	corn	oat/clover cc	corn
D	III	16	hay3/oat cc	corn	soybean	oat/clover cc	corn
D	III	17	hay3/oat cc	corn	soybean	corn/ryegrass	soybean
D	III	18	hay3/oat cc	corn	soybean	corn/ryegrass	soybean

Check your crop mix, as in step 23, to be sure that the field plan provides the correct amount of each crop.

Now fill in cover crops for next winter that make sense given the crops that precede and follow them. Consider especially (1) the harvest time of the preceding crop, (2) the planting time of the following crop, and (3) the needs of the following crop (N demand, ability to incorporate cover crop before planting, etc.).

25. *Plan future years.*

Repeat, as in step 23, for each succeeding year. Plan as far ahead as you feel will be useful. Realize that your plans may need to change due to weather events and market conditions.

3 years from now	4 years from now	5 years from now	6 years from now
hay3/oat cc	corn	soybean	oat/clover/spelt
spelt/hay	hay2	hay3/oat cc	corn
corn	soybean	oat/clover/spelt	spelt/hay
hay2	hay3/oat cc	corn	soybean
soybean	oat/clover/spelt	spelt/hay	hay2
oat/clover/spelt	spelt/hay	hay2	hay3/oat cc
spelt/hay	hay2	hay3/spelt	spelt/hay
spelt/hay	hay2	hay3/spelt	spelt/hay
hay2	hay3/spelt	spelt/hay	hay2
hay2	hay3/spelt	spelt/hay	hay2
hay3/spelt	spelt/hay	hay2	hay3
hay2/spelt	spelt/hay	hay2	hay3
corn	soybean	oat/clover cc	corn
corn	soybean	oat/clover cc	corn
soybean	oat/clover cc	corn	soybean
soybean	oat/clover cc	corn	soybean
oat/clover cc	corn	soybean	corn
oat/clover cc	corn	soybean	corn

Refining Your Plan

26. *Put your plans on maps.*

Copy the information from the Field Futures Worktable onto blank maps. Put the crops for next summer on one map, the crops for next winter on another, etc., for as many seasons as you have planned ahead.

27. *Take the maps to the field.*

Take these maps and walk through your fields. For each cluster of adjacent MUs, farm the cropping sequence through in your head. Compare the maps with your feel for the various management units and how they have performed in the past. Take notes on what seems right and what may not work.

Write down what you could do if problems arise. This is an important consideration. Think about what will happen if rain delays timely incorporation of a cover crop or timely planting of a cash crop. What will you do if cultivation is delayed and the crop becomes excessively weedy? Consider other potential problems and whether they may require a change in the planned sequence. Make notes on potential alternative strategies to meet circumstances you may encounter.

28. *Modify planned sequences.*

Return to your office (or kitchen table) and lay out your maps and notes. Based on insights gained from walking the fields, modify the planned sequences where necessary on the Field Futures Worktable.

29. *Recheck your crop mix.*

When you have a reasonable plan, add up the number of MUs of each crop in each year and check this against your intended production, as indicated on the Crop Characteristics Worktable. Make further adjustments on the Crop Characteristics Worktable or the Field Futures Worktable if necessary. Remember, however, that year-to-year variation in productivity may swamp out slight variation in the number of MUs grown for major crops.

TABLE 5.9 Crop characteristics worktable for Summer Acres Vegetable Farm

Crop[1]	Acres/ year	MUs/ year	Family	Plant Time[2]	Harvest Ends[2]	Harvested Part	Cold Tolerance
Garlic	0.16	2	Lily	lfall	msum	root	very hardy
Pea	0.32	4	Legume	espr	msum	fruit	hardy
Lettuce 5	0.16	2	Lettuce	espr	esum	leaf	half-hardy
Lettuce 6	0.16	2	Lettuce	esum	msum	leaf	half-hardy
Lettuce 7e	0.16	2	Lettuce	msum	lsum	leaf	half-hardy
Lettuce 7l	0.16	2	Lettuce	msum	efall	leaf	half-hardy
Lettuce 8	0.16	2	Lettuce	lsum	lfall	leaf	half-hardy
Potato	0.32	4	Nightshade	lspr	lsum	root	half-hardy
Tomato	0.48	6	Nightshade	lspr	efall	fruit	tender
Pepper	0.24	3	Nightshade	lspr	efall	fruit	tender
Carrot	0.16	2	Carrot	espr	efall	root	half-hardy
Kohlrabi	0.08	1	Mustard	espr	msum	leaf	hardy
Broccoli	0.16	2	Mustard	lspr	lsum	flower bud	hardy
Summer squash	0.24	3	Cucurbit	esum	efall	fruit	tender
Winter squash	0.48	6	Cucurbit	lspr	efall	fruit	tender
Spinach 5	0.16	2	Beet	espr	esum	leaf	hardy
Spinach 8e	0.16	2	Beet	lsum	efall	leaf	hardy
Spinach 8l	0.16	2	Beet	lsum	lfall	leaf	hardy
Beet 5	0.08	1	Beet	lspr	msum	root	half-hardy
Beet 7	0.08	1	Beet	msum	lfall	root	half-hardy
Total	4.08	51					

[1] The number after the names of some crops refers to the planting month; e and l refer to early and late in the month.
[2] Abbreviations for planting time and the end of harvest are given in Sidebar 5.3 (page 70).

30. **Note your contingency plans.**

When you have the Field Futures Worktable adjusted the way you want it, add notes indicating your contingency plans (see your field notes from step 27). Enter these either in the margins if they are few or on a separate piece of paper if there are many. If necessary create a separate page to show the contingency plans for a given group of MUs. Staple the contingency plans to the Field Futures Worktable, so that they stay together.

Small Valley has multiple possibilities for meeting contingencies. For example, if weather hopelessly delays planting of oat, the farmer can substitute corn. Similarly, soybean can be substituted if planting corn is not feasible. If plowing down the hay or planting spelt proves impossible, the hay can be left for an extra year. Each of these essentially moves the rotation ahead one year, which is

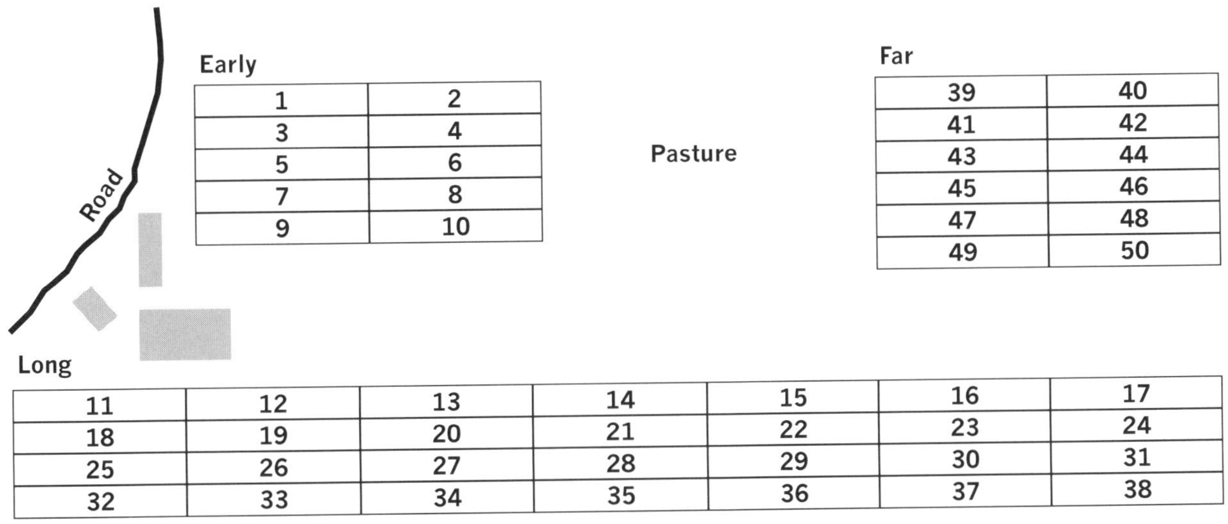

FIGURE 5.4 Map of Summer Acres Farm showing division into management units.

fairly easy to compensate for in the future. Obviously, all of these circumstances result in a crop mix that is different from the original plan, but that is necessarily the case when a crop cannot be planted.

The Small Valley example also illustrates potential for adjusting the crop mix to meet market demand without significant modification of the basic rotation plan. For example, a different spring grain could be substituted for oat, dry bean or snap bean for soybean, or a heavy-feeding vegetable crop like cabbage or pumpkin for corn.

31. **Make your crop placement maps match your revised Field Futures Worktable.**

Finally, modify the maps for each year so that they match the Field Futures Worktable. Make several copies of these maps so that you can take them into the field when you are preparing seedbeds and planting while still retaining a clean copy for your records.

Congratulations! You have created a complete cropping plan for your farm. Be prepared to modify it as you gain knowledge and experience. Continue to grow with your farm.

A More Complex Example: Summer Acres Vegetable Farm

Table 5.9 shows the Crop Characteristics Worktable for Summer Acres Farm, and figure 5.4 shows a map of the farm divided into management units. Table 5.10 (pages 84–88) gives completed Field Conditions and Field Futures Worktables. The example is fictitious, but it is based on a sample crop mix and planting and harvest times provided by a New York vegetable grower.

This sample farm is sufficiently land limited to constrain the cropping sequences but not so land limited as to force a serious departure from good rotation practices. The farmers grow 51 management units of cash crops on 50 MUs of land, so some double cropping is necessary.

Because of the land area constraint, the farmers' primary rotation goal is to maximize the time between crops in the same or similar families. Within this constraint, they choose sequences that supply cover crop nitrogen whenever possible, especially before heavy-feeding crops. The farmers attempt to keep the ground covered with a cash or cover crop throughout the year to prevent erosion

(continued on page 89)

TABLE 5.10 Field history and future for Summer Acres Farm

Field Name	Mgmt Unit	Crop 3 Summers Ago	Crop 2 Winters Ago	Crop 2 Summers Ago	Crop Last Winter
Early	1	Lettuce5/beet7	Bare	Carrot	Oat
Early	2	Lettuce5/cowpea	Oat	Carrot	Oat
Early	3	Pea/sorgh	Oat	Kohlrabi/cowpeaw	Oat & HV
Early	4	Pea/sorgh	Oat	Beet5/buckwheat	Oat & HV
Early	5	Pea/sorgh	Oat	Spinach5/cowpea	Oat & HV
Early	6	Pea/sorgh	Oat	Spinach5/cowpea	Oat
Early	7	Carrot	Oat	Pea/sorgh	Oat
Early	8	Carrot	Oat	Pea/sorgh	Oat
Early	9	Kohlrabi/buckwheat	Oat	Pea/sorgh	Oat
Early	10	Beet5/buckwheat	Oat	Pea/sorgh	Oat
Long	11	Pepper	Oat	Summer squash	Oat
Long	12	Pepper	Oat	Summer squash	Oat
Long	13	Pepper	Oat	Summer squash	Oat
Long	14	Spinach5/cowpea	Garlic	Garlic/field pea-oat	Oat
Long	15	Spinach5/cowpea	Garlic	Garlic/field pea-oat	Oat
Long	16	Lettuce6/fallow/spinach8e	Oat	Oat-red clover	Red clover
Long	17	Lettuce6/fallow/spinach8e	Oat	Oat-red clover	Red clover
Long	18	Lettuce7e/fallow/spinach8l	Bare	Oat-red clover	Red clover
Long	19	Tomato	Rye	Lettuce6/fallow/spinach8e	Rye
Long	20	Tomato	Rye	Lettuce6/fallow/spinach8e	Rye
Long	21	Tomato	Oat	Broccoli/fallow/lettuce8	Bare/field pea
Long	22	Tomato	Oat	Broccoli/fallow/lettuce8	Bare
Long	23	Tomato	Rye	Fallow/lettuce7e/fallow/spinach8l	Bare
Long	24	Tomato	Rye	Fallow/lettuce7e/fallow/spinach8l	Bare
Long	25	Lettuce7e/fallow/spinach8l	Bare	Oat-red clover	Red clover
Long	26	Winter squash	Oat	Tomato	Rye
Long	27	Winter squash	Oat	Tomato	Rye
Long	28	Winter squash	Oat	Tomato	Rye
Long	29	Winter squash	Oat	Tomato	Rye
Long	30	Winter squash	Oat	Tomato	Rye
Long	31	Winter squash	Oat	Tomato	Rye
Long	32	Summer squash	Oat	Pepper	Rye
Long	33	Summer squash	Oat	Pepper	Rye
Long	34	Summer squash	Oat	Pepper	Rye
Long	35	Potato	Oat & HV	Lettuce5/fallow	Rye & HV
Long	36	Potato	Oat & HV	Lettuce5/fallow	Rye & HV
Long	37	Potato	Oat & HV	Sorgh/lettuce7l	Bare
Long	38	Potato	Oat & HV	Sorgh/lettuce7l	Bare
Far	39	Broccoli/fallow/lettuce8	Bare	Oat/beet7	Rye
Far	40	Broccoli/fallow/lettuce8	Bare	Oat-red clover	Red clover
Far	41	Lettuce7l-interseeded HV	HV	Potato/oat	Garlic
Far	42	Lettuce7l-interseeded HV	HV	Potato/oat	Garlic
Far	43	Garlic/fallow	Oat & HV	Potato	Oat
Far	44	Garlic/fallow	Oat & HV	Potato	Oat
Far	45	Oat-red clover	Red clover	Winter squash	Oat
Far	46	Oat-red clover	Red clover	Winter squash	Oat
Far	47	Oat-red clover	Red clover	Winter squash	Oat
Far	48	Oat-red clover	Red clover	Winter squash	Oat
Far	49	Oat-red clover	Red clover	Winter squash	Oat
Far	50	Oat-red clover	Red clover	Winter squash	Oat

TABLE 5.10 Field history and future for Summer Acres Farm (*continued*)

Field Name	Mgmt Unit	Crop Last Summer	Current Winter Crop	Plant	Harv.
Early	1	Pea/sorgh	Oat	efall	espr
Early	2	Pea/sorgh	Oat	efall	espr
Early	3	Pepper	Oat	efall	espr
Early	4	Pepper	Oat	efall	espr
Early	5	Pepper	Oat	efall	espr
Early	6	Kohlrabi/buckwheat	Oat	efall	espr
Early	7	Spinach5/cowpea	Oat	efall	espr
Early	8	Spinach5/cowpea	Oat	efall	espr
Early	9	Carrot	Oat	efall	espr
Early	10	Carrot	Oat & HV	lsum	lspr
Long	11	Pea/sorgh	Rye	efall	lspr
Long	12	Pea/sorgh	Rye	efall	lspr
Long	13	Fallow/spinach8l	Rye	efall	lspr
Long	14	Oat-red clover	Red clover	—	lspr
Long	15	Oat-red clover	Red clover	—	lspr
Long	16	Potato	Rye & HV	lsum	lspr
Long	17	Potato	Rye & HV	lsum	lspr
Long	18	Potato	Rye & HV	lsum	espr
Long	19	Summer squash	Oat	efall	espr
Long	20	Summer squash	Oat	efall	espr
Long	21	Summer squash	Oat	efall	espr
Long	22	Lettuce7e	Rye & HV	lsum	lspr
Long	23	Oat-red clover	Red clover	—	lspr
Long	24	Oat-red clover	Red clover	—	lspr
Long	25	Potato	Oat & HV	lsum	lspr
Long	26	Lettuce6/fallow/spinach8e	Garlic	lfall	—
Long	27	Lettuce6/fallow/spinach8e	Garlic	lfall	—
Long	28	Fallow/spinach8l	Bare	—	—
Long	29	Broccoli/lettuce8	Bare	—	—
Long	30	Broccoli/lettuce8	Bare	—	—
Long	31	Lettuce7e	Oat & HV	efall	esum
Long	32	Cowpea/lettuce7l	Rye	efall	lspr
Long	33	Cowpea/lettuce7l	Rye	efall	lspr
Long	34	Beet5/buckwheat	Rye	efall	lspr
Long	35	Winter squash	Oat	efall	espr
Long	36	Winter squash	Oat	efall	espr
Long	37	Winter squash	Oat	efall	espr
Long	38	Winter squash	Oat	efall	espr
Far	39	Winter squash	Oat	efall	espr
Far	40	Winter squash	Oat	efall	espr
Far	41	Garlic/field pea-oat	CC residue	—	—
Far	42	Garlic/field pea-oat	CC residue	—	—
Far	43	Lettuce5/fallow/cowpea	CC residue	—	—
Far	44	Lettuce5/beet7	Rye	efall	espr
Far	45	Tomato	Rye	efall	lspr
Far	46	Tomato	Rye	efall	lspr
Far	47	Tomato	Rye	efall	lspr
Far	48	Tomato	Rye	efall	lspr
Far	49	Tomato	Rye	efall	esum
Far	50	Tomato	Rye	efall	esum

TABLE 5.10 Field history and future for Summer Acres Farm (*continued*)

Field Name	Mgmt Unit	Next Summer Crop	Plant	Harv.	Next Winter Crop	Plant	Harv.
Early	1	Spinach5/cowpea	espr/esum	esum/efall	Oat	efall	espr
Early	2	Spinach5/cowpea	espr/esum	esum/efall	Oat	efall	espr
Early	3	Pea/sorgh	espr/msum	msum/efall	Oat	efall	espr
Early	4	Pea/sorgh	espr/msum	msum/efall	Oat	efall	espr
Early	5	Pea/sorgh	espr/msum	msum/efall	Oat	efall	espr
Early	6	Pea/sorgh	espr/msum	msum/efall	Oat	efall	espr
Early	7	Carrot	espr	efall	Oat	efall	espr
Early	8	Carrot	espr	efall	Oat	efall	espr
Early	9	Kohlrabi/buckwheat	espr/msum	msum/efall	Oat	efall	espr
Early	10	Beet5/buckwheat	lspr/msum	msum/lsum	Oat	efall	espr
Long	11	Cowpea/Lettuce7l	esum/msum	msum/efall	Rye	efall	lspr
Long	12	Potato	lspr	lsum	Rye & HV	lsum	esum
Long	13	Potato	lspr	lsum	Rye & HV	lsum	esum
Long	14	Potato	lspr	lsum	Rye & HV	lsum	esum
Long	15	Potato	lspr	lsum	Rye & HV	lsum	lspr
Long	16	Cowpea/lettuce8	esum/lsum	lsum/lfall	Bare	—	—
Long	17	Cowpea/lettuce8	esum/lsum	lsum/lfall	Bare	—	—
Long	18	Winter squash	lspr	efall	Rye	lfall	lspr
Long	19	Pepper	lspr	efall	Oat & HV	efall	lspr
Long	20	Pepper	lspr	efall	Oat & HV	efall	lspr
Long	21	Pepper	lspr	efall	Rye	efall	lspr
Long	22	Summer squash	esum	efall	Oat & HV	efall	espr
Long	23	Summer squash	esum	efall	Oat & HV	efall	lspr
Long	24	Summer squash	esum	efall	Oat & HV	efall	lspr
Long	25	Winter squash	lspr	efall	Rye	lfall	lspr
Long	26	Garlic/field pea&oat	—/lsum	msum	CC residue		
Long	27	Garlic/field pea&oat	—/lsum	msum	CC residue		
Long	28	Field pea/buckwheat/spinach8e	espr/msum/lsum	esum/lsum/efall	Rye	efall	lspr
Long	29	Field pea/buckwheat/spinach8e	espr/msum/lsum	esum/lsum/efall	Rye	efall	lspr
Long	30	Oat-red clover	espr	mow esum	Red clover		lspr
Long	31	Fallow/Beet7	msum	lfall	Rye	efall	lspr
Long	32	Broccoli	lspr	lsum	Oat & HV	lsum	lspr
Long	33	Broccoli	lspr	lsum	Oat & HV	lsum	lspr
Long	34	Cowpea/lettuce7l	esum/msum	msum/efall	Rye	efall	lspr
Long	35	Tomato	lspr	efall	Rye & HV	efall	esum
Long	36	Tomato	lspr	efall	Rye & HV	efall	esum
Long	37	Tomato	lspr	efall	Rye & HV	efall	esum
Long	38	Tomato	lspr	efall	Rye & HV	efall	esum
Far	39	Tomato&Lettuce5	lspr	efall	Rye	efall	espr
Far	40	Tomato&Lettuce5	lspr	efall	Rye & HV	efall	esum
Far	41	Winter squash	lspr	efall	Rye	efall	espr
Far	42	Winter squash	lspr	efall	Rye	efall	espr
Far	43	Winter squash	lspr	efall	Rye	efall	espr
Far	44	Winter squash	lspr	efall	Rye	efall	espr
Far	45	Lettuce6/cowpea&oat	esum/msum	msum	CC residue	—	—
Far	46	Lettuce6/cowpea&oat	esum/msum	msum	CC residue	—	—
Far	47	Cowpea/spinach8l	esum/lsum	lsum/lfall	Bare	—	—
Far	48	Cowpea/spinach8l	esum/lsum	lsum/lfall	Bare	—	—
Far	49	Fallow/Lettuce7e	msum	lsum	Garlic	lfall	—
Far	50	Fallow/Lettuce7e	msum	lsum	Garlic	lfall	—

TABLE 5.10 Field history and future for Summer Acres Farm (*continued*)

Field Name	Mgmt Unit	Two Summers from Now			Two Winters from Now		
		Crop	Plant	Harv.	Crop	Plant	Harv.
Early	1	Kohlrabi/buckwheat	espr/msum	msum/lsum	Oat	efall	espr
Early	2	Pepper	lspr	efall	Oat	efall	espr
Early	3	Spinach5/cowpea	espr/esum	esum/efall	Oat	efall	espr
Early	4	Spinach5/cowpea	espr/esum	esum/efall	Oat	efall	espr
Early	5	Carrot	espr	efall	Oat	efall	espr
Early	6	Carrot	espr	efall	Oat	efall	espr
Early	7	Pea/fallow	espr	msum	Oat & HV	lsum	espr
Early	8	Pea/fallow	espr	msum	Oat & HV	lsum	espr
Early	9	Pea/fallow	espr	msum	Oat & HV	lsum	espr
Early	10	Pea/fallow	espr	msum	Oat	efall	espr
Long	11	Pepper	lspr	efall	Oat	efall	espr
Long	12	Lettuce6/buckwheat	esum/msum	msum/lsum	Oat	efall	lspr
Long	13	Lettuce6/buckwheat	esum/msum	msum/lsum	Oat	efall	lspr
Long	14	Cowpea/spinach8l	esum/lsum	lsum/lfall	Bare	efall	lspr
Long	15	Summer squash	esum	efall	Rye	efall	lspr
Long	16	Summer squash	esum	efall	Rye	efall	lspr
Long	17	Summer squash	esum	efall	Rye	efall	lspr
Long	18	Cowpea/lettuce8	esum/lsum	lsum/lfall	Bare	—	—
Long	19	Broccoli	lspr	lsum	Oat & HV	lsum	espr
Long	20	Broccoli	lspr	lsum	Oat & HV	lsum	espr
Long	21	Cowpea/spinach8l	esum/lsum	lsum/lfall	Bare	—	—
Long	22	Pepper	lspr	efall	Bare	—	—
Long	23	Potato	lspr	lsum	Rye	efall	lspr
Long	24	Potato	lspr	lsum	Rye	efall	lspr
Long	25	Cowpea/lettuce8	esum/lsum	lsum/lfall	Bare	—	—
Long	26	Winter squash	lspr	efall	Rye	efall	lspr
Long	27	Winter squash	lspr	efall	Rye	efall	lspr
Long	28	Winter squash	lspr	efall	Rye	efall	lspr
Long	29	Winter squash	lspr	efall	Rye	efall	lspr
Long	30	Potato	lspr	lsum	Rye & HV	lsum	lspr
Long	31	Potato	lspr	lsum	Rye & HV	lsum	lspr
Long	32	Beet5/buckwheat	lspr/msum	msum/lsum	Rye & HV	lsum	lspr
Long	33	Tomato	lspr	efall	Rye	efall	lspr
Long	34	Tomato	lspr	efall	Rye	efall	lspr
Long	35	Fallow/Buckwheat/spinach8e	msum/lsum	lsum/efall	Rye & HV	lsum	lspr
Long	36	Fallow/Buckwheat/spinach8e	msum/lsum	lsum/efall	Bare	—	—
Long	37	Fallow/Lettuce7e	msum	lsum	Rye	lsum	esum
Long	38	Fallow/Lettuce7e	msum	lsum	Rye	lsum	esum
Far	39	Oat-red clover	espr	mow esum	Garlic	lfall	—
Far	40	Fallow/beet7	msum	lfall	Garlic	lfall	—
Far	41	Tomato&Lettuce5	lspr	esum&efall	Rye	efall	lspr
Far	42	Tomato&Lettuce5	lspr	esum&efall	Rye	efall	lspr
Far	43	Tomato	lspr	efall	Rye	efall	lspr
Far	44	Tomato	lspr	efall	Rye	efall	lspr
Far	45	Winter squash	lspr	efall	Rye	efall	espr
Far	46	Winter squash	lspr	efall	Rye	efall	espr
Far	47	Cowpea/lettuce7l	esum/msum	msum/efall	Rye	efall	espr
Far	48	Cowpea/lettuce7l	esum/msum	msum/efall	Rye	efall	espr
Far	49	Garlic/field pea&oat	—/lsum	msum	CC residue	—	—
Far	50	Garlic/field pea&oat	—/lsum	msum	CC residue	—	—

TABLE 5.10 Field history and future for Summer Acres Farm (*continued*)

Field Name	Mgmt Unit	Three Summers from Now		
		Crop	Plant	Harv.
Early	1	Pea/sorgh	espr/msum	msum/efall
Early	2	Pea/sorgh	espr/msum	msum/efall
Early	3	Carrot	espr	efall
Early	4	Carrot	espr	efall
Early	5	Tomato & spinach5	lspr	esum&efall
Early	6	Tomato&spinach5	lspr	esum&efall
Early	7	Pepper	lspr	efall
Early	8	Pepper	lspr	efall
Early	9	Pepper	lspr	efall
Early	10	Kohlrabi/cowpea	espr/msum	msum/lsum
Long	11	Pea/sorgh	espr/msum	msum/efall
Long	12	Pea/sorgh	espr/msum	esum/lsum
Long	13	Winter squash	lspr	efall
Long	14	Winter squash	lspr	efall
Long	15	Beet5/buckwheat	lspr/msum	msum/lsum
Long	16	Tomato	lspr	efall
Long	17	Tomato	lspr	efall
Long	18	Tomato	lspr	efall
Long	19	Lettuce5/cowpea	espr/esum	esum/lsum
Long	20	Lettuce5/cowpea	espr/esum	esum/lsum
Long	21	Field pea/lettuce7e	espr/msum	esum/lsum
Long	22	Field pea/lettuce7e	espr/msum	esum/lsum
Long	23	Cowpea/lettuce8	esum/lsum	lsum/lfall
Long	24	Cowpea/lettuce8	esum/lsum	lsum/lfall
Long	25	Field pea/beet7	espr/msum	esum/lfall
Long	26	Potato	lspr	lsum
Long	27	Potato	lspr	lsum
Long	28	Potato	lspr	lsum
Long	29	Potato	lspr	lsum
Long	30	Lettuce6/cowpea	esum/msum	msum/efall
Long	31	Lettuce6/cowpea	esum/msum	msum/efall
Long	32	Winter squash	lspr	efall
Long	33	Winter squash	lspr	efall
Long	34	Winter squash	lspr	efall
Long	35	Winter squash	lspr	efall
Long	36	Oat-red clover	espr	mow esum
Long	37	Fallow/Buckwheat/spinach8e	msum/lsum	lsum/efall
Long	38	Fallow/Buckwheat/spinach8e	msum/lsum	lsum/efall
Far	39	Garlic/field pea&oat	—/lsum	msum
Far	40	Garlic/field pea&oat	—/lsum	msum
Far	41	Cowpea/spinach8l	esum/lsum	lsum/lfall
Far	42	Cowpea/spinach8l	esum/lsum	lsum/lfall
Far	43	Cowpea/lettuce7l	esum/msum	msum/efall
Far	44	Cowpea/lettuce7l	esum/msum	msum/efall
Far	45	Broccoli	lspr	lsum
Far	46	Broccoli	lspr	lsum
Far	47	Tomato	lspr	efall
Far	48	Summer squash	esum	efall
Far	49	Summer squash	esum	efall
Far	50	Summer squash	esum	efall

Abbreviations:

Plant	Planting time
Harv	End of harvest, or for cover crops, the time of incorporation
Sorgh	Sorghum-sudan grass hybrid
HV	Hairy vetch
CC residue	Winter-killed cover crop residue

Abbreviations for planting and harvest times are given in sidebar 5.3 (page 70).

> **"The farmers attempt to keep the ground covered with a cash or cover crop throughout the year to prevent erosion and improve soil quality..."**

and improve soil quality, even when the opportunity for biomass production by a cover crop is limited. The exception is that they include a one-month fallow period in late spring or early summer for weed control whenever this is convenient.

Mostly, the Summer Acres farmers manage to plant a given crop in adjacent MUs. However, since they grow most crops in even numbers of MUs, the configuration of the "Long" field in figure 5.4 (page 83), with its strips of seven MUs, poses a problem. If they cannot manage to plant the same crop in a long strip, they try to plant pairs of MUs that are side by side. This reduces time spent planting and managing the crop. Pepper, tomato, summer squash, and winter squash are less bothersome to have in multiple locations since the farmers grow several varieties of each of these crops. To the extent possible, they attempt to separate successive plantings of lettuce and spinach with one or more MUs of other crops. When successive plantings are forced onto adjacent MUs by other considerations, they try to provide a time lag within the season, so that insect pests and diseases cannot easily spread from one planting to the next.

Before the planning process, the growers often double-cropped short-season crops (for example, an early lettuce planting with a late spinach planting). This allowed them to produce 51 MUs of crops on 50 MUs of land. It also allowed them to plant a soil-building full-season cover crop of oat (mowed in June) and red clover on a few MUs each year. However, it made including shorter-season legume cover crops like cowpea and field pea difficult on an even greater number of MUs, thereby requiring substantial use of compost to meet N needs. Consequently, this practice was discontinued. In order to continue to grow more MUs of crops than they have land, they began intercropping

early lettuce or spinach with tomato (see chapter 7, pages 95–100). The lettuce or spinach is planted at the same time as the tomato in an adjacent row on the same bed and is harvested in early summer before the tomatoes crowd it. Although double-cropping and intercropping allow intensive use of the land, they also mean that more different crop families are grown within a given number of years on those MUs. This can increase the difficulty of separating families in time.

The only MUs with special properties are in the field called "Early." That field is well drained and has a south-facing slope that warms early in the spring. Consequently, the farmers attempt to grow their earliest crops on this field whenever possible. These crops include pea, carrot, kohlrabi, and early plantings of lettuce and spinach. Since kohlrabi requires only one MU, whereas the other early crops use two or four MUs, the farmers sometimes use the first planting of beet (beet5 in tables 5.9, page 82 and 5.10, pages 84–88), which also requires only one MU, as a "fill-in" crop to balance the rotation plan. When possible, they also like to grow peppers on the field, since peppers are a high-value crop that takes advantage of the warm temperatures provided by the field's southerly aspect.

The rotation on this field is complicated, however, by the need to grow four MUs of peas and the use of cowpea and hairy vetch cover crops (close relatives of peas) as nitrogen sources for the other crops. To minimize problems, they decide to plant peas on a given MU only one year out of three, and to avoid preceding them with a cowpea cover crop during summer the year before. Since nitrogen-fixing cover crops are limited by these decisions, they also decide to use a purchased amendment, if necessary, to supply N needs. To meet the first of these decisions, in some years they plant two MUs of peas on MU 11 and 12 of the field Long. Even with their precautions, the frequency of peas and pea relatives may eventually lead to disease problems for this crop.

Many of the early-season crops grown on field Early are harvested in time for a late planting of lettuce, spinach, or beet. Lettuce, however, shares diseases with peas (see appendix 2, pages 104–123), which is the crop most dependent on field Early. Similarly, since the farmers want to grow early-season crops of spinach and beet on field Early, if late-season plantings of these same crops are grown after peas, or kohlrabi, adequately long lags between beet family crops would be difficult to obtain. Consequently, the spring cash crops on field Early are followed by summer cover crops.

The principal limiting factor on the remaining 40 MUs in fields Long and Far relate to the need to grow 13 MUs of species in the nightshade family (tomato, potato, and peppers). The farmers have to juggle their crops carefully to avoid growing a nightshade crop more often than one year in three (40/13 ≈ 3). A longer interval between nightshade crops is desirable (see appendix 3, pages 124–137), and they sometimes manage this on some MUs by growing peppers in field Early. To minimize the problem of finding locations for nightshades that maximize return times, they begin the placement process for fields Long and Far by locating these crops first.

The farmers then proceed to place the winter and summer squashes. Squash also occupies a large percentage of fields Long and Far, and therefore providing adequate breaks between squash crops is difficult. In addition, they grow six MUs of winter squash, and management is easier if it is planted in a block of adjacent MUs. Other crops are then filled in wherever they can fit given the goals discussed above.

With the exception of the nightshades, which are probably planted too frequently, the farmers in this example manage a reasonable separation in time for most families on most MUs in most years. Accomplishing this, however, requires considerable juggling of crop placement: Regular repetition of particular crop sequences is largely impossible, and development of a general crop rotation plan would probably require a shift in the crop mix. Increasing the land base could simplify the rotation and avoid the problem of too many MUs of nightshade crops. In addition, increased land would allow greater use of legumes to supply nitrogen for heavy-feeding crops and allow more convenient placement of crops on the farm.

6

CROP ROTATION DURING THE TRANSITION FROM CONVENTIONAL TO ORGANIC AGRICULTURE

Charles L. Mohler

The primary purpose of this manual is to help organic farmers plan crop rotations on land that is already being farmed organically. Nevertheless, a brief discussion of how to sequence crops during the transition from conventional to organic management may be useful for beginning organic farmers and those who are adding new land to their farms. Organic farms in the northeastern US usually begin either with land that has been actively farmed using conventional practices or with land that has been semi-fallow for several years (for example, an old hay field). In both cases, soil improvement and weed management are usually large challenges.

Transition from Old Sod to Vegetable Production

Many small organic vegetable farms in the northeastern US begin on land that has been a hay field or pasture for several years. Often the previous manager applied no fertilizers or pesticides for several years, and thus the land can be quickly certified as organic. The long period in sod will have improved soil physical quality, but export of several tons of hay per acre over several years may have depleted soil nutrients.

Old hay fields and pastures are excellent habitats for establishment of perennial weed species. Also, some forage grasses like smooth brome can be challenging weeds in organic vegetable fields. At the start, making a systematic assessment of the plant species present and mapping potential weed problems may be worthwhile. *Weeds of the Northeast* is a useful guide for weed identification (116). Taking an initial survey will help you avoid spreading a few patches of weeds like johnsongrass or bindweed all over the field during tillage. If any bad perennial weeds are

> ## "Old hay fields and pastures are excellent habitats for establishment of perennial weed species."

abundant, consider choosing a different field or using conventional methods to get the weed under control before attempting the transition. If taking an initial weed survey is not practical, it will be safest to assume that perennial weeds pose a substantial problem. *Reducing weed numbers to manageable levels at the outset will pay lasting dividends in reduced labor over the coming years.* Consequently, a full growing season of cover crops and fallow periods is often a good investment when converting old sod to vegetable production (see sidebar 6.1, page 92). If perennials show up in the fall cover crop after the fallow, a second year of fallow and cover crops may be necessary.

If a full year of summer fallow and cover crops to control weeds and improve soil quality is not practical, working a summer fallow period into the first year's cropping sequence may help get the weeds under control. For example, a fallow can be worked in after a spring lettuce crop or before fall broccoli. However, avoid leaving the soil bare in the spring or mid to late fall, when conditions may prevent working the soil for long periods, as this will allow weed growth and nutrient leaching.

Whether or not the transition process begins with a full season of fallow and cover crops, the first cash crop after a sod should be transplanted, not direct seeded. In general, transplants compete better with weeds because they begin larger, and they can be cultivated or hoed sooner after planting. Also, unless mulch is used, avoid widely spreading vine crops like winter squash or pumpkins in the first two years after sod, because these become impossible to weed late in their growth cycle.

In general, working a lot of cover crops into the rotation during the first few years of transition is advisable to build soil physical quality, increase nutrient storage, and compete with weeds. Soil that has been built up in physical quality and nutrient storage over several years will often support multiple vegetable crops within a single growing season. During transition, however, multiple cropping may result in low yields and poor-quality produce, whereas investing in soil development and weed control through cover cropping and mulching will provide a basis for long-term prosperity.

Transition from Conventional Cropping on a Farm with Forages

When the land has been actively farmed by conventional means, often soil organic matter and soil tilth are low. If the land has been in field crops, the dominant weeds will likely be full-season, spring-germinating annuals like lambsquarters, pigweed, and foxtail. No-till farmed land may have a lot of perennial weeds, as well.

If the farm has a use for forages, beginning the transition with a sod crop like alfalfa or a mixed grass–legume hay has multiple advantages. A few years in sod will build soil structure and organic matter better than any alternative crop will (68). Moreover, annual weeds do not get a chance to go to seed in a mowed hay field, so the density of their seeds in the soil will decline by natural mortality. However, heavy weed seed production may occur during the establishment year of the sod crop, and steps should be taken to prevent this.

Usually, organic growers sow perennial forages with a small grain nurse crop. The nurse crop helps compete with weeds while the forage crop establishes. Winter grains like winter wheat and spelt are better at competing with weeds than spring grains because they are already well established in the spring when the dominant weeds in the field begin to germinate. Also, they are harvested before most of the spring-germinating weeds go to seed. Red clover will establish well if overseeded onto the soil surface in very early spring, while the ground is freezing and thawing (frost seeding). For alfalfa and grasses, planting with a no-till drill is safer. Spring grains and forages can be planted together at the same time. If the farm has a use or market for cereal grain, hay, or green chop, taking the spring grain crop off for one of those uses can prevent most mid-season weed seed production. The young forage crop should be mowed at four to five inches in late summer to further reduce weed seed production.

Often the sod is broken in the fall to allow it to break down over the winter, and a cover crop like rye is planted to protect the soil. If the sod includes a substantial component of legumes, planting a heavy feeder like corn the next year is advisable. Avoid planting this first corn crop after transition too early in the spring. A late spring planting will let more weeds germinate before final seedbed preparation, reduce seed losses to rot and insects, and ensure that the corn grows rapidly enough to be competitive. The corn will do nothing for restoring soil quality, so if it is harvested for silage, sow a winter grain cover crop after harvest. If the corn is harvested as grain, consider interseeding a cover crop like red clover or annual ryegrass just after last cultivation (96). Planting the cover crop after the corn is well established will not reduce yield (96), but it will allow plenty of time for good cover to develop before winter.

Transition to Cash Grain or Vegetables on a Farm Without Forages

If the farm does not need forages, the transition cropping sequence will probably rely on cover crops to build soil quality. Stale seedbeds (see table 3.6, page 43) and other fallow periods may be needed to reduce weed density.

In vegetables, rely on transplanted crops and large-seeded crops like sweet corn and snap beans the first few years. These are more competitive and easier to cultivate and hoe than direct-seeded crops with small seeds. Short-season crops like transplanted lettuce are useful early in transition because they can be harvested before weeds have a chance to go to seed. They also allow time for a fallow period for weed control or an additional cover crop to build soil quality. Early in the transition, winter cover

> ## "The extensive fine root system of the grain will help build soil quality."

crops are especially important to build soil quality. Accordingly, avoid crops that are harvested too late to plant a winter cover, or overseed a cover crop into the cash crop. Establishment will be better if the cover crop seed is covered by hoeing or cultivation.

On cash grain farms, avoid starting the transition with corn, even if this would be the logical next crop for the field (see table 6.1 for potential sequences). Corn is likely to suffer from nitrogen deficiency early in the transition process (58, 119) unless large amounts of manure, compost, or expensive organic fertilizer are applied. In contrast, soybean supplies its own N. If possible, plant a winter grain like wheat or spelt after soybean is harvested. This may require using a short-season soybean. A winter grain has multiple benefits early in the transition and represents an alternative to soybean as a starting point. Since the soil does not yet have good N supplying power, however, compost or some other source of N may be required to reach full yield potential. The extensive fine root system of the grain will help build soil quality. Also, a densely

TABLE 6.1 Some cropping sequences for transition on a cash grain farm

Year	Sequence 1	Sequence 2
1	Soybean (short-season) followed by winter grain	Winter grain with frost-seeded red clover
2	Winter grain with frost-seeded red clover	Corn with interseeded annual ryegrass at last cultivation
3	Corn with interseeded red clover or annual ryegrass at last cultivation	Soybean
4	Spring grain or soybean	Winter or spring grain

sown winter grain will suppress weeds well, and it will be harvested before most spring-germinating weeds can go to seed.

Many organic grain growers in the northeastern US overseed winter grains with clover in late winter, when frost can work the seed into the soil. The clover establishes slowly but will be ready for rapid growth by the time the grain is harvested. If weeds have started to go to seed, set the combine head low at grain harvest to cut off the seed-producing parts of the weeds. If the weeds have not yet flowered at harvest, set the combine head high, and then return and mow the field at a height of about five inches before weed seeds set. The clover will compete heavily with weed regrowth if the weeds are cut after they have flowered.

The full year's growth of clover will supply enough N for a corn crop the following year. If the growing season is long enough, sow a winter cover crop after harvest. Otherwise, interseed a cover crop at last cultivation to ensure continued soil building. Small seeds like clover will fall into the broken soil after cultivation, but large-seeded species should be sown before cultivation. Interseeding into corn at last cultivation usually produces good stands but may occasionally fail due to drought during cover crop establishment (see chapter 7, pages 95–100) for more on interseeding cover crops).

7

GUIDELINES FOR INTERCROPPING
CHARLES L. MOHLER AND KIMBERLY A. STONER

Intercropping is an all-encompassing term for the practice of growing two or more crops in close proximity: in the same row or bed, or in rows or strips that are close enough for biological interaction. Mixed cropping, companion planting, relay cropping, interseeding, overseeding, underseeding, smother cropping, planting polycultures, and using living mulch are all forms of intercropping (see glossary at the end of this chapter). Intercropping includes the growing of two or more cash crops together. It also includes the growing of a cash crop with a cover crop or other non-cash crop that provides benefits to the primary crop or to the overall farm system. Cover crops can also be intercropped with one another. The purpose of this chapter is to outline some of the basic principles for using intercropping successfully and to relate these to the principles of crop rotation detailed in the rest of this manual.

Advantages of intercropping fall into three basic categories. First, an intercrop may use resources of light, water, and nutrients more efficiently than single crops planted in separate areas, and this can improve yields and income. Second, crop mixtures frequently have lower pest densities, especially of insect pests. This occurs both because the mixture confuses the insects and, if the mixture is chosen carefully, because the mixture attracts beneficial predators. Finally, intercropping may allow more effective management of cover crops.

The advantages of intercropping, however, do not come for free. Intercropping systems require additional management. They often call for careful timing of field operations, and they may necessitate special interventions to keep competition between the intercropped species in balance. A crop mix that works well in one year may fail the next if weather favors one crop over another. A mixture of crops with different growth forms or timing of development may make cultivation and use of mulches

> **"[Intercropping systems] call for careful timing of field operations, and they may necessitate special interventions to keep competition between the intercropped species in balance."**

more difficult and less effective. Planting crops in alternate rows or strips greatly simplifies management and captures some of the benefits of intercropping for pest control. It may do little, however, to increase resource capture by the crops, unless alternating strips are close together.

Intercropping also poses a special problem for crop rotation. One fundamental principle of crop rotation is the separation of plant families in time. As explained in chapters 2 and 3, pages 3–46, this is critical for management of diseases and, to a lesser extent, insects. If plants from two families are mixed in the same bed or field, however, achieving a substantial time lag before replanting either of those families may be difficult. Suppose, for example, that a farm grows an acre each of tomato, squash, broccoli, and mid-season lettuce. A simple rotation would put each of the crops in a different year, with a three-year interval before a crop is repeated on the same bed. If, however, the lettuce and tomato are grown together (see the next section), crops would be separated by only a two-year interval, which may be insufficient to keep some diseases under control (see appendix 3, pages 124–137). Thus, intercropping requires extra care and effort in planning and maintaining a viable crop rotation.

For an intercropping scheme to be useful, it should improve the overall economics of the farm. A new intercropping idea should be tested first on a relatively small area. This will allow evaluation of whether it fits into the overall management system and whether benefits outweigh extra costs, labor, or yield reduction. Note that some consequences of intercropping—such as better or worse weed control, or difficulties in timing planting or harvest—may not show up in a single test year.

Interplanting Crops with Partially Overlapping Growing Seasons

Interplanting crops that share the field for only part of the season can increase the capture of sunlight over the course of the whole year. Expert panel farmer Drew Norman (page 51) provides an example of this sort of intercropping. He transplants lettuce next to his tomato plants. The lettuce uses the space that is not yet occupied by the tomatoes and is harvested about the time the tomatoes are branching out to cover the full width of the bed. Usually, when two cash crops are intercropped, they are either planted at the same time or harvested at the same time. Mechanical planting may be difficult if the crops are not planted simultaneously. Without careful planning, harvesting the early crop may damage the late crop.

Nurse crops are another variation on staggered-season intercropping. Forage legumes and grasses establish so slowly that weeds tend to take over the field if a fast-growing, competitive nurse crop like oats, barley, or wheat is not there to use the available sunlight. After the grain is harvested, the forages continue to grow through the remainder of the season and are ready for a first cutting in the autumn.

Interseeding cover crops into established cash crops can increase cover crop productivity and the range of cover crop species that can be used in a region. For example, clover can be interseeded into corn during the last inter-row cultivation (96), whereas clovers sown after corn harvest establish poorly and have little time for growth before winter. Similarly, in New York and New England, hairy vetch sown after September 15 often winter-kills, which potentially restricts it to use following early-harvested crops. It can, however, be interplanted successfully into many full-season crops. For example, NEON collaborators Eric and Anne Nordell plant single rows of hairy vetch between rows of many types of late-season vegetables. Despite trampling during harvest, the vetch sprawls out and provides good winter ground cover and nitrogen for crops the following year.

Most cover crops will compete heavily with the cash crop unless seeding is delayed until the cash crop is well established. Consequently, cover crops planted into established cash crops usually produce negligible organic matter or nitrogen by the time of crop harvest. Attempts to use interseeded cover crops to smother weeds have generally shown that if the cover crop is sufficiently dense and vigorous to suppress the weeds, it also competes with the cash crop. Successful exceptions require subtleties of timing, sowing densities, and relative growth rates of the cash and cover crops that are difficult to repeat consistently. Thus, the primary use of interseeded cover crops is the early establishment of cover. Note that if the cover crop is left after the cash crop is harvested, cleanup of weeds after harvest is restricted to mowing or hand weeding. Consequently, interseeded cover crops are most useful in late-harvested crops or fields with low weed pressure. Table 7.1 shows opportunities and problems with interseeding cover crops into established cash crops.

Intercropping Legumes with Nonlegumes

Legumes like beans and alfalfa have nitrogen-fixing bacteria associated with their roots. Consequently they compete only slightly with nonlegumes for soil nitrogen and in some cases even supply nitrogen to adjacent plants via leakage and root decomposition (fine roots grow and die rapidly within the season, even in healthy plants).

For example, field pea can be grown with a small grain and the two crops combine-harvested together (119). Intercropping of beans and corn (usually with squash, as well) formed the basic farming system of Native Americans from Central America to the northeastern US. The scientific literature has documented the value of intercropping legumes with nonlegumes, especially grain crops, though much of this work has been done in the tropics (for example, see reference 126).

TABLE 7.1 Cover crop interseeding systems

Cover crop	Cash crop	Method	Benefits	Problems
Red clover, annual or perennial ryegrass[1]	Corn, late sweet corn	Broadcast after last cultivation[2]	Good organic matter production; N-fixation by red clover	Establishment may be poor in a dry summer; annual ryegrass may winter-kill
Rye	Corn, late sweet corn	Broadcast in early fall at 3 bu/A	Reasonable establishment most years[3]	Stand may be patchy; stand may be poor if the fall is dry
Annual ryegrass, creeping red fescue, red clover, white clover, alfalfa[4]	Soybean (planted in rows)	Broadcast after last cultivation[2]	No interference with harvest; N-fixation by legumes	Establishment may be poor in a dry summer
Rye, winter wheat, spelt	Soybean	Broadcast at 1.5X usual rate at leaf yellowing	Allows establishment in wet years and late harvested soybean	Timing is critical[5]; stand may be poor if the fall is dry
Crimson clover	Soybean	Broadcast at 20 lb/A at leaf yellowing	N-fixation; good production	Useful only from zone 6 & south – further north it winter-kills after little growth
Red clover, alsike clover, alfalfa, yellow sweet clover	Winter wheat, spelt	Sow on frozen ground in early spring	Good organic matter production and N-fixation before next spring crop	Ground may not freeze sufficiently to support tractor
Bell bean[6]	Fall brassicas	Plant two rows of bell bean between crop rows after last cultivation	N-fixation for next crop; grows fast and then winter-kills; upright growth does not interfere with crop	Expensive seed. Cover crop will be damaged at harvest.
Annual ryegrass	Tomato, pepper	Broadcast after last cultivation[2]	Good dry matter production by next spring	May winter-kill
Hairy vetch	Late harvested vegetables	Plant 1 or 2 rows between rows of vegetables after last cultivation	N-fixation for next crop; no interference with crop; spreads out to give fair winter cover and good spring production	None apparent
Rye	Late harvested vegetables	Plant 1 or 2 rows between rows of vegetables after last cultivation	Falls over to give fair winter cover; no interference with crop	None apparent
Rye	Late harvested vegetables	Broadcast at 2 to 3 bu/A 3 to 5 weeks before harvest	Provides more uniform cover than drilling between rows[3]	Stand may be patchy; stand may be poor if the fall is dry; interferes with harvest of short, leafy crops

Note: Only systems that cause negligible yield reduction have been included. All of these systems provide either a living or winter-killed cover through the winter. All resist damage during harvest of the cash crop unless otherwise noted, but some damage is inevitable.

[1] Alfalfa, yellow sweetclover, crimson clover, birdsfoot trefoil, white clover, alsike clover and hairy vetch can also be established by this method, but fall cover and spring dry matter production tend to be less than for red clover, annual ryegrass or perennial ryegrass.

[2] Seed can be applied at cultivation by attaching a forage seeder box to dribble seed onto the ground behind the cultivator tools. It can also be spun on with an attachment or by hand. Seeding should be completed before the first rain after cultivation.

[3] Rye is the only cover crop that usually establishes well when surface sown in the fall. Spelt and annual ryegrass also have a reasonable chance of success. Other surface seeded cover crops usually either fail to germinate or are heavily consumed by seed and seedling feeding insects (species that are normally considered beneficials due to their consumption of weed seeds and pest insects).

[4] Wheat or rye seeded by this method will grow several inches above the height of the lowest pods by harvest.

[5] If the grain is sown too soon before leaf drop, grain establishment will be poor due to shading by the soybeans. If the grain is sown after leaf drop, many seeds will not make contact with the soil and those that do will not have the benefit of coverage by dead leaves.

[6] Bell bean is a small seeded variety of fava bean. It is preferred over field pea in this application because it does not fall over or twine into the crop.

Grass-legume combinations are often used for forage and for cover crops. Hairy vetch combined with a winter grain like rye, wheat, or spelt is a good combination for a fall-planted, overwintering cover crop. Oat and field pea planted in August in the northern US and southern Canada will produce substantial organic matter and will then winter-kill, allowing early tillage the following spring. Hay meadows and pastures are often planted with a mixture of grasses and legumes. In all of these cases, the legume provides nitrogen, while the grass produces the bulk of the organic matter. Some research indicates that a pound of clover will fix more nitrogen into plant-usable form when grown with grasses than when grown in a pure stand. In some cases this can result in as much nitrogen fixation by the mixture as by a pure stand, but with a greater yield of organic matter (44).

Using Tall Crops to Reduce Drought or Heat Stress of Shorter Crops

Two mechanisms are involved in using tall crops to reduce drought or heat stress of shorter crops: partial shading and reduction in wind speed. Partial shade cast by a trellised crop or a well-spaced planting of sweet corn can reduce heat stress of summer crops of spinach or lettuce (19). This may be useful in preventing early bolting. On windy sites, periodic rows of tall crops can reduce water stress by slowing wind speed. For example, one study showed that soybean yields in Minnesota increased by as much as 28 percent when pairs of corn rows were interspersed in the fields to block wind (89).

Using Intercropping to Disrupt Host Finding by Some Host-Specific Insect Pests

Intercropping reduced densities of insect and mite pests in about 50 percent of the cases that have been studied, usually by disrupting the ability of the pest to find its host (2). Choosing an intercrop that does not host key pests on the main crop is critical. Intercropping usually does not reduce, and may even increase, the density of generalist pests. Whether insects are actually repelled by the odor of non-host plants is a matter of controversy. The odor of non-hosts does confuse insects that search for hosts by smell (110), making mixtures of dissimilar crops less attractive than monocultures. A mixture of leaf shapes can similarly confuse insects that search for their hosts by sight. For some pests, simply alternating rows or strips of different crops can be sufficient to interfere with insect movement or host-finding ability.

Specialist pests have different ways of finding their host plants, and non-host plants disrupt some species more easily than others. Crucifer flea beetles (*Phyllotreta cruciferae*), for example, are attracted to an area by odors of plants in the cabbage family. Since they move somewhat randomly within that area, landing on anything green, intercropping tends to reduce flea beetle numbers on the host plants (although often not enough to control damage). Imported cabbageworm butterflies (*Pieris rapae*), on the other hand, are good at finding their host plants in a mixture of other plants, and many studies have found that intercropping has no effect on their numbers. In the spring, newly emerged Colorado potato beetles find their hosts primarily by walking, and densely planted grass or heavy mulch interferes with their ability to do that. Expert farmer Eero Ruuttila (page 50) leaves strips of rye–hairy vetch cover crop between widely spaced rows of potatoes, which interfere with the beetles' movement. He later mows the cover strips and uses the clippings as mulch, which interferes with beetle movement and provides habitat for beetle predators.

How Intercrops Affect Populations of Beneficial Parasitoids and Pest Predators

The effects of intercropping on pest species vary, depending on the specific behaviors and life cycles of the beneficial insects. Many parasitoids are limited to a narrow range of insect hosts. Some of these use plant odors or visual cues to locate their hosts by first finding the plants on which the hosts are located. In those cases, intercropping can interfere with host finding by the beneficial parasitoids (99).

For the intercrop to increase the numbers of beneficial insects, it should provide the beneficials with an important resource, such as pollen, nectar, alternate prey, shelter, or overwintering sites. Organic growers often plant buckwheat, alyssum, and other flowering plants as sources of nectar and pollen for beneficials. Corn and other grasses also produce large quantities of pollen. Many major groups of beneficial insects—including predators such as lacewings, lady beetles, minute pirate bugs, and hover flies, as well as parasitoids and pollinators—feed on pollen or nectar. But beware: So do many pests, including tarnished plant bug and imported cabbageworm butterflies. One way to evaluate "insectary plantings" is to look at both the pests and the beneficials attracted by the flowers and evaluate the beneficial/pest ratio (64).

Alternate food or prey, shelter, and overwintering sites can be important in building up a buffer of generalist insect predators to prevent chance colonization of the field from turning into a major outbreak. Some generalist predators, like spiders, ground beetles, and rove beetles, typically have only one or two generations per year and are not highly mobile; so they need steady food sources and undisturbed vegetation nearby to colonize the field when pests arrive. For example, grass strips between fields provide overwintering sites for ground beetles, which colonize adjacent fields during the growing season.

Using Trap Crops to Reduce Pests

Designing a successful strategy for trap cropping requires a sophisticated understanding of the pest insect: its host plant preferences, pattern of movement, and timing of infestation and reproduction. One strategy that has recently proved successful for several species is perimeter trap cropping. This method is used for pest species that move into a field from the edges, have strong preferences for particular species or varieties of hosts, and generally require several months to a year for reproduction. The trap crop, which is strongly preferred to the main crop, is planted all around the main crop, like walls of a fortress. The pest, arriving in the field from the edges, encounters the trap crop first and stops, staying along the edge of the field. The trap crop may be sprayed with an insecticide or flamed to kill the pest before it moves to the main crop. This strategy is currently used to manage pepper maggot on bell peppers, with hot cherry peppers as the trap crop. It is also used to manage cucumber beetles and squash vine borers on yellow summer squash, with blue Hubbard squash as the trap crop. Research into various combinations of mustard family crops for trap cropping of flea beetles and diamondback moth is under way (8).

> "For the intercrop to increase the numbers of beneficial insects, it should provide the beneficials with an important resource."

A Glossary of Intercropping Terms

Alley cropping: Growing annual crops in tilled strips between rows of a tree or shrub crop.

Biostrips: Permanent sod strips, usually of high botanical diversity, maintained to provide food and habitat for beneficial organisms and disrupt dispersal of pests.

Companion planting: A general term essentially synonymous with *intercropping* but often used to refer to the planting of non-crop or ornamental species with vegetables for attraction of beneficial insects.

Insectary planting: Planting strips or patches in a field with species that attract beneficial insects.

Interplanting: Intercropping.

Interseeding: Planting a direct-seeded crop into another crop, either at planting of the first crop or later, after it is established.

Living mulch: Permanent sod strips of perennial grasses or legumes between rows or beds.

Monoculture: A field with a single crop in it, or pertaining to such a field.

Nurse crop: A fast-growing crop that suppresses weeds while a slow-growing crop establishes.

Overseeding, oversowing: Planting a direct-seeded crop or cover crop into an already established crop, usually by surface sowing of the seeds.

Parasitoid: An insect that lays its eggs in or on another arthropod. The larvae develop inside the host, eventually killing it.

Polyculture: A field (or cropping system) with multiple, interacting crops, or pertaining to such a field or cropping system.

Relay (inter)cropping: Planting a second crop into an already established crop. Usually the first crop is harvested before the second matures.

Smother crop: An interseeded crop sown with the intent of smothering weeds; sometimes also applied to a weed-suppressive cover crop grown alone.

Underseeding, undersowing: Overseeding or oversowing.

APPENDIX 1 Characteristics of Crops Commonly Grown in the Northeastern United States
Compiled by Charles L. Mohler and Anusuya Rangarajan

Yield and nutrient removal data are unavailable for some minor crops. Vegetable crops are arranged alphabetically by family.

| | Family | Har-vested Part | Average Yield[1] (lbs/acre) | Net Removal (lb/1000 lb product, fresh wt.) | | | Cold Tolerance | Weed Competi-tion | Seedbed Required |
				N	P[2]	K[2]			
Vegetable crops									
Beet[3]	Beet	root, leaf	25,000	2.7	0.9	3.4	half hardy	moderate	fine
Spinach & chard	Beet	leaf	8,000	5.0	1.0	5.0	hardy	moderate	fine
Carrot, parsnip	Carrot	root	26,000	1.6	0.4	4.0	half hardy	low	fine
Celeriac	Carrot	root	n/a	n/a	n/a	n/a	half hardy	low	fine
Celery	Carrot	leaf	50,000	1.7	0.3	3.8	half hardy	low	fine
Fennel	Carrot	leaf	n/a	n/a	n/a	n/a	half hardy	low	fine
Cucumber	Cucurbit	fruit	20,000	3.1	1.1	5.2	tender	moderate	medium
Melons[4]	Cucurbit	fruit	15,000	4.2	0.8	5.3	tender	high	medium
Pumpkin, winter squash	Cucurbit	fruit	30,000	5.4	1.2	n/a	tender	high	coarse
Summer squash	Cucurbit	fruit	17,000	1.8	0.4	n/a	tender	high	medium
Sweet corn	Grass	seed	11,000	5.0	0.7	2.5	tender	high	coarse
Bean, snap	Legume	fruit	6,000	4.0	2.0	5.0	tender	moderate	medium
Pea, in pods	Legume	fruit	9,000	n/a	n/a	n/a	hardy	low	medium
Endive etc.[5]	Lettuce	leaf	23,000	n/a	n/a	n/a	half hardy	low	fine/medium
Lettuce	Lettuce	leaf	24,000	2.5	1.2	5.0	half hardy	moderate	medium[7]
Salsify, scorzonera	Lettuce	root	n/a	n/a	n/a	n/a	hardy	low	fine
Garlic	Lily	bulb	16,500	n/a	n/a	n/a	very hardy	low	medium
Leek	Lily	bulb	16,000	3.6	0.5	n/a	hardy	low	fine
Onion[6]	Lily	bulb	25,000	2.7	0.5	2.7	hardy	low	fine
Scallion	Lily	bulb	18,000	n/a	n/a	n/a	half hardy	low	fine
Okra	Mallow	fruit	15,000	n/a	n/a	n/a	tender	low	fine
Sweet potato	Morning glory	root	15,000	n/a	n/a	n/a	tender	moderate	medium
Broccoli, cauliflower	Mustard	flower bud	10,000	2.8	0.8	4.0	hardy	moderate	medium[7]
Brussels sprouts	Mustard	bud	10,000	9.4	1.2	7.8	hardy	moderate	medium[7]
Cabbage	Mustard	bud	35,000	3.1	0.8	3.3	hardy	moderate	medium[7]
Mustard greens[8]	Mustard	leaf	12,000	6.2	1.5	5.5	hardy	low	fine
Radish	Mustard	root	6,000	n/a	n/a	n/a	half hardy	low	medium[7]
Turnip, rutabaga, daikon	Mustard	root	3,650	n/a	n/a	n/a	hardy	moderate	fine
Eggplant	Nightshade	fruit	20,000	1.6	0.3	n/a	tender	moderate	medium[7]
Pepper	Nightshade	fruit	20,000	2.0	0.3	2.3	tender	moderate	medium[7]
Potato	Nightshade	root	30,000	3.7	0.7	5.0	half hardy	high	coarse
Tomato	Nightshade	fruit	20,000	1.7	0.8	3.0	tender	moderate	medium[7]
Strawberry	Rose	fruit	10,000	1.0	0.3	2.2	very hardy	moderate	medium[7]

	Family	Har-vested Part	Average Yield[10] (lbs/acre)	Net Removal (lb/1000 lb of produce)			Cold Tolerance	Weed Competi-tion	Seedbed Required
				N	P	K			
Field crops									
Field corn—grain	Grass	seed	5,600	17	1.7	2.1	tender	moderate	coarse
Spring barley									
grain	Grass	seed	2,880	18	1.7	2.2	hardy	moderate	medium
straw	Grass	stem	1,210	18	1.3	15.4	—	—	—
Oat									
grain	Grass	seed	3,030	16	1.4	2.1	hardy	moderate	medium
straw	Grass	stem	4,020	5	0.8	8.3	—	—	—
Spring wheat									
grain	Grass	seed	2,410	25	2.1	2.9	hardy	moderate	medium
straw	Grass	stem	2,770	9	0.5	8.3	—	—	—
Winter wheat									
grain	Grass	seed	2,410	25	2.1	2.9	very hardy	high	medium
straw	Grass	stem	3,030	8	0.4	7.5	—	—	—
Spelt—grain	Grass	seed	2,000	n/a	n/a	n/a	very hardy	high	medium
Rye									
grain	Grass	seed	2,500	22	1.3	2.5	very hardy	high	medium
straw	Grass	stem	1,610	12	1.4	7.8	—	—	—
Buckwheat	Buckwheat	seed	950	17	3.2	4.5	tender	high	medium
Soybean	Legume	seed	2,410	59	6.0	14.0	tender	high	coarse
Dry bean	Legume	seed	1,790	36	4.0	9.5	tender	moderate	medium
Alfalfa hay	Legume	leaf	5,220	25	2.4	19.1	very hardy	high	fine
Grass & grass—leg. hay[9]	Grass-legume	leaf	3,790	21	3.5	18.1	very hardy	high	fine

Note: Appendix 1 is divided into sections for vegetable, grain, and cover crops. The type of data available differ slightly between these crop types.

[1] Averages are for all producers, not just organic producers. Turnip yield is for Maryland, and garlic and sweet potato yields are U.S. averages; all other vegetable crop yields are for New York.

[2] P and K removal and capture rates are for elemental P and K, not P_2O_5 or K_2O.

[3] Yield and nutrients are for roots only.

[4] Includes cantelope and watermelon.

[5] Includes endive, escarole, radicchio, Italian dandelion.

[6] Yield and nutrients are for bulbs only.

[7] For transplants.

[8] Includes kale, collards, mustard greens, Asian greens, napa cabbage, arugula, cress

[9] Nutrient removals are an average of alfalfa-smooth brome, alfalfa-orchardgrass and alfalfa-timothy. Afalfa-timothy removes more P than the others.

[10] Average yield data for field crops is from Canada (119).

	Family	Harvested Part	Capture N[11]	P	K	Cold Tolerance	Weed Competitiveness	Seedbed Required
Cover crops								
Winter grain, cc[12]	Grass	whole plant	high	moderate	moderate	very hardy	high	medium
Spring grain, cc[13]	Grass	whole plant	moderate	low	low	hardy	moderate	medium
Annual ryegrass	Grass	whole plant	moderate	moderate	moderate	very hardy	moderate	medium
Sorghum/ sudangrass	Grass	whole plant	high	moderate	moderate	tender	high	medium
Buckwheat	Buckwheat	whole plant	low	high	high	tender	high	medium
White clover	Legume	whole plant	fixes 80–200	low	low	very hardy	moderate	medium
Clovers, hardy[14]	Legume	whole plant	fixes 70–150	moderate	moderate	very hardy	moderate	medium
Clovers, not hardy[15]	Legume	whole plant	fixes 70–130	moderate	moderate	tender	moderate	medium
Sweet clover	Legume	whole plant	fixes 90–170	high	high	very hardy	moderate	medium
Hairy vetch	Legume	whole plant	fixes 90–200	moderate	moderate	very hardy	moderate	medium
Field pea	Legume	whole plant	fixes 90–150	low	low	hardy	high	coarse
Bell bean	Legume	whole plant	fixes 70–220	n/a	n/a	hardy	moderate	coarse
Rape, canola	Mustard	whole plant	high	high	n/a	hardy	moderate	medium
Oilseed radish	Mustard	whole plant	high	high	n/a	hardy	high	medium

[11] N fixation rates are in pounds per acre.

[12] cc, as a cover crop. Includes rye winter wheat, spelt.

[13] cc, as a cover crop. Includes barley, oat, spring wheat.

[14] Includes red clover, alsike clover, and crimson clover in the south.

[15] Includes berseem clover and crimson clover in the north.

Sources:
Some vegetable nutrient composition data adapted from (69). Other results are based upon Cornell laboratory testing of harvested portions.
Cold tolerance and weed competitiveness for vegetable crops partially from (39).
Field crop nutrient data computed from (119) and, if missing there, from (78).
Cover crop information was adapted largely from (107).

APPENDIX 2 Crop Sequence Problems and Opportunities
Compiled by Charles L. Mohler

Find the preceding crop in the second column and the following crop in the 5th row. The row goes across pp. 104–108. Using the row number and column number, locate the detailed note in the notes section, pp. 109–123.

		A	B	C	D	E	F	G	H	I
FAMILY										
		—	Lily	Lily	Lily	Lily	Legume	Legume	Lettuce	Night-shade
FOLLOWING CROP										
FAMILY	**PRECEDING CROP**	General	Onion	Scallion	Leek	Garlic	Bean, snap	Pea	Lettuce, etc.[1]	Potato
1	—	General		W-							W-
2	Lily	Onion	C	XXXX		D	D				
3	Lily	Scallion	C		XXXX						
4	Lily	Leek	C	D		XXXX	D, S				S
5	Lily	Garlic	C	D		D, S	XXXX				S, S-, N-
6	Legume	Bean, snap						XXXX		D	D
7	Legume	Pea							XXXX	D, C-	
8	Lettuce	Lettuce etc.[1]		W-		W-		D	D	XXXX	D
9	Nightshade	Potato	W-			S	S, C-	D		D	XXXX
10	Nightshade	Tomato						D		D	D, I
11	Nightshade	Eggplant									D, I
12	Nightshade	Pepper									D
13	Carrot	Carrot, parsnip		W		S	S	D		D	D, S
14	Carrot	Celery, herbs etc.[2]									D
15	Carrot	Celeriac									D
16	Mustard	Crucifer greens[3]									
17	Mustard	Broccoli, cauliflower						D		D	D
18	Mustard	Cabbage, b. sprouts[4]						D	D-	D	D
19	Mustard	Kale, collards						D	D-	D	D
20	Mustard	Radish							D-		D
21	Mustard	Turnip, rutabaga, daikon							D-		D
22	Cucurbit	Cucumber	W-					W-		W	
23	Cucurbit	Melons[5]	W-					W-		W	
24	Cucurbit	Pumpkin, winter squash	W-					W-		W	
25	Cucurbit	Summer squash	W-							W	
26	Beet	Spinach, chard		W-		W-				C-	
27	Beet	Beet									D
28	Grass	Sweet corn						D-			C-
29	Rose	Strawberry									D
30	Grass	Field corn						D-			C-
31	Grass	Oat	D-, W	W, I	W, I	W, I		D-		D-	D-, I
32	Grass	Spring barley	D-, W	W, I	W, I	W, I		D-	D-	D-	D-, I
33	Grass	Winter wheat, spelt	D-	W, I	W, I	W, I		D-		D-	D-, I
34	Grass	Rye	D-	W, I	W, I	W, I		D-		D-	D-, I
35	Legume	Soybean						D			D-
36	Legume	Dry bean						D		D	D
37	Legume	Alfalfa hay									D-
38	Grass-legume	Grass & grass-leg. hay		I	I	I					D-
39	Grass	Winter grain, cc[6]	W-, I-, N, S, C, C-	I	I	I		D-	D-	C	D-
40	Grass	Spring grain, cc[7]	D-, I-, N, S, C-	I	I	I		D-			D-
41	Grass	Annual ryegrass	N, S	I	I	I					D-
42	Grass	Sorghum-sudangrass	D-	I	I	I					D-
43	Buckwheat	Buckwheat									D-, S
44	Legume	White clover	I, N-							I	
45	Legume	Clovers, hardy[8]	I, N-						D	D, I	
46	Legume	Clovers, not hardy[9]	N-							I	
47	Legume	Sweet clover	N-					D			D
48	Legume	Hairy vetch	D, N-, C-						D		
49	Legume	Field pea	N-, C-						D	D	
50	Legume	Bell bean	N-						D	D	
51	Mustard	Rape, canola	D-								D-
52	Mustard	Oilseed radish	D-								D-

	J	K	L	M	N	O	P	Q	R	S	T	U	V
FAMILY													
	Night-shade	Night-shade	Night-shade	Carrot	Carrot	Carrot	Mustard	Mustard	Mustard	Mustard	Mustard	Mustard	Cucurbit
FOLLOWING CROP													
	Tomato	Eggplant	Pepper	Carrot, parsnip	Celery, herbs etc.[2]	Celeriac	Crucifer greens[3]	Broccoli, cauliflower	Cabbage, b. sprouts[4]	Kale, collards	Radish	Turnip, ruta-baga, daikon	Cucumber
1													
2													
3													
4				S								S	
5				S								S	
6								D-	D-	D-	D-	D-	
7							C-				C-		
8	D, C-	C-	C-	W-									C-
9	D, I	D, I		D, S, W-	D, S-	D	S-					S	
10	XXXX	D, I	D					D-	D-	D-	D-	D-	D
11	D, I	XXXX	D										D
12	D	D	XXXX										D
13				XXXX	D	D						S	D
14				D	XXXX	D							
15				D	D	XXXX							
16	D, C-	C-	C-				XXXX	D	D	D	D	D	N-, C-
17							D	XXXX	D	D	D	D	N-
18	D						D	D	XXXX	D	D	D	N-
19							D	D	D	XXXX	D	D	N-
20							D	D	D	D	XXXX	D	N-
21							D	D	D	D	D	XXXX	D, N-
22		D	D	W			W, N-	D-, N-	D-, N-	D-, N-	D-	D-	XXXX
23		D	D	W			W, N-	N-	N-	N-			D
24		D	D	W			W, N-	N-	N-	N-			D
25		D	D	W			W, N-	N-	N-	N-			D
26				W-							C-		
27							D	D	D				
28							D-	D-	D-				
29	D	D											
30							D-	D-	D-				
31				W, I	W		D-	D-	D-				I
32				W, I	W		D-	D-	D-				I
33				W, I	W		D	D-	D-				I
34				W, I	W		D-	D-	D-				I
35													
36													
37				D									
38				W, I									I
39				C	C		C	D-	D-	D-			
40								D-, W-, S-	D-, W-, S-	D-, W-, S-			
41							D-	D-	D-	D-	D-	D-	
42													
43								D-	D-	D-	D-	D-	
44													
45							C-	C-		C-			
46													
47													
48													N-
49								N-, W-	N-, W-	N-, W-			
50							N-	N-	N-	N-	N-	N-	
51							D	D	D	D	D	D	
52							D	D	D	D	D	D	

Find the preceding crop in the second column and the following crop in the 5th row. The row goes across pp. 104–108. Using the row number and column number, locate the detailed note in the notes section, pp. 109–123.

		W	X	Y	Z	AA	AB	AC	AD	AE
FAMILY										
		Cucurbit	Cucurbit	Cucurbit	Beet	Beet	Grass	Rose	Grass	Grass
FOLLOWING CROP										
FAMILY	**PRECEDING CROP**	Melons[5]	Pumpkin, w. squash	Summer squash	Spinach, chard	Beet	Sweet corn	Strawberry	Field corn	Oat
1	—	General									
2	Lily	Onion									
3	Lily	Scallion									
4	Lily	Leek									
5	Lily	Garlic									
6	Legume	Bean, snap									
7	Legume	Pea				C-					
8	Lettuce	Lettuce etc.[1]	C-	C-	C-						
9	Nightshade	Potato					D		D		
10	Nightshade	Tomato	D	D	D				D		
11	Nightshade	Eggplant	D	D	D						
12	Nightshade	Pepper	D	D	D						
13	Carrot	Carrot, parsnip									
14	Carrot	Celery, herbs etc.[2]									
15	Carrot	Celeriac									
16	Mustard	Crucifer greens[3]	N-, C-	N-, C-	N-, C-						
17	Mustard	Broccoli, cauliflower	N-	N-	N-, C-				D-		
18	Mustard	Cabbage, b. sprouts[4]	N-	N-	N-		D				
19	Mustard	Kale, collards	N-	N-	N-						
20	Mustard	Radish	N-	N-	N-						
21	Mustard	Turnip, rutabaga, daikon	N-	N-	N-						
22	Cucurbit	Cucumber	D	D	D			I		I	
23	Cucurbit	Melons[5]	XXXX	D	D			I		I	
24	Cucurbit	Pumpkin, winter squash	D	XXXX	D			I		I	
25	Cucurbit	Summer squash	D	D	XXXX			I		I	
26	Beet	Spinach, chard				XXXX					
27	Beet	Beet					XXXX				
28	Grass	Sweet corn		D			D-	XXXX		I	D
29	Rose	Strawberry							XXXX		
30	Grass	Field corn		D			D-	I		XXXX	D
31	Grass	Oat	I				D-, I	I		I	XXXX
32	Grass	Spring barley	I				D-, I	I		I	
33	Grass	Winter wheat, spelt	I				D-, I	I		D, I	
34	Grass	Rye	I				D-, I	I		I	I
35	Legume	Soybean								D-	
36	Legume	Dry bean									
37	Legume	Alfalfa hay									
38	Grass-legume	Grass & grass-leg. hay	I				I	D-, I, N-	I	D-, I, N-	D, I
39	Grass	Winter grain, cc[6]					D-				
40	Grass	Spring grain, cc[7]					D-				
41	Grass	Annual ryegrass									
42	Grass	Sorghum-sudangrass									
43	Buckwheat	Buckwheat									
44	Legume	White clover									
45	Legume	Clovers, hardy[8]									
46	Legume	Clovers, not hardy[9]									
47	Legume	Sweet clover									
48	Legume	Hairy vetch	D-, N-	N-	N-						
49	Legume	Field pea									
50	Legume	Bell bean									
51	Mustard	Rape, canola									
52	Mustard	Oilseed radish									

	AF	AG	AH	AI	AJ	AK	AL	AM	AN	AO	AP	AQ	AR
FAMILY													
	Grass	Grass	Grass	Legume	Legume	Legume	Grass-legume	Grass	Grass	Grass	Grass	Buck-wheat	Legume
FOLLOWING CROP													
	Spring barley	Winter wheat, spelt	Rye	Soybean	Dry bean	Alfalfa	Grass-legume hay	Winter grain, cc[6]	Spring grain, cc[7]	Annual ryegrass	Sorghum-sudangrass	Buck-wheat	White clover
1													
2													
3													
4													
5													
6				D	D								
7													
8													
9													
10													
11													
12													
13									W-, S-				
14													
15													
16													
17													
18													
19													
20													
21													
22					W-								
23					W-								
24					W-								
25													
26													
27													
28		D			D-								
29													
30	D	D, D-			D-								
31		D, D-, I	I		D-								
32	XXXX	D, I	D, I		D-								
33	D	XXXX	D, I		D-								
34			XXXX		D-		D						
35				XXXX	D								
36		D-		D	XXXX								
37					N-, S-	XXXX							
38		D, I	D, I		N-, S-		XXXX	C-					
39	D				D-			XXXX					
40					D-				XXXX				
41										XXXX			
42											XXXX		
43												XXXX	
44													XXXX
45				D	D								
46													
47				D				C-					
48								W					
49													
50													
51													
52				D-									

Find the preceding crop in the second column and the following crop in the 5th row. The row goes across pp. 104–108. Using the row number and column number, locate the detailed note in the notes section, pp. 109–123.

		AS	AT	AU	AV	AW	AX	AY	AZ
	FAMILY								
		Legume	Legume	Legume	Legume	Legume	Legume	Mustard	Mustard
	FOLLOWING CROP								
FAMILY	PRECEDING CROP	Clovers, hardy[8]	Clovers, not hardy[9]	Sweet clover	Hairy vetch	Field pea	Bell bean	Rape, canola	Oilseed radish
1 —	General								
2 Lily	Onion								
3 Lily	Scallion								
4 Lily	Leek								
5 Lily	Garlic								
6 Legume	Bean, snap					D	D		
7 Legume	Pea	D				D	D		
8 Lettuce	Lettuce etc.[1]	D				D	D		
9 Nightshade	Potato								
10 Nightshade	Tomato								
11 Nightshade	Eggplant								
12 Nightshade	Pepper								
13 Carrot	Carrot, parsnip					W-, N-			
14 Carrot	Celery, herbs etc.[2]								
15 Carrot	Celeriac								
16 Mustard	Crucifer greens[3]							D	D
17 Mustard	Broccoli, cauliflower							D	D
18 Mustard	Cabbage, b. sprouts[4]							D	D
19 Mustard	Kale, collards							D	D
20 Mustard	Radish							D	D
21 Mustard	Turnip, rutabaga, daikon							D	D
22 Cucurbit	Cucumber								
23 Cucurbit	Melons[5]								
24 Cucurbit	Pumpkin, winter squash			C-					
25 Cucurbit	Summer squash								
26 Beet	Spinach, chard								
27 Beet	Beet								
28 Grass	Sweet corn								
29 Rose	Strawberry								
30 Grass	Field corn								
31 Grass	Oat								
32 Grass	Spring barley								
33 Grass	Winter wheat, spelt								
34 Grass	Rye								
35 Legume	Soybean							D	
36 Legume	Dry bean					D	D		
37 Legume	Alfalfa hay					D	D		
38 Grass-legume	Grass & grass-leg. hay			C-					
39 Grass	Winter grain, cc[6]								
40 Grass	Spring grain, cc[7]								
41 Grass	Annual ryegrass								
42 Grass	Sorghum-sudangrass								
43 Buckwheat	Buckwheat								
44 Legume	White clover								
45 Legume	Clovers, hardy[8]	XXXX				D	D		
46 Legume	Clovers, not hardy[9]		XXXX						
47 Legume	Sweet clover	D		XXXX			D		
48 Legume	Hairy vetch				XXXX				
49 Legume	Field pea	D				XXXX	D		
50 Legume	Bell bean	D				D	XXXX		
51 Mustard	Rape, canola							XXXX	D
52 Mustard	Oilseed radish							D	XXXX

Notes:

A blank cell indicates that the sequence has no known advantages or disadvantages. Follow general rotation guidelines described in this book.

Shading indicates that the crops are in the same family.

XXXX = Crops are the same; do not plant.
D = Disease problems.
D- = Decreases disease problems.
W = Weed problems.
W- = Decreases weed problems.
I = Insect problems.
I- = Decreases insect problems.
N = Crop nutrition problems.
N- = Decreases crop nutrition problems.
S = Soil structural problems.
S- = Decreases soil structural problems.
C = Crop management problems.
C- = Decreases crop management problems.

[1] Includes lettuce, chicory, endive, and escarole.
[2] Includes celery, fennel, parsley, dill, and related herbs.
[3] Includes mustard greens, Asian greens, napa cabbage, arugula, and cress.
[4] Includes cabbage, Brussels sprouts, and kohlrabi.
[5] Includes cantaloupe and watermelon.
[6] Includes winter wheat, spelt, and rye.
[7] Includes barley, oat, and spring wheat.
[8] Includes red clover, alsike clover, and crimson clover in the south.
[9] Includes berseem clover and crimson clover in the north.

Notes on Interactions:

Row	Col.	Notes
1	B	**W-**, weed control in onion, which is a weak competitor, is easier following the good weed suppression that results when a competitive crop like tomato or squash is heavily mulched with hay (80).
1	I	**W-**, due to cultivation, hilling, and digging, potato is useful for cleaning up after a weedy crop (83).
2	A	**C**, many crops do well after alliums, possibly due to mycorrhizal buildup (82, 83).
2	B	**XXXX**
2	D	**D**, white rot, onion smut (danger is primarily to seedlings before transplanting) (36).
2	E	**D**, white rot (36).
3	A	**C**, many crops do well after alliums, possibly due to mycorrhizal buildup (82, 83).
3	C	**XXXX**
4	A	**C**, many crops do well after alliums, possibly due to mycorrhizal buildup (82, 83).

Row	Col.	Notes
4	B	**D**, onion smut (danger is primarily to seedlings before transplanting), white rot (36).
4	D	**XXXX**
4	E	**D**, white rot (36). **S**, root crops tend to reduce soil structure due to the additional soil disturbance during harvest; consequently, growing "soil building" crops before and after a root crop is often desirable (80).
4	I	**S**, root crops tend to reduce soil structure due to the additional soil disturbance during harvest; consequently, growing "soil building" crops before and after a root crop is often desirable (80).
4	M	**S**, root crops tend to reduce soil structure due to the additional soil disturbance during harvest; consequently, growing "soil building" crops before and after a root crop is often desirable (80).
4	U	**S**, root crops tend to reduce soil structure due to the additional soil disturbance during harvest; consequently, growing "soil building" crops before and after a root crop is often desirable (80).
5	A	**C**, many crops do well after Alliums, possibly due to mycorrhizal buildup (82, 83).
5	B	**D**, white rot (36).
5	D	**D**, white rot (36). **S**, root crops tend to reduce soil structure due to the additional soil disturbance during harvest; consequently, growing "soil building" crops before and after a root crop is often desirable (80).
5	E	**XXXX**
5	I	**S**, root crops tend to reduce soil structure due to the additional soil disturbance during harvest; consequently, growing "soil building" crops before and after a root crop is often desirable (80). **S-**, **N-**, mulched garlic, however, tends to restore soil structure and fertility after the relatively extractive potato crop (80).
5	M	**S**, root crops tend to reduce soil structure due to the additional soil disturbance during harvest; consequently, growing "soil building" crops before and after a root crop is often desirable (80).
5	U	**S**, root crops tend to reduce soil structure due to the additional soil disturbance during harvest; consequently, growing "soil building" crops before and after a root crop is often desirable (80).
6	F	**XXXX**
6	H	**D**, sclerotinia drop (67; see appendix 3, p. 124).
6	I	**D**, sclerotinia stalk rot (67; see appendix 3, p. 124).
6	Q	**D-**, clubroot declines more quickly when tomato, cucumber, snap bean, or buckwheat is grown (see chapter 3, p. 21).
6	R	**D-**, clubroot declines more quickly when tomato, cucumber, snap bean, or buckwheat is grown (see chapter 3, p. 21).
6	S	**D-**, clubroot declines more quickly when tomato, cucumber, snap bean, or buckwheat is grown (see chapter 3, p. 21).

Row	Col.	Notes
6	T	**D-**, clubroot declines more quickly when tomato, cucumber, snap bean, or buckwheat is grown (see chapter 3, p. 21).
6	U	**D-**, clubroot declines more quickly when tomato, cucumber, snap bean, or buckwheat is grown (see chapter 3, p. 21).
6	AI	**D**, common bacterial blight (*Xanthomonas campestris*; appendix 3, p. 124); soybean cyst nematode (*Heterodera glycines*) increases to high density on bean, though the bean crop is scarcely affected (28, 41).
6	AJ	**D**, common bacterial blight (*Xanthomonas campestris*; appendix 3, p. 124); soybean cyst nematode (*Heterodera glycines*) (28).
6	AW	**D**, field pea and bell bean should not be planted after bean due to *Fusarium*, *Pythium*, and *Sclerotinia* (119).
6	AX	**D**, field pea and bell bean should not be planted after bean due to *Fusarium*, *Pythium*, and *Sclerotinia* (119).
7	G	**XXXX**
7	H	**D**, sclerotinia disease of broad bean (presumably including bell bean) and red clover rot are closely related (varieties of *S. trifoliorum*); each can attack a variety of crops, including pea, lettuce, and possibly other plants (36). **C-**, there is time for a short-season crop after harvesting pea, and the second crop benefits from N supplied by the pea (81).
7	P	**C-**, there is time for a crop of crucifer greens or spinach after harvesting pea, and the second crop benefits from N supplied by the pea (81).
7	T	**C-**, timing works well to plant lettuce or radish after pea or spinach within a year (82).
7	Z	**C-**, there is time for a crop of crucifer greens or spinach after harvesting pea, and the second crop benefits from N supplied by the pea (81).
7	AS	**D**, sclerotinia disease of broad bean (presumably including bell bean) and red clover rot are closely related (varieties of *S. trifoliorum*); each can attack a variety of crops, including pea, lettuce, and possibly other plants (36).
7	AW	**D**, sclerotinia disease of broad bean (presumably including bell bean) and red clover rot are closely related (varieties of *S. trifoliorum*); each can attack a variety of crops, including pea, lettuce, and possibly other plants (36).
7	AX	**D**, sclerotinia disease of broad bean (presumably including bell bean) and red clover rot are closely related (varieties of *S. trifoliorum*); each can attack a variety of crops, including pea, lettuce, and possibly other plants (36).
8	B	**W-**, a short-season crop like lettuce or spinach allows good weed control and low weed seed production prior to slow-growing, long-season, hard-to-weed crops like onion and carrot (83).

Row	Col.	Notes
8	D	**W-**, a short-season crop like lettuce or spinach allows good weed control and low weed seed production prior to slow-growing, long-season, hard-to-weed crops like onion and carrot (83).
8	F	**D**, sclerotinia white mold (67; see appendix 3, p. 124).
8	G	**D**, sclerotinia disease of broad bean (presumably including bell bean) and red clover rot are closely related (varieties of *S. trifoliorum*); each can attack a variety of crops, including pea, lettuce, and possibly other plants (36).
8	H	**XXXX**
8	I	**D**, sclerotinia stalk rot (67; see appendix 3, p. 124).
8	J	**D**, lettuce, cabbage, and cress can be symptomless carriers of *Colletotrichum coccodes*, which causes tomato anthracnose and black dot. **C-**, short-season salad greens act as a cover crop and are harvested in time to plant tomato, eggplant, or pepper (83).
8	K	**C-**, short-season salad greens act as a cover crop and are harvested in time to plant tomato, eggplant, or pepper (83).
8	L	**C-**, short-season salad greens act as a cover crop and are harvested in time to plant tomato, eggplant, or pepper (83).
8	M	**W-**, a short-season crop like lettuce or spinach allows good weed control and low weed seed production prior to slow-growing, long-season, hard-to-weed crops like onion and carrot (83).
8	V	**C-**, leafy greens can make a crop before cucurbits need to be planted, and residue from the greens act as a green manure (81).
8	W	**C-**, leafy greens can make a crop before cucurbits need to be planted, and residue from the greens act as a green manure (81).
8	X	**C-**, leafy greens can make a crop before cucurbits need to be planted, and residue from the greens act as a green manure (81).
8	Y	**C-**, leafy greens can make a crop before cucurbits need to be planted, and residue from the greens act as a green manure (81).
8	AS	**D**, sclerotinia disease of broad bean (presumably including bell bean) and red clover rot are closely related (varieties of *S. trifoliorum*); each can attack a variety of crops, including pea, lettuce, and possibly other plants (36).
8	AW	**D**, sclerotinia disease of broad bean (presumably including bell bean) and red clover rot are closely related (varieties of *S. trifoliorum*); each can attack a variety of crops, including pea, lettuce, and possibly other plants (36).
8	AX	**D**, sclerotinia disease of broad bean (presumably including bell bean) and red clover rot are closely related (varieties of *S. trifoliorum*); each can attack a variety of crops, including pea, lettuce, and possibly other plants (36).

Row	Col.	Notes
9	A	**W-**, due to cultivation, hilling, and digging, potatoes are useful for cleaning up weeds prior to other crops (83, 81).
9	D	**S**, root crops tend to reduce soil structure due to the additional soil disturbance during harvest; consequently, preceding and following root crops with "soil building" crops is often desirable (80).
9	E	**S**, root crops tend to reduce soil structure due to the additional soil disturbance during harvest; consequently, growing "soil building" crops before and after a root crop is often desirable (80). **C-**, the timing of potato harvest and garlic planting are well suited for following potato with garlic (83).
9	F	**D**, sclerotinia white mold (67; see appendix 3, p. 124).
9	H	**D**, sclerotinia drop (67; see appendix 3, p. 124).
9	I	**XXXX**
9	J	**D**, early blight, anthracnose, verticillium wilt (67; see appendix 3, p. 124); stem canker (36). **I**, Colorado potato beetle (see table 3.5, p. 40).
9	K	**D**, verticillium wilt (67; see appendix 3, p. 124). **I**, Colorado potato beetle (see table 3.5, p. 40).
9	M	**D**, any 2-year sequence involving carrot, celery, and potato should be avoided due to root-knot nematode (*Meloidogyne hapla*) (20). **S**, root crops tend to reduce soil structure due to the additional soil disturbance during harvest; consequently, preceding and following root crops with "soil building" crops is often desirable (80). **W-**, due to cultivation and competitiveness, potato cleans up weeds prior to carrots, which are a poor competitor and hard to weed (83).
9	N	**D**, any 2-year sequence involving carrot, celery, and potato should be avoided due to root-knot nematode (*Meloidogyne hapla*) (20). **S-**, potatoes improve soil structure before small direct-seeded crops due to low traffic (83).
9	O	**D**, any 2-year sequence involving carrot, celery, and potato should be avoided due to root-knot nematode (*Meloidogyne hapla*) (20).
9	P	**S-**, potatoes improve soil structure before small direct-seeded crops due to low traffic (83).
9	U	**S**, root crops tend to reduce soil structure due to the additional soil disturbance during harvest; consequently, preceding and following root crops with "soil building" crops is often desirable (80).
9	AA	**D**, scab of beet is caused by several of the Actinomycete species that cause common scab of potato (36).
9	AC	**D**, verticillium wilt (36); brown and black root rot of strawberries can be caused by the same organism as rhizoctonia canker (black scurf) of potato (36).
10	F	**D**, sclerotinia white mold (67; see appendix 3, p. 124).
10	H	**D**, sclerotinia drop (67; see appendix 3, p. 124).
10	I	**D**, verticillium wilt, sclerotinia stalk rot, early blight (67; see appendix 3, p. 124). **I**, Colorado potato beetle (see table 3.5, p. 40).

Row	Col.	Notes
10	J	**XXXX**
10	K	**D**, verticillium wilt (67; see appendix 3, p. 124), phytophthora crown, and collar rot (31; see appendix 3). **I**, Colorado potato beetle (see table 3.5, p. 40).
10	L	**D**, phytophthora blight (67; see appendix 3, p. 124).
10	Q	**D-**, clubroot declines more quickly when tomato, cucumber, snap bean, or buckwheat is grown (see chapter 3, p. 21).
10	R	**D-**, clubroot declines more quickly when tomato, cucumber, snap bean, or buckwheat is grown (see chapter 3, p. 21).
10	S	**D-**, clubroot declines more quickly when tomato, cucumber, snap bean, or buckwheat is grown (see chapter 3, p. 21).
10	T	**D-**, clubroot declines more quickly when tomato, cucumber, snap bean, or buckwheat is grown (see chapter 3, p. 21).
10	U	**D-**, clubroot declines more quickly when tomato, cucumber, snap bean, or buckwheat is grown (see chapter 3, p. 21).
10	V	**D**, phytophthora blight (31; see appendix 3, p. 124).
10	W	**D**, phytophthora blight (31; see appendix 3, p. 124).
10	X	**D**, phytophthora blight (67; see appendix 3, p. 124).
10	Y	**D**, phytophthora blight (31; see appendix 3, p. 124).
10	AC	**D**, verticillium wilt (36); brown and black root rot by *Corticium solani* (36).
11	I	**D**, verticillium wilt (67; see appendix 3, p. 124). **I**, Colorado potato beetle (see table 3.5, p. 40).
11	J	**D**, verticillium wilt (67; see appendix 3, p. 124). **I**, Colorado potato beetle (see table 3.5, p. 40).
11	K	**XXXX**
11	L	**D**, phytophthora blight (67; see appendix 3, p. 124).
11	V	**D**, phytophthora blight (see appendix 3, p. 124).
11	W	**D**, phytophthora blight (see appendix 3, p. 124).
11	X	**D**, phytophthora blight (67; see appendix 3, p. 124).
11	Y	**D**, phytophthora blight (see appendix 3, p. 124).
12	I	**D**, verticillium wilt (67; see appendix 3, p. 124).
12	J	**D**, bacterial spot (67; see appendix 3, p. 124).
12	K	**D**, verticillium wilt (67; see appendix 3, p. 124); phytophthora crown and collar rot (see appendix 3).
12	L	**XXXX**
12	V	**D**, phytophthora blight (see appendix 3, p. 124).
12	W	**D**, phytophthora blight (see appendix 3, p. 124).
12	X	**D**, phytophthora blight (67; see appendix 3, p. 124).
12	Y	**D**, phytophthora blight (see appendix 3, p. 124).
13	B	**W**, weed control is difficult in carrots and can lead to heavy weed pressure in onions, which is also a difficult-to-weed crop.
13	D	**S**, root crops tend to reduce soil structure due to the additional soil disturbance during harvest; consequently, growing "soil building" crops before and after a root crop is often desirable (80).

Row	Col.	Notes
13	E	**S**, root crops tend to reduce soil structure due to the additional soil disturbance during harvest; consequently, growing "soil building" crops before and after a root crop is often desirable (80).
13	F	**D**, sclerotinia white mold (67; see appendix 3, p. 124).
13	H	**D**, sclerotinia drop (67; see appendix 3, p. 124).
13	I	**D**, sclerotinia stalk rot, common scab (67; see appendix 3, p. 124); any 2-year sequence involving carrot, celery, and potato should be avoided due to root-knot nematode (*Meloidogyne hapla*) (20). **S**, root crops tend to reduce soil structure due to the additional soil disturbance during harvest; consequently, preceding and following root crops with "soil building" crops is often desirable (80).
13	M	**XXXX**
13	N	**D**, any 2-year sequence involving carrot, celery, and potato should be avoided due to root-knot nematode (*Meloidogyne hapla*) (20).
13	O	**D**, any 2-year sequence involving carrot, celery, and potato should be avoided due to root-knot nematode (*Meloidogyne hapla*) (20).
13	U	**S**, root crops tend to reduce soil structure due to the additional soil disturbance during harvest; consequently, growing "soil building" crops before and after a root crop is often desirable (80).
13	V	**D**, Cucumber can be infected with canker from soil containing diseased remains of carrots or turnips (36).
13	AN	**W-, S-**, a spring oat cover crop (often with field pea) helps control weeds and restore soil structure after late-harvested root crops like parsnip.
13	AW	**W-, N-**, a spring-planted field pea cover crop (often with oat) controls weeds and helps restore N after late-harvested root crops like parsnip.
14	I	**D**, any 2-year sequence involving carrot, celery, and potato should be avoided due to root-knot nematode (*Meloidogyne hapla*) (20).
14	M	**D**, any 2-year sequence involving carrot, celery, and potato should be avoided due to root-knot nematode (*Meloidogyne hapla*) (20).
14	N	**XXXX**
14	O	**D**, celery root rot and celeriac scab are caused by the same organism (*Phoma apiicola*); once a crop has shown infection, neither crop should be grown for 3–4+ years (36); any 2-year sequence involving carrot, celery, and potato should be avoided due to root-knot nematode (*Meloidogyne hapla*) (20).
15	I	**D**, any 2-year sequence involving carrot, celery, and potato should be avoided due to root-knot nematode (*Meloidogyne hapla*) (20).
15	M	**D**, any 2-year sequence involving carrot, celery, and potato should be avoided due to root-knot nematode (*Meloidogyne hapla*) (20).

Row	Col.	Notes
15	N	**D**, celery root rot and celeriac scab are caused by the same organism (*Phoma apiicola*); once a crop has shown infection, neither crop should be grown for 3–4+ years (36); any 2-year sequence involving carrot, celery, and potato should be avoided due to root-knot nematode (*Meloidogyne hapla*) (20).
15	O	**XXXX**
16	J	**D**, lettuce, cabbage, and cress can be symptomless carriers of *Colletotrichum coccodes*, which causes tomato anthracnose and black dot (chapter 3, p. 21). **C-**, short-season salad greens act as a cover crop and are harvested in time to plant tomato, eggplant, or pepper (83).
16	K	**C-**, short-season salad greens act as a cover crop and are harvested in time to plant tomato, eggplant, or pepper (83).
16	L	**C-**, short-season salad greens act as a cover crop and are harvested in time to plant tomato, eggplant, or pepper (83).
16	P	**XXXX**
16	Q	**D**, clubroot attacks many crops in the mustard family, including cabbage and its relatives, mustard, radish, Chinese cabbage, turnip, canola, and many weeds (36).
16	R	**D**, clubroot attacks many crops in the mustard family, including cabbage and its relatives, mustard, radish, Chinese cabbage, turnip, canola, and many weeds (36).
16	S	**D**, clubroot attacks many crops in the mustard family, including cabbage and its relatives, mustard, radish, Chinese cabbage, turnip, canola, and many weeds (36).
16	T	**D**, clubroot attacks many crops in the mustard family, including cabbage and its relatives, mustard, radish, Chinese cabbage, turnip, canola, and many weeds (36).
16	U	**D**, clubroot attacks many crops in the mustard family, including cabbage and its relatives, mustard, radish, Chinese cabbage, turnip, canola, and many weeds (36).
16	V	**N-**, brassicas can follow cucurbits within the same year and vice versa without need for additional compost (83). **C-**, leafy greens can make a crop before cucurbits need to be planted, and residue from the greens act as a green manure (81).
16	W	**N-**, brassicas can follow cucurbits within the same year and vice versa without need for additional compost (83). **C-**, leafy greens can make a crop before cucurbits need to be planted, and residue from the greens act as a green manure (81).
16	X	**N-**, brassicas can follow cucurbits within the same year and vice versa without need for additional compost (83). **C-**, leafy greens can make a crop before cucurbits need to be planted, and residue from the greens act as a green manure (81).
16	Y	**N-**, brassicas can follow cucurbits within the same year and vice versa without need for additional compost (83). **C-**, leafy greens can make a crop before cucurbits need to be planted, and residue from the greens act as a green manure (81).

Row	Col.	Notes
16	AY	**D**, clubroot attacks many crops in the mustard family, including cabbage and its relatives, mustard, radish, Chinese cabbage, turnip, canola, and many weeds (36).
16	AZ	**D**, clubroot attacks many crops in the mustard family, including cabbage and its relatives, mustard, radish, Chinese cabbage, turnip, canola, and many weeds (36).
17	F	**D**, sclerotinia white mold (67; see appendix 3, p. 124).
17	H	**D**, sclerotinia drop (67; see appendix 3, p. 124).
17	I	**D**, sclerotinia stalk rot (67; see appendix 3, p. 124).
17	P	**D**, clubroot attacks many crops in the mustard family, including cabbage and its relatives, mustard, radish, Chinese cabbage, turnip, canola, and many weeds (36).
17	Q	**XXXX**
17	R	**D**, clubroot, fusarium yellows, blackleaf, black rot, white mold (67).
17	S	**D**, clubroot, fusarium yellows, blackleaf, black rot, white mold (67).
17	T	**D**, clubroot (67; see appendix 3, p. 124).
17	U	**D**, clubroot (67; see appendix 3, p. 124).
17	V	**N-**, brassicas can follow cucurbits within the same year and vice versa without need for additional compost (83).
17	W	**N-**, brassicas can follow cucurbits within the same year and vice versa without need for additional compost (83).
17	X	**N-**, brassicas can follow cucurbits within the same year and vice versa without need for additional compost (83).
17	Y	**N-**, brassicas can follow cucurbits within the same year and vice versa without need for additional compost (83). **C-**, two rows of broccoli fit comfortably in the space needed for one row of summer squash.
17	AC	**D-**, broccoli residue reduces the severity of verticillium wilt (*Verticillium dahliae*) in subsequent strawberry (106).
17	AY	**D**, clubroot attacks many crops in the mustard family, including cabbage and its relatives, mustard, radish, Chinese cabbage, turnip, canola, and many weeds (36).
17	AZ	**D**, clubroot attacks many crops in the mustard family, including cabbage and its relatives, mustard, radish, Chinese cabbage, turnip, canola, and many weeds (36).
18	F	**D**, sclerotinia white mold (67; see appendix 3, p. 124).
18	G	**D-**, residues of crops in the mustard family suppress aphanomyces root rot of pea (85).
18	H	**D**, sclerotinia drop (67; see appendix 3, p. 124).
18	I	**D**, sclerotinia stalk rot (67; see appendix 3, p. 124); black scurf and stem canker (*Corticum solani*) (36).
18	J	**D**, lettuce, cabbage, and cress can be symptomless carriers of *Colletotrichum coccodes*, which causes tomato anthracnose and black dot (chapter 3, p. 21).
18	P	**D**, clubroot attacks many crops in the mustard family, including cabbage and its relatives, mustard, radish, Chinese cabbage, turnip, canola. and many weeds (36).
18	Q	**D**, clubroot, fusarium yellows, blackleaf, black rot, white mold (67).
18	R	**XXXX**
18	S	**D**, clubroot, fusarium yellows, blackleaf, black rot, white mold (67).
18	T	**D**, clubroot (67; see appendix 3, p. 124).
18	U	**D**, clubroot (67; see appendix 3, p. 124).
18	V	**N-**, brassicas can follow cucurbits within the same year and vice versa without need for additional compost (83).
18	W	**N-**, brassicas can follow cucurbits within the same year and vice versa without need for additional compost (83).
18	X	**N-**, brassicas can follow cucurbits within the same year and vice versa without need for additional compost (83).
18	Y	**N-**, brassicas can follow cucurbits within the same year and vice versa without need for additional compost (83).
18	AA	**D**, beet cyst nematode attacks both cabbage and beet (10).
18	AY	**D**, clubroot attacks many crops in the mustard family, including cabbage and its relatives, mustard, radish, Chinese cabbage, turnip, canola, and many weeds (36).
18	AZ	**D**, clubroot attacks many crops in the mustard family, including cabbage and its relatives, mustard, radish, Chinese cabbage, turnip, canola, and many weeds (36).
19	F	**D**, sclerotinia white mold (67; see appendix 3, p. 124).
19	G	**D-**, residues of crops in the mustard family suppress aphanomyces root rot of pea (85).
19	H	**D**, sclerotinia drop (67; see appendix 3, p. 124).
19	I	**D**, sclerotinia stalk rot (67; see appendix 3, p. 124).
19	P	**D**, clubroot attacks many crops in the mustard family, including cabbage and its relatives, mustard, radish, Chinese cabbage, turnip, canola, and many weeds (36).
19	Q	**D**, clubroot, fusarium yellows, blackleaf, black rot, white mold (67).
19	R	**D**, clubroot, fusarium yellows, blackleaf, black rot, white mold (67).
19	S	**XXXX**
19	T	**D**, clubroot (67; see appendix 3, p. 124).
19	U	**D**, clubroot (67; see appendix 3, p. 124).
19	V	**N-**, brassicas can follow cucurbits within the same year and vice versa without need for additional compost (83).
19	W	**N-**, brassicas can follow cucurbits within the same year and vice versa without need for additional compost (83).
19	X	**N-**, brassicas can follow cucurbits within the same year and vice versa without need for additional compost (83).
19	Y	**N-**, brassicas can follow cucurbits within the same year and vice versa without need for additional compost (83).
19	AY	**D**, clubroot attacks many crops in the mustard family, including cabbage and its relatives, mustard, radish, Chinese cabbage, turnip, canola, and many weeds (36).

Row	Col.	Notes
19	AZ	**D**, clubroot attacks many crops in the mustard family, including cabbage and its relatives, mustard, radish, Chinese cabbage, turnip, canola, and many weeds (36).
20	G	**D-**, residues of crops in the mustard family suppress aphanomyces root rot of pea (85).
20	I	**D**, common scab (67; see appendix 3, p. 124).
20	P	**D**, clubroot attacks many crops in the mustard family, including cabbage and its relatives, mustard, radish, Chinese cabbage, turnip, canola, and many weeds (36).
20	Q	**D**, clubroot (67; see appendix 3, p. 124).
20	R	**D**, clubroot (67; see appendix 3, p. 124).
20	S	**D**, clubroot (67; see appendix 3, p. 124).
20	T	**XXXX**
20	U	**D**, clubroot (67; see appendix 3, p. 124).
20	V	**N-**, brassicas can follow cucurbits within the same year and vice versa without need for additional compost (83).
20	W	**N-**, brassicas can follow cucurbits within the same year and vice versa without need for additional compost (83).
20	X	**N-**, brassicas can follow cucurbits within the same year and vice versa without need for additional compost (83).
20	Y	**N-**, brassicas can follow cucurbits within the same year and vice versa without need for additional compost (83).
20	AY	**D**, clubroot attacks many crops in the mustard family, including cabbage and its relatives, mustard, radish, Chinese cabbage, turnip, canola, and many weeds (36).
20	AZ	**D**, clubroot attacks many crops in the mustard family, including cabbage and its relatives, mustard, radish, Chinese cabbage, turnip, canola, and many weeds (36).
21	G	**D-**, residues of crops in the mustard family suppress aphanomyces root rot of pea (85).
21	I	**D**, common scab (67; see appendix 3, p. 124).
21	P	**D**, clubroot attacks many crops in the mustard family, including cabbage and its relatives, mustard, radish, Chinese cabbage, turnip, canola, and many weeds (36).
21	Q	**D**, clubroot, blackleaf, blackrot (67; see appendix 3, p. 124).
21	R	**D**, clubroot, blackleaf, blackrot (67; see appendix 3, p. 124).
21	S	**D**, clubroot, blackleaf, blackrot (67; see appendix 3, p. 124).
21	T	**D**, clubroot (67; see appendix 3, p. 124).
21	U	**XXXX**
21	V	**D**, Cucumber can be infected with canker from soil containing diseased remains of carrots or turnips (36). **N-**, brassicas can follow cucurbits within the same year and vice versa without need for additional compost (83).
21	W	**N-**, brassicas can follow cucurbits within the same year and vice versa without need for additional compost (83).
21	X	**N-**, brassicas can follow cucurbits within the same year and vice versa without need for additional compost (83).
21	Y	**N-**, brassicas can follow cucurbits within the same year and vice versa without need for additional compost (83).

Row	Col.	Notes
21	AY	**D**, clubroot attacks many crops in the mustard family, including cabbage and its relatives, mustard, radish, Chinese cabbage, turnip, canola, and many weeds (36).
21	AZ	**D**, clubroot attacks many crops in the mustard family, including cabbage and its relatives, mustard, radish, Chinese cabbage, turnip, canola, and many weeds (36).
22	A	**W-**, mulched vine crops clean up weeds before hard-to-weed crops (83).
22	F	**W-**, intense cultivation of bean can help clean up weeds following a weedy vine crop (83).
22	H	**W**, unmulched vine crops get weedy; therefore, do not follow them with direct-seeded salad greens or carrots (83).
22	K	**D**, phytophthora crown and collar rot (see appendix 3, p. 124).
22	L	**D**, phytophthora blight (67; see appendix 3, p. 124).
22	M	**W**, unmulched vine crops get weedy; therefore, do not follow them with direct-seeded salad greens or carrots (83).
22	P	**W**, unmulched vine crops get weedy; therefore, do not follow them with direct-seeded salad greens or carrots (83). **N-**, brassicas can follow vine crops within the same year and vice versa without need for additional compost (83).
22	Q	**D-**, clubroot declines more quickly when tomato, cucumber, snap bean, or buckwheat is grown (see chapter 3, p. 21). **N-**, brassicas can follow vine crops within the same year and vice versa without need for additional compost (83).
22	R	**D-**, clubroot declines more quickly when tomato, cucumber, snap bean, or buckwheat is grown (see chapter 3, p. 21). **N-**, brassicas can follow vine crops within the same year and vice versa without need for additional compost (83).
22	S	**D-**, clubroot declines more quickly when tomato, cucumber, snap bean, or buckwheat is grown (see chapter 3, p. 21). **N-**, brassicas can follow vine crops within the same year and vice versa without need for additional compost (83).
22	T	**D-**, clubroot declines more quickly when tomato, cucumber, snap bean, or buckwheat is grown (see chapter 3, p. 21).
22	U	**D-**, clubroot declines more quickly when tomato, cucumber, snap bean, or buckwheat is grown (see chapter 3, p. 21).
22	V	**XXXX**
22	W	**D**, leaf spots, black rot (gummy stem blight), scab (67; see appendix 3, p. 124); phytophthora blight (see appendix 3).
22	X	**D**, blackrot (gummy stem blight), fusarium crown and fruit rot, phytophthora blight (67; see appendix 3, p. 124).
22	Y	**D**, phytophthora blight (see appendix 3, p. 124).
22	AB	**I**, corn rootworm adults are attracted to cucurbits; they lay their eggs at the base of the plants, and the larvae attack corn roots the following year (see table 3.5, p. 40).

Row	Col.	Notes
22	AD	**I**, corn rootworm adults are attracted to cucurbits; they lay their eggs at the base of the plants, and the larvae attack corn roots the following year (see table 3.5, p. 40).
22	AJ	**W-**, intense cultivation of bean can help clean up weeds following a weedy vine crop (83).
23	A	**W-**, mulched vine crops clean up weeds before hard-to-weed crops (83).
23	F	**W-**, intense cultivation of bean can help clean up weeds following a weedy vine crop (83).
23	H	**W**, unmulched vine crops get weedy; therefore, do not follow them with direct-seeded salad greens or carrots (83).
23	K	**D**, phytophthora crown and collar rot (see appendix 3, p. 124).
23	L	**D**, phytophthora blight (67; see appendix 3, p. 124).
23	M	**W**, unmulched vine crops get weedy; therefore, do not follow them with direct-seeded salad greens or carrots (83).
23	P	**W**, unmulched vine crops get weedy; therefore, do not follow them with direct-seeded salad greens or carrots (83). **N-**, brassicas can follow vine crops within the same year and vice versa without need for additional compost (83).
23	Q	**N-**, brassicas can follow vine crops within the same year and vice versa without need for additional compost (83).
23	R	**N-**, brassicas can follow vine crops within the same year and vice versa without need for additional compost (83).
23	S	**N-**, brassicas can follow vine crops within the same year and vice versa without need for additional compost (83).
23	V	**D**, leaf spots, gummy stem blight, scab (67; see appendix 3, p. 124); phytophthora blight (see appendix 3).
23	W	**XXXX**
23	X	**D**, blackrot (gummy stem blight), fusarium crown and fruit rot, phytophthora blight (67; see appendix 3, p. 124).
23	Y	**D**, phytophthora blight (see appendix 3, p. 124).
23	AB	**I**, corn rootworm adults are attracted to cucurbits; they lay their eggs at the base of the plants, and the larvae attack corn roots the following year (see table 3.5, p. 40).
23	AD	**I**, corn rootworm adults are attracted to cucurbits; they lay their eggs at the base of the plants, and the larvae attack corn roots the following year (see table 3.5, p. 40).
23	AJ	**W-**, intense cultivation of bean can help clean up weeds following a weedy vine crop (83).
24	A	**W-**, mulched vine crops clean up weeds before hard-to-weed crops (83).
24	F	**W-**, intense cultivation of bean can help clean up weeds following a weedy vine crop (83).
24	H	**W**, unmulched vine crops get weedy; therefore, do not follow them with direct-seeded salad greens or carrots (83).
24	K	**D**, phytophthora crown and collar rot (see appendix 3, p. 124).
24	L	**D**, phytophthora blight (67; see appendix 3, p. 124).
24	M	**W**, unmulched vine crops get weedy; therefore, do not follow them with direct-seeded salad greens or carrots (83).
24	P	**W**, unmulched vine crops get weedy; therefore, do not follow them with direct-seeded salad greens or carrots (83). **N-**, brassicas can follow vine crops within the same year and vice versa without need for additional compost (83).
24	Q	**N-**, brassicas can follow vine crops within the same year and vice versa without need for additional compost (83).
24	R	**N-**, brassicas can follow vine crops within the same year and vice versa without need for additional compost (83).
24	S	**N-**, brassicas can follow vine crops within the same year and vice versa without need for additional compost (83).
24	V	**D**, black rot (gummy stem blight) (67; see appendix 3, p. 124); phytophthora blight (see appendix 3).
24	W	**D**, leaf spots, black rot (gummy stem blight), scab (67; see appendix 3, p. 124); phytophthora blight (see appendix 3).
24	X	**XXXX**
24	Y	**D**, phytophthora blight (see appendix 3, p. 124).
24	AB	**I**, corn rootworm adults are attracted to cucurbits; they lay their eggs at the base of the plants, and the larvae attack corn roots the following year (see table 3.5, p. 40).
24	AD	**I**, corn rootworm adults are attracted to cucurbits; they lay their eggs at the base of the plants, and the larvae attack corn roots the following year (see table 3.5, p. 40).
24	AJ	**W-**, intense cultivation of bean can help clean up weeds following a weedy vine crop (83).
24	AV	**C-**, hairy vetch can be overseeded into winter squash in July to provide a winter cover crop after harvest (83).
25	A	**W-**, mulched vine crops clean up weeds before hard-to-weed crops (83).
25	H	**W**, unmulched vine crops get weedy; therefore, do not follow them with direct-seeded salad greens or carrots (83).
25	K	**D**, phytophthora crown and collar rot (see appendix 3, p. 124).
25	L	**D**, phytophthora blight (67; see appendix 3, p. 124).
25	M	**W**, unmulched vine crops get weedy; therefore, do not follow them with direct-seeded salad greens or carrots (83).
25	P	**W**, unmulched vine crops get weedy; therefore, do not follow them with direct-seeded salad greens or carrots (83). **N-**, brassicas can follow vine crops within the same year and vice versa without need for additional compost (83).
25	Q	**N-**, brassicas can follow vine crops within the same year and vice versa without need for additional compost (83).
25	R	**N-**, brassicas can follow vine crops within the same year and vice versa without need for additional compost (83).

Row	Col.	Notes
25	S	**N-**, brassicas can follow vine crops within the same year and vice versa without need for additional compost (83).
25	V	**D**, phytophthora blight (see appendix 3, p. 124).
25	W	**D**, leaf spots, black rot (gummy stem blight), scab (67; see appendix 3, p. 124); phytophthora blight (see appendix 3).
25	X	**D**, blackrot (gummy stem blight), fusarium crown and fruit rot, phytophthora blight (67; see appendix 3, p. 124).
25	Y	**XXXX**
25	AB	**I**, corn rootworm adults are attracted to cucurbits; they lay their eggs at the base of the plants, and the larvae attack corn roots the following year (see table 3.5, p. 40).
25	AD	**I**, corn rootworm adults are attracted to cucurbits; they lay their eggs at the base of the plants, and the larvae attack corn roots the following year (see table 3.5, p. 40).
26	B	**W-**, a short-season crop like lettuce or spinach allows good weed control and low weed seed production prior to slow-growing, long-season, hard-to-weed crops like onion and carrot (83).
26	D	**W-**, a short-season crop like lettuce or spinach allows good weed control and low weed seed production prior to slow-growing, long-season, hard-to-weed crops like onion and carrot (83).
26	H	**C-**, timing works well to plant lettuce or radish after pea or spinach within a year (82).
26	M	**W-**, a short-season crop like lettuce or spinach allows good weed control and low weed seed production prior to slow-growing, long-season, hard-to-weed crops like onion and carrot (83).
26	T	**C-**, timing works well to plant lettuce or radish after pea or spinach within a year (82).
26	Z	**XXXX**
27	I	**D**, scab of beet is caused by several of the Actinomycete species that cause common scab of potato (36).
27	Q	**D**, beet cyst nematode attacks both cabbage and beet (10), and thus presumably also broccoli and cauliflower.
27	R	**D**, beet cyst nematode attacks both cabbage and beet (10).
27	S	**D**, beet cyst nematode attacks both cabbage and beet (10), and thus presumably also kale and collards.
27	AA	**XXXX**
28	F	**D-**, use grain crops or sweet corn in rotation with bean to decrease root rots (67).
28	I	**C-**, potato works well after corn because it tolerates corn stover (82).
28	Q	**D-**, use grain crops or sweet corn in rotation with cabbage and related species to decrease white mold (67).
28	R	**D-**, use grain crops or sweet corn in rotation with cabbage and related species to decrease white mold (67).
28	S	**D-**, use grain crops or sweet corn in rotation with cabbage and related species to decrease white mold (67).

Row	Col.	Notes
28	X	**D**, fusarium fruit rot is more common on pumpkin following corn (chapter 3, p. 21).
28	AA	**D-**, use grain crops or sweet corn in rotation with beet to decrease root rots (67).
28	AB	**XXXX**
28	AD	**I**, corn rootworm (see table 3.5, p. 40).
28	AE	**D**, scab (*Gibberella zeae*) on barley and spring wheat tends to be worse following corn even than following another spring grain, unless the corn stalks are removed for silage or by clean tillage (10).
28	AG	**D**, fusarium can be a problem when wheat follows corn (83).
28	AJ	**D-**, use grain crops or sweet corn in rotation with bean to decrease root rots (67).
29	I	**D**, verticillium wilt (36).
29	J	**D**, verticillium wilt (36).
29	K	**D**, verticillium wilt (67; see appendix 3, p. 124).
29	AC	**XXXX**
30	F	**D-**, use grain crops or sweet corn in rotation with bean to decrease root rots (67).
30	I	**C-**, potato works well after corn because it tolerates corn stover (82).
30	Q	**D-**, use grain crops or sweet corn in rotation with cabbage and related species to decrease white mold (67).
30	R	**D-**, use grain crops or sweet corn in rotation with cabbage and related species to decrease white mold (67).
30	S	**D-**, use grain crops or sweet corn in rotation with cabbage and related species to decrease white mold (67).
30	X	**D**, fusarium fruit rot is more common on pumpkin following corn (chapter 3, p. 21).
30	AA	**D-**, use grain crops or sweet corn in rotation with beet to decrease root rots (67).
30	AB	**I**, corn rootworm (see table 3.5, p. 40).
30	AD	**XXXX**
30	AE	**D**, scab (*Gibberella zeae*) on barley and spring wheat tends to be worse following corn even than following another spring grain, unless the corn stalks are removed for silage or by clean tillage (10).
30	AF	**D**, barley should not be grown after corn due to possibility of scab (119).
30	AG	**D**, scab (*Fusarium* spp. and *Gibberella* spp.) can be a problem when wheat follows corn (83, 20). **D-**, foot rot is negligible when wheat follows oat, corn, or beans (20); take-all is better suppressed by corn than by other crops like soybean and sunflower (65).
30	AJ	**D-**, use grain crops or sweet corn in rotation with bean to decrease root rots (67).

Row	Col.	Notes
31	A	**D-**, small grains decrease nematode populations (chapter 3, p. 21). **W**, broadleaf weeds have time to set seeds in a grain crop before harvest (39, based on experience of Eric and Anne Nordell).
31	B	**W**, broadleaf weeds have time to set seeds in a grain crop before harvest, which is particularly a problem in noncompetitive or difficult-to-cultivate crops like onion and carrot (39, based on experience of Eric and Anne Nordell). **I**, onion thrips may be a problem when grain or any grass precedes onions (83).
31	C	**W**, broadleaf weeds have time to set seeds in a grain crop before harvest, which is particularly a problem in noncompetitive or difficult-to-cultivate crops like onion and carrot (39, based on experience of Eric and Anne Nordell). **I**, onion thrips may be a problem when grain or any grass precedes onions (83).
31	D	**W**, broadleaf weeds have time to set seeds in a grain crop before harvest, which is particularly a problem in noncompetitive or difficult-to-cultivate crops like onion and carrot (39, based on experience of Eric and Anne Nordell). **I**, onion thrips may be a problem when grain or any grass precedes onions (83).
31	F	**D-**, use grain crops or sweet corn in rotation with bean to decrease root rots (67).
31	H	**D-**, rotation with small grains decreases root-knot nematode (*Meloidogyne hapla*) effects on lettuce (22).
31	I	**D-**, use of 2 years of grass or 1 year of cereal in rotation with potato helps reduce rhizoctonia canker (67). **I**, wireworms (*Melanotus communis* and *Limonius* spp.) (see table 3.5, p. 40).
31	M	**W**, broadleaf weeds have time to set seeds in a grain crop before harvest, which is particularly a problem in noncompetitive or difficult-to-cultivate crops like onion and carrot (39, based on experience of Eric and Anne Nordell). **I**, wireworms (*Melanotus communis* and *Limonius* spp.) (see table 3.5, p. 40).
31	N	**W**, broadleaf weeds have time to set seeds in a grain crop before harvest, which is particularly a problem in noncompetitive or difficult-to-cultivate crops like onion and carrot (39, based on experience of Eric and Anne Nordell).
31	Q	**D-**, use grain crops or sweet corn in rotation with cabbage and related species to decrease white mold (67).
31	R	**D-**, use grain crops or sweet corn in rotation with cabbage and related species to decrease white mold (67).
31	S	**D-**, use grain crops or sweet corn in rotation with cabbage and related species to decrease white mold (67).
31	V	**I**, wireworms (*Melanotus communis* and *Limonius* spp.) (see table 3.5, p. 40).
31	W	**I**, wireworms (*Melanotus communis* and *Limonius* spp.) (see table 3.5, p. 40).
31	AA	**D-**, use grain crops or sweet corn in rotation with beet to decrease root rots (67). **I**, wireworms (*Melanotus communis* and *Limonius* spp.) (see table 3.5, p. 40).
31	AB	**I**, wireworms (*Melanotus communis* and *Limonius* spp.) (see table 3.5, p. 40).
31	AD	**I**, wireworms (*Melanotus communis* and *Limonius* spp.) (see table 3.5, p. 40).
31	AE	**XXXX**
31	AG	**D**, incidence of foot rot of wheat caused by *Fusarium culmorum* (but not by *Helminthosporium sativum*) declines more slowly if oat is part of the rotation (56). **D-**, foot rot is negligible when wheat follows oat, corn, or bean (20). **I**, wireworms (*Melanotus communis* and *Limonius* spp.) (see table 3.5, p. 40).
31	AH	**I**, wireworms (*Melanotus communis* and *Limonius* spp.) (see table 3.5, p. 40).
31	AJ	**D-**, use grain crops or sweet corn in rotation with bean to decrease root rots (67).
32	A	**D-**, small grains decrease nematode populations (chapter 3, p. 21). **W**, broadleaf weeds have time to set seeds in a grain crop before harvest (39, based on experience of Eric and Anne Nordell).
32	B	**W**, broadleaf weeds have time to set seeds in a grain crop before harvest, which is particularly a problem in noncompetitive or difficult-to-cultivate crops like onion and carrot (39, based on experience of Eric and Anne Nordell). **I**, onion thrips may be a problem when grain or any grass precedes onions (83).
32	C	**W**, broadleaf weeds have time to set seeds in a grain crop before harvest, which is particularly a problem in noncompetitive or difficult-to-cultivate crops like onion and carrot (39, based on experience of Eric and Anne Nordell). **I**, onion thrips may be a problem when grain or any grass precedes onions (83).
32	D	**W**, broadleaf weeds have time to set seeds in a grain crop before harvest, which is particularly a problem in noncompetitive or difficult-to-cultivate crops like onion and carrot (39, based on experience of Eric and Anne Nordell). **I**, onion thrips may be a problem when grain or any grass precedes onions (83).
32	F	**D-**, use grain crops or sweet corn in rotation with bean to decrease root rots (67).
32	G	**D-**, a preceding oat crop reduces aphanomyces (common) root rot (*Aphanomyces euteiches*) (54).
32	H	**D-**, rotation with small grains decreases root-knot nematode (*Meloidogyne hapla*) effects on lettuce (22).
32	I	**D-**, use of 2 years of grass or 1 year of cereal in rotation with potato helps reduce rhizoctonia canker (67). **I**, wireworms (*Melanotus communis* and *Limonius* spp.) (see table 3.5, p. 40).
32	M	**W**, broadleaf weeds have time to set seeds in a grain crop before harvest, which is particularly a problem in noncompetitive or difficult to cultivate crops like onion and carrot (39, based on experience of Eric and Anne Nordell). **I**, wireworms (*Melanotus communis* and *Limonius* spp.) (see table 3.5, p. 40).

Row	Col.	Notes
32	N	**W**, broadleaf weeds have time to set seeds in a grain crop before harvest, which is particularly a problem in noncompetitive or difficult to cultivate crops like onion and carrot (39, based on experience of Eric and Anne Nordell).
32	Q	**D-**, use grain crops or sweet corn in rotation with cabbage and related species to decrease white mold (67).
32	R	**D-**, use grain crops or sweet corn in rotation with cabbage and related species to decrease white mold (67).
32	S	**D-**, use grain crops or sweet corn in rotation with cabbage and related species to decrease white mold (67).
32	V	**I**, wireworms (*Melanotus communis* and *Limonius* spp.) (see table 3.5, p. 40).
32	W	**I**, wireworms (*Melanotus communis* and *Limonius* spp.) (see table 3.5, p. 40).
32	AA	**D-**, use grain crops or sweet corn in rotation with beet to decrease root rots (67). **I**, wireworms (*Melanotus communis* and *Limonius* spp.) (see table 3.5, p. 40).
32	AB	**I**, wireworms (*Melanotus communis* and *Limonius* spp.) (see table 3.5, p. 40).
32	AD	**I**, wireworms (*Melanotus communis* and *Limonius* spp.) (see table 3.5, p. 40).
32	AF	**XXXX**
32	AG	**D**, barley is a good host for take-all, even though it is less affected by the disease than wheat (52); foot rot is highest when following barley (20). **I**, wireworms (*Melanotus communis* and *Limonius* spp.) (see table 3.5, p. 40).
32	AH	**D**, barley is a host for ergot (119). **I**, wireworms (*Melanotus communis* and *Limonius* spp.) (see table 3.5, p. 40).
32	AJ	**D-**, use grain crops or sweet corn in rotation with bean to decrease root rots (67).
33	A	**D-**, small grains decrease nematode populations (chapter 3, p. 21).
33	B	**W**, broadleaf weeds have time to set seeds in a grain crop before harvest, which is particularly a problem in noncompetitive or difficult-to-cultivate crops like onion and carrot (39, based on experience of Eric and Anne Nordell). **I**, onion thrips may be a problem when grain or any grass precedes onions (83).
33	C	**W**, broadleaf weeds have time to set seeds in a grain crop before harvest, which is particularly a problem in noncompetitive or difficult-to-cultivate crops like onion and carrot (39, based on experience of Eric and Anne Nordell). **I**, onion thrips may be a problem when grain or any grass precedes onions (83).
33	D	**W**, broadleaf weeds have time to set seeds in a grain crop before harvest, which is particularly a problem in noncompetitive or difficult-to-cultivate crops like onion and carrot (39, based on experience of Eric and Anne Nordell). **I**, onion thrips may be a problem when grain or any grass precedes onions (83).
33	F	**D-**, use grain crops or sweet corn in rotation with bean to decrease root rots (67).

Row	Col.	Notes
33	H	**D-**, rotation with small grains decreases root-knot nematode (*Meloidogyne hapla*) effects on lettuce (22).
33	I	**D-**, use of 2 years of grass or 1 year of cereal in rotation with potato helps reduce rhizoctonia canker (67). **I**, wireworms (*Melanotus communis* and *Limonius* spp.) (see table 3.5, p. 40).
33	M	**W**, broadleaf weeds have time to set seeds in a grain crop before harvest, which is particularly a problem in noncompetitive or difficult-to-cultivate crops like onion and carrot (39, based on experience of Eric and Anne Nordell). **I**, wireworms (*Melanotus communis* and *Limonius* spp.) (see table 3.5, p. 40).
33	N	**W**, broadleaf weeds have time to set seeds in a grain crop before harvest, which is particularly a problem in noncompetitive or difficult-to-cultivate crops like onion and carrot (39, based on experience of Eric and Anne Nordell).
33	Q	**D-**, use grain crops or sweet corn in rotation with cabbage and related species to decrease white mold (67).
33	R	**D-**, use grain crops or sweet corn in rotation with cabbage and related species to decrease white mold (67).
33	S	**D-**, use grain crops or sweet corn in rotation with cabbage and related species to decrease white mold (67).
33	V	**I**, wireworms (*Melanotus communis* and *Limonius* spp.) (see table 3.5, p. 40).
33	W	**I**, wireworms (*Melanotus communis* and *Limonius* spp.) (see table 3.5, p. 40).
33	AA	**D-**, use grain crops or sweet corn in rotation with beet to decrease root rots (67). **I**, wireworms (*Melanotus communis* and *Limonius* spp.) (see table 3.5, p. 40).
33	AB	**I**, wireworms (*Melanotus communis* and *Limonius* spp.) (see table 3.5, p. 40).
33	AD	**D**, seedling root rots of corn are more common following wheat than following oat (20). **I**, wireworms (*Melanotus communis* and *Limonius* spp.) (see table 3.5, p. 40).
33	AE	**I**, wireworms (*Melanotus communis* and *Limonius* spp.) (see table 3.5, p. 40).
33	AF	**D**, To avoid leaf diseases, avoid planting barley after wheat (107); barley should not be planted after wheat due to leaf diseases and root rot (119).
33	AG	**XXXX**
33	AH	**D**, wheat is a host for ergot (119). **I**, wireworms *Melanotus communis* and *Limonius* spp.) (see table 3.5, p. 40).
33	AJ	**D-**, use grain crops or sweet corn in rotation with bean to decrease root rots (67).
34	A	**D-**, small grains decrease nematode populations (chapter 3, p. 21).
34	B	**W**, broadleaf weeds have time to set seeds in a grain crop before harvest, which is particularly a problem in noncompetitive or difficult-to-cultivate crops like onion and carrot (39, based on experience of Eric and Anne Nordell). **I**, onion thrips may be a problem when grain or any grass precedes onions (83).

Row	Col.	Notes
34	C	**W**, broadleaf weeds have time to set seeds in a grain crop before harvest, which is particularly a problem in noncompetitive or difficult-to-cultivate crops like onion and carrot (39, based on experience of Eric and Anne Nordell). **I**, onion thrips may be a problem when grain or any grass precedes onions (83).
34	D	**W**, broadleaf weeds have time to set seeds in a grain crop before harvest, which is particularly a problem in noncompetitive or difficult-to-cultivate crops like onion and carrot (39, based on experience of Eric and Anne Nordell). **I**, onion thrips may be a problem when grain or any grass precedes onions (83).
34	F	**D-**, use grain crops or sweet corn in rotation with beans to decrease root rots (67).
34	H	**D-**, rotation with small grains decreases root-knot nematode (*Meloidogyne hapla*) effects on lettuce (22).
34	I	**D-**, use of 2 years of grass or 1 year of cereal in rotation with potato helps reduce rhizoctonia canker (67). **I**, wireworms (*Melanotus communis* and *Limonius* spp.) (see table 3.5, p. 40).
34	M	**W**, broadleaf weeds have time to set seeds in a grain crop before harvest, which is particularly a problem in noncompetitive or difficult-to-cultivate crops like onion and carrot (39, based on experience of Eric and Anne Nordell). **I**, wireworms (*Melanotus communis* and *Limonius* spp.) (see table 3.5, p. 40).
34	N	**W**, broadleaf weeds have time to set seeds in a grain crop before harvest, which is particularly a problem in noncompetitive or difficult-to-cultivate crops like onion and carrot (39, based on experience of Eric and Anne Nordell).
34	Q	**D-**, use grain crops or sweet corn in rotation with cabbage and related species to decrease white mold (67).
34	R	**D-**, use grain crops or sweet corn in rotation with cabbage and related species to decrease white mold (67).
34	S	**D-**, use grain crops or sweet corn in rotation with cabbage and related species to decrease white mold (67).
34	V	**I**, wireworms (*Melanotus communis* and *Limonius* spp.) (see table 3.5, p. 40).
34	W	**I**, wireworms (*Melanotus communis* and *Limonius* spp.) (see table 3.5, p. 40).
34	AA	**D-**, use grain crops or sweet corn in rotation with beet to decrease root rots (67). **I**, wireworms (*Melanotus communis* and *Limonius* spp.) (see table 3.5, p. 40).
34	AB	**I**, wireworms (*Melanotus communis* and *Limonius* spp.) (see table 3.5, p. 40).
34	AD	**I**, wireworms (*Melanotus communis* and *Limonius* spp.) (see table 3.5, p. 40).
34	AE	**I**, wireworms (*Melanotus communis* and *Limonius* spp.) (see table 3.5, p. 40).
34	AH	**XXXX**
34	AJ	**D-**, use grain crops or sweet corn in rotation with bean to decrease root rots (67).
34	AL	**D**, avoid planting crops that are hosts to ergot, such as forage grasses, before and after rye in the rotation (119).
35	F	**D**, common bacterial blight (*Xanthomonas campestris*; appendix 3, p. 124); soybean cyst nematode (28).
35	I	**D-**, soybean before potato prevents scab (82).
35	AD	**D-**, a previous crop of soybean reduces red root rot of corn (*Phoma terrestris* + *Pythium* spp. and *Fusarium* spp.) (123).
35	AI	**XXXX**
35	AJ	**D**, common bacterial blight (*Xanthomonas campestris*; appendix 3, p. 124); soybean cyst nematode (28).
35	AY	**D**, following soybean with rape or canola fosters buildup of *Sclerotinia* (119).
36	F	**D**, common bacterial blight (appendix 3, p. 124); soybean cyst nematode (28).
36	H	**D**, sclerotinia drop (67; see appendix 3, p. 124).
36	I	**D**, sclerotinia stalk rot (67; see appendix 3, p. 124).
36	AG	**D-**, foot rot is negligible when wheat follows oat, corn, or beans (20).
36	AI	**D**, common bacterial blight (*Xanthomonas campestris*; appendix 3, p. 124); soybean cyst nematode increases to high density on bean, though the bean crop is scarcely affected (28, 41).
36	AJ	**XXXX**
36	AW	**D**, field pea and bell bean should not be planted after bean due to *Fusarium*, *Pythium*, and *Sclerotinia* (119).
36	AX	**D**, field pea and bell bean should not be planted after bean due to *Fusarium*, *Pythium*, and *Sclerotinia* (119).
37	I	**D-**, alfalfa decreases fusarium wilt (20).
37	M	**D**, carrot root dieback can be severe after alfalfa; alfalfa is a host for *Pythium violae*, which causes cavity spot (see chapter 3, p. 21).
37	AJ	**N-**, **S-**, dry beans do well after sod crops due to good tilth and nutrition (83).
37	AK	**XXXX**
37	AW	**D**, field pea and bell bean should not be planted after alfalfa due to *Fusarium* and *Pythium* (119).
37	AX	**D**, field pea and bell bean should not be planted after alfalfa due to *Fusarium* and *Pythium* (119).
38	B	**I**, onion thrips may be a problem when grain or any grass precedes onions (83).
38	C	**I**, onion thrips may be a problem when grain or any grass precedes onions (83).
38	D	**I**, onion thrips may be a problem when grain or any grass precedes onions (83).
38	I	**D-**, green manure of rye or other grass reduces common scab and black scurf (rhizoctonia canker) (36); also, use of 2 years of grass or 1 year of cereal in rotation with potato helps reduce rhizoctonia canker (67).

Row	Col.	Notes
38	M	**W**, perennial grasses and weeds from plowed-down sod make weeding carrots difficult (82). **I**, wireworms (*Melanotus communis* and *Limonius* spp.) (see table 3.5, p. 40).
38	V	**I**, wireworms (*Melanotus communis* and *Limonius* spp.) (see table 3.5, p. 40).
38	W	**I**, wireworms (*Melanotus communis* and *Limonius* spp.) (see table 3.5, p. 40).
38	AA	**I**, wireworms (*Melanotus communis* and *Limonius* spp.) (see table 3.5, p. 40).
38	AB	**D-**, **N-**, corn does well after sod; it is a heavy feeder and can use the high N available, and diseases are not a problem (82). **I**, wireworms (*Melanotus communis* and *Limonius* spp.) and white grubs (*Phyllophaga* spp.) (see table 3.5, p. 40).
38	AC	**I**, white grubs (*Phyllophaga* spp.) (see table 3.5, p. 40).
38	AD	**D-**, **N-**, corn does well after sod; it is a heavy feeder and can use the high N available, and diseases are not a problem (82). **I**, wireworms (*Melanotus communis* and *Limonius* spp.) and white grubs (*Phyllophaga* spp.) (see table 3.5, p. 40).
38	AE	**D**, "If scald is a problem, barley should not be grown after bromegrass" (119). **I**, wireworms (*Melanotus communis* and *Limonius* spp.) (see table 3.5, p. 40).
38	AG	**D**, smooth brome should not be used in rotation with wheat if take-all is a problem (52). **I**, wireworms (*Melanotus communis* and *Limonius* spp.) and white grubs (*Phyllophaga* spp.) (see table 3.5, p. 40).
38	AH	**D**, avoid planting crops that are hosts to ergot, such as forage grasses, before and after rye in the rotation (119). **I**, wireworms` (*Melanotus communis* and *Limonius* spp.) and white grubs (*Phyllophaga* spp.) (see table 3.5, p. 40).
38	AJ	**N-**, **S-**, dry beans do well after sod crops due to good tilth and nutrition (83).
38	AL	**XXXX**
38	AM	**C-**, rye and hairy vetch establish well in plowed sod and make a good transition from grass sod to vegetables (81).
38	AV	**C-**, rye and hairy vetch establish well in plowed sod and make a good transition from grass sod to vegetables (81).
39	A	**W-**, **C**, decomposing rye releases allelopathic toxins that suppress weeds but may also harm crops. Problems can be avoided by incorporating residue 3 weeks before planting (95). **I-**, "High-biomass cover crops such as barley or rye increased population of centipedes, predator mites and other important predators" (107). **N**, incorporation of large amounts of grain straw can tie up nitrogen in microbial tissues, thereby making it unavailable to succeeding crops. **S**, the lag between incorporation and planting, however, leaves the soil open to erosion. **C-**, for maximum dry matter accumulation, use before late spring or early summer crops (81).

Row	Col.	Notes
39	B	**I**, onion thrips may be a problem when grain precedes onions (82, 83).
39	C	**I**, onion thrips may be a problem when grain precedes onions (82, 83).
39	D	**I**, onion thrips may be a problem when grain or any grass precedes onions (83).
39	F	**D-**, use grain crops or sweet corn in rotation with beans to decrease root rots (67).
39	G	**D-**, rye suppresses thielaviopsis (black) root rot (*Thielaviopsis basicola*) (54).
39	H	**C**, avoid direct seeding of small-seeded crops after a rye cover crop due to interference from the straw (82).
39	I	**D-**, green manure of rye or other grass reduces common scab and black scurf (rhizoctonia canker) (20, 36).
39	M	**C**, avoid direct seeding small-seeded crops after a rye cover crop due to interference from the straw (82).
39	N	**C**, avoid direct seeding small-seeded crops after a rye cover crop due to interference from the straw (82).
39	P	**C**, avoid direct seeding small-seeded crops after a rye cover crop due to interference from the straw (82).
39	Q	**D-**, use grain crops or sweet corn in rotation with cabbage and related species to decrease white mold (67).
39	R	**D-**, use grain crops or sweet corn in rotation with cabbage and related species to decrease white mold (67).
39	S	**D-**, use grain crops or sweet corn in rotation with cabbage and related species to decrease white mold (67).
39	AA	**D-**, use grain crops or sweet corn in rotation with beet to decrease root rots (67).
39	AF	**D**, to avoid leaf diseases, avoid planting barley after wheat (107).
39	AJ	**D-**, use grain crops or sweet corn in rotation with bean to decrease root rots (67).
39	AM	**XXXX**
40	A	**D-**, unlike most crops, an oat cover crop decreases density of lesion nematodes (*Pratylenchus* spp.) (41). **I-**, "High-biomass cover crops such as barley or rye increased population of centipedes, predator mites, and other important predators" (107). **N**, incorporating annual ryegrass can tie up N in microbial tissues, thereby making it unavailable to succeeding crops. Problems can be avoided by incorporating residue a few weeks before planting (107). **S**, the lag between incorporation and planting, however, leaves the soil open to erosion. **C-**, "Winter killed cover crops like field pea and oats made the most sense before early planted vegetables, allowing us to work the ground early in the spring" (39, quoting Eric and Anne Nordell).
40	B	**I**, onion thrips may be a problem when grain or any grass precedes onions (83).
40	C	**I**, onion thrips may be a problem when grain or any grass precedes onions (83).

Row	Col.	Notes
40	D	**I**, onion thrips may be a problem when grain or any grass precedes onions (83).
40	F	**D-**, use grain crops or sweet corn in rotation with bean to decrease root rots (67).
40	I	**D-**, use of 2 years of grass or 1 year of cereal in rotation with potato helps reduce rhizoctonia canker (67).
40	Q	**D-**, use grain crops or sweet corn in rotation with cabbage and related species to decrease white mold (67). **W-**, **S-**, oat cover crop (often with field pea) controls weeds and improves soil structure before summer-transplanted brassicas (83).
40	R	**D-**, use grain crops or sweet corn in rotation with cabbage and related species to decrease white mold (67). **W-**, **S-**, oat cover crop (often with field pea) controls weeds and improves soil structure before summer-transplanted brassicas (83).
40	S	**D-**, use grain crops or sweet corn in rotation with cabbage and related species to decrease white mold (67). **W-**, **S-**, oat cover crop (often with field pea) controls weeds and improves soil structure before summer-transplanted brassicas (83).
40	AA	**D-**, use grain crops or sweet corn in rotation with beet to decrease root rots (67).
40	AJ	**D-**, use grain crops or sweet corn in rotation with beans to decrease root rots (67).
40	AN	**XXXX**
41	A	**N**, incorporating annual ryegrass can tie up N in microbial tissues, thereby making it unavailable to succeeding crops. Problems can be avoided by incorporating residue a few weeks before planting (107). **S**, the lag between incorporation and planting, however, leaves the soil open to erosion.
41	B	**I**, onion thrips may be a problem when grain or any grass precedes onions (83).
41	C	**I**, onion thrips may be a problem when grain or any grass precedes onions (83).
41	D	**I**, onion thrips may be a problem when grain or any grass precedes onions (83).
41	I	**D-**, use of 2 years of grass or 1 year of cereal in rotation with potato helps reduce rhizoctonia canker (67).
41	P	**D-**, ryegrass reduces clubroot infection rates more than other rotation species (20).
41	Q	**D-**, ryegrass reduces clubroot infection rates more than other rotation species (20).
41	R	**D-**, ryegrass reduces clubroot infection rates more than other rotation species (20).
41	S	**D-**, ryegrass reduces clubroot infection rates more than other rotation species (20).
41	T	**D-**, ryegrass reduces clubroot infection rates more than other rotation species (20).
41	U	**D-**, ryegrass reduces clubroot infection rates more than other rotation species (20).

Row	Col.	Notes
41	AO	**XXXX**
42	A	**D-**, sorghum-sudangrass cover crop reduces southern root-knot nematode (*Meloidogyne incognita*) populations in subsequent vegetable crops (30).
42	B	**I**, onion thrips may be a problem when grain or any grass precedes onions (83).
42	C	**I**, onion thrips may be a problem when grain or any grass precedes onions (83).
42	D	**I**, onion thrips may be a problem when grain or any grass precedes onions (83).
42	I	**D-**, use of 2 years of grass or 1 year of cereal in rotation with potato helps reduce rhizoctonia canker (67).
42	AP	**XXXX**
43	I	**D-**, severity of verticillium wilt was lower following buckwheat green manure than following canola or a fallow period (see chapter 3, p. 21). **S-**, buckwheat leaves the soil in a good state of tilth for potato (83).
43	Q	**D-**, clubroot declines more quickly when tomato, cucumber, snap bean, or buckwheat is grown (see chapter 3, p. 21).
43	R	**D-**, clubroot declines more quickly when tomato, cucumber, snap bean, or buckwheat is grown (see chapter 3, p. 21).
43	S	**D-**, clubroot declines more quickly when tomato, cucumber, snap bean, or buckwheat is grown (see chapter 3, p. 21).
43	T	**D-**, clubroot declines more quickly when tomato, cucumber, snap bean, or buckwheat is grown (see chapter 3, p. 21).
43	U	**D-**, clubroot declines more quickly when tomato, cucumber, snap bean, or buckwheat is grown (see chapter 3, p. 21).
43	AQ	**XXXX**
44	A	**I**, "Grubs, wireworms, maggots, and slugs were also a nuisance after even one year of clover sod" (39, quoting Eric and Anne Nordell). **N-**, nitrogen-fixing cover crop (107).
44	H	**I**, clovers before lettuce increases tarnished plant bug attack (82).
44	AR	**XXXX**
45	A	**I**, "Grubs, wireworms, maggots, and slugs were also a nuisance after even one year of clover sod" (39, quoting Eric and Anne Nordell). **N-**, nitrogen-fixing cover crop (107).
45	G	**D**, sclerotinia disease of broad bean (presumably including bell bean) and red clover rot are closely related (varieties of *S. trifoliorum*); each can attack a variety of crops, including pea, lettuce, and possibly other plants (36).
45	H	**D**, clover rot fungus (*Sclerotinia trifoliorum*) occasionally attacks lettuce (36). **I**, clover before lettuce increases tarnished plant bug attack (82).

Row	Col.	Notes
45	P	**C-**, fall-sown red clover provides a drought-tolerant cover crop the next summer prior to fall-sown brassicas (83).
45	Q	**C-**, fall-sown red clover provides a drought-tolerant cover crop the next summer prior to fall-sown brassicas (83).
45	S	**C-**, fall-sown red clover provides a drought-tolerant cover crop the next summer prior to fall-sown brassicas (83).
45	AI	**D**, "Never plant dry beans or soybeans after clover unless the cover has been thoroughly incorporated by plowing" (107).
45	AJ	**D**, "Never plant dry beans or soybeans after clover unless the cover has been thoroughly incorporated by plowing" (107).
45	AS	**XXXX**
45	AW	**D**, sclerotinia disease of broad bean (presumably including bell bean) and red clover rot are closely related (varieties of *S. trifoliorum*); each can attack a variety of crops, including pea, lettuce, and possibly other plants (36).
45	AX	**D**, sclerotinia disease of broad bean (presumably including bell bean) and red clover rot are closely related (varieties of *S. trifoliorum*); each can attack a variety of crops, including pea, lettuce, and possibly other plants (36).
46	A	**N-**, nitrogen-fixing cover crop (107).
46	H	**I**, clover before lettuce increases tarnished plant bug attack (82).
46	AT	**XXXX**
47	A	**N-**, nitrogen-fixing cover crop (107).
47	F	**D**, white sweet clover is an important host in which yellow bean mosaic virus 2 overwinters. It can infect also broad bean (and presumably bell bean), soybean, and alsike and other clovers (36).
47	I	**D**, sweet clover green manure is more conducive to scab development than alfalfa or rye (20).
47	AI	**D**, white sweet clover is an important host in which yellow bean mosaic virus 2 overwinters. It can infect also broad bean (and presumably bell bean), soybean, and alsike and other clovers (36).
47	AM	**C-**, a winter grain can be overseeded into a previously established hairy vetch cover crop to create a mixed grass–legume winter cover (83).
47	AS	**D**, white sweet clover is an important host in which yellow bean mosaic virus 2 overwinters. It can infect also broad bean (and presumably bell bean), soybean, and alsike and other clovers (36).
47	AU	**XXXX**
47	AX	**D**, white sweet clover is an important host in which yellow bean mosaic virus 2 overwinters. It can infect also broad bean (and presumably bell bean), soybean, and alsike and other clovers (36).

Row	Col.	Notes
48	A	**D**, hairy vetch is a good host for northern root-knot nematode (*Meloidogyne hapla*) (113). **N-**, nitrogen-fixing cover crop (107). **C-**, use of hairy vetch (often with rye) before late-planted crops allows maximum accumulation of dry matter and nitrogen (81).
48	G	**D**, avoid hairy vetch in rotation with pea due to black stem fungus (*Ascochyta pinodella*) (20).
48	V	**N-**, cucurbits have a high nitrogen need that vetch can supply (83).
48	W	**D-**, hairy vetch residue incorporated into the soil reduces fusarium wilt in watermelon. **N-**, cucurbits have a high nitrogen need that vetch can supply (83).
48	X	**N-**, cucurbits have a high nitrogen need that vetch can supply (83).
48	Y	**N-**, cucurbits have a high nitrogen need that vetch can supply (83).
48	AM	**W**, hairy vetch can be a severe weed in all winter grains, decreasing both yield and quality. Dormant seeds in the cover-crop sowing may persist in the soil for several years and infest subsequent winter grain crops even if the cover crop is not allowed to seed (59).
48	AV	**XXXX**
49	A	**N-**, nitrogen-fixing cover crop (107). **C-**, "Winter killed cover crops like field pea and oats made the most sense before early planted vegetables, allowing us to work the ground early in the spring" (39, quoting Eric and Anne Nordell).
49	G	**D**, sclerotinia disease of broad bean (presumably including bell bean) and red clover rot are closely related (varieties of *S. trifoliorum*); each can attack a variety of crops, including pea, lettuce, and possibly other plants (36).
49	H	**D**, sclerotinia disease of broad bean (presumably including bell bean) and red clover rot are closely related (varieties of *S. trifoliorum*); each can attack a variety of crops, including pea, lettuce, and possibly other plants (36).
49	Q	**N-**, **W-**, a field pea cover crop (often with oat) controls weeds and provides nitrogen for summer-transplanted brassicas (83).
49	R	**N-**, **W-**, a field pea cover crop (often with oat) controls weeds and provides nitrogen for summer-transplanted brassicas (83).
49	S	**N-**, **W-**, a field pea cover crop (often with oat) controls weeds and provides nitrogen for summer-transplanted brassicas (83).
49	AS	**D**, sclerotinia disease of broad bean (presumably including bell bean) and red clover rot are closely related (varieties of *S. trifoliorum*); each can attack a variety of crops, including pea, lettuce, and possibly other plants (36).
49	AW	**XXXX**

Row	Col.	Notes
49	AX	**D**, sclerotinia disease of broad bean (presumably including bell bean) and red clover rot are closely related (varieties of *S. trifoliorum*); each can attack a variety of crops, including pea, lettuce, and possibly other plants (36).
50	A	**N-**, nitrogen-fixing cover crop.
50	G	**D**, sclerotinia disease of broad bean (presumably including bell bean) and red clover rot are closely related (varieties of *S. trifoliorum*); each can attack a variety of crops, including pea, lettuce, and possibly other plants (36).
50	H	**D**, sclerotinia disease of broad bean (presumably including bell bean) and red clover rot are closely related (varieties of *S. trifoliorum*); each can attack a variety of crops, including pea, lettuce, and possibly other plants (36).
50	P	**N-**, brassicas do well after incorporating bell bean due to abundant N supply (83).
50	Q	**N-**, brassicas do well after incorporating bell bean due to abundant N supply (83).
50	R	**N-**, brassicas do well after incorporating bell beans due to abundant N supply (83).
50	S	**N-**, brassicas do well after incorporating bell bean due to abundant N supply (83).
50	T	**N-**, brassicas do well after incorporating bell bean due to abundant N supply (83).
50	U	**N-**, brassicas do well after incorporating bell bean due to abundant N supply (83).
50	AS	**D**, sclerotinia disease of broad bean (presumably including bell bean) and red clover rot are closely related (varieties of *S. trifoliorum*); each can attack a variety of crops, including pea, lettuce, and possibly other plants (36).
50	AW	**D**, sclerotinia disease of broad bean (presumably including bell bean) and red clover rot are closely related (varieties of *S. trifoliorum*); each can attack a variety of crops, including pea, lettuce, and possibly other plants (36).
50	AX	**XXXX**
51	A	**D-**, incorporated mustard family cover crops suppress a variety of soilborne diseases (see chapter 3, p. 21).
51	I	**D-**, plowed-down brassica cover crops act as a fumigant against potato diseases (83).
51	P	**D**, clubroot attacks many crops in the mustard family, including cabbage and its relatives, mustard, radish, Chinese cabbage, turnip, canola, and many weeds (36).
51	Q	**D**, clubroot attacks many crops in the mustard family, including cabbage and its relatives, mustard, radish, Chinese cabbage, turnip, canola, and many weeds (36).
51	R	**D**, clubroot attacks many crops in the mustard family, including cabbage and its relatives, mustard, radish, Chinese cabbage, turnip, canola, and many weeds (36).

Row	Col.	Notes
51	S	**D**, clubroot attacks many crops in the mustard family, including cabbage and its relatives, mustard, radish, Chinese cabbage, turnip, canola, and many weeds (36).
51	T	**D**, clubroot attacks many crops in the mustard family, including cabbage and its relatives, mustard, radish, Chinese cabbage, turnip, canola, and many weeds (36).
51	U	**D**, clubroot attacks many crops in the mustard family, including cabbage and its relatives, mustard, radish, Chinese cabbage, turnip, canola, and many weeds (36).
51	AY	**XXXX**
51	AZ	**D**, clubroot attacks many crops in the mustard family, including cabbage and its relatives, mustard, radish, Chinese cabbage, turnip, canola, and many weeds (36).
52	A	**D-**, incorporated mustard family cover crops suppress a variety of soilborne diseases (see chapter 3, p. 21).
52	I	**D-**, plowed-down brassica cover crops act as a fumigant against potato diseases (83).
52	P	**D**, clubroot attacks many crops in the mustard family, including cabbage and its relatives, mustard, radish, Chinese cabbage, turnip, canola, and many weeds (36).
52	Q	**D**, clubroot attacks many crops in the mustard family, including cabbage and its relatives, mustard, radish, Chinese cabbage, turnip, canola, and many weeds (36).
52	R	**D**, clubroot attacks many crops in the mustard family, including cabbage and its relatives, mustard, radish, Chinese cabbage, turnip, canola, and many weeds (36).
52	S	**D**, clubroot attacks many crops in the mustard family, including cabbage and its relatives, mustard, radish, Chinese cabbage, turnip, canola, and many weeds (36).
52	T	**D**, clubroot attacks many crops in the mustard family, including cabbage and its relatives, mustard, radish, Chinese cabbage, turnip, canola, and many weeds (36).
52	U	**D**, clubroot attacks many crops in the mustard family, including cabbage and its relatives, mustard, radish, Chinese cabbage, turnip, canola, and many weeds (36).
52	AI	**D-**, oilseed radish can decrease nematode populations in soybean (119).
52	AY	**D**, clubroot attacks many crops in the mustard family, including cabbage and its relatives, mustard, radish, Chinese cabbage, turnip, canola, and many weeds (36).
52	AZ	**XXXX**

APPENDIX 3 Sources of Inoculum for Crop Diseases in the Northeastern United States
Compiled by Margaret Tuttle McGrath

Disease	Pathogen Name	Rotation (years)[1]	Seed Borne	Wind-blown Spores[2]	Insect Vectored	Weed Hosts
VEGETABLE CROPS						
Asparagus						
Fusarium crown rot	*Fusarium* spp.	Y (long)	Y (crown)	N	N	wide host range[3]
Fusarium root rot	*Fusarium* spp.	Y (long)	Y (crown)	N	N	wide host range[3]
Phytophthora spear rot	*Phytophthora* spp.	N	Maybe	N	N	common purslane, horsenettle, velvetleaf, eastern black nightshade (*P. capsici*)
Rust	*Puccinia asparagi*	Y (3)	N	Y	N	no records located
Bean, snap and dry						
Anthracnose	*Colletotrichum lindemuthianum*	Y (3)	Y	Y (local, rain)	N	no records located
Bacterial brown spot	*Pseudomonas syringae* pv. *syringae*	Y (2)	Y	NA	N	wide host range
Bean common mosaic virus (BCMV)	Bean common mosaic virus (BCMV)	NA	Y	NA	Y (aphid)	common chickweed, common lambsquarters, black medic, Canada thistle
Bean rust	*Uromyces appendiculatus*	Y (3)	N	Y	N	no records located
Bean yellow mosaic virus (BYMV)	Bean yellow mosaic virus (BYMV)	NA	N	NA	Y (aphid)	many, mostly legumes[7]
Botrytis gray mold	*Botrytis cinerea*	Y	N	Y	N	common sunflower
Clover yellow vein virus (CYVV)	Clover yellow vein virus (CYVV)	NA	N	NA	Y	common lambsquarters, black medic, clover, and possibly other perennial weeds
Common bacterial blight	*Xanthomonas campestris*	Y (2-3)	Y	NA	N	mustard, shepherd's purse, some other weeds in the mustard family, soybean
Cucumber mosaic virus (CMV)	Cucumber mosaic virus (CMV)	NA	Y	NA	Y (aphid)	wide host range[8]
Halo blight	*Pseudomonas syringae* pv. *phaseolicola*	Y (3)	Y	NA	N	wide host range
Root rot, damping-off	*Pythium, Rhizoctonia, Thielaviopsis, Fusarium,* and *Pratylenchus* spp.	Y (3-4)	Y	N	N	wide host range[3,4,5]
White mold	*Sclerotinia sclerotiorum*	Y (5)	N	Y (local)	N	wide host range[6]
Bean, lima						
Downy mildew	*Phytophthora phaseoli*	Y (2)	Y	Y	N	no records located
Pod blight	*Phytophthora capsici*	Y (>3)	N	Y (local, rain)	N	common purslane, eastern black nightshade, horsenettle, velvetleaf

Disease	Pathogen Name	Rotation (years)[1]	Seed Borne	Wind-blown Spores[2]	Insect Vectored	Weed Hosts
Root-knot nematodes	*Meloidogyne hapla, M. incognita*	Y (long); small grains	N	NA	N	wide host range[9]
White mold	*Sclerotinia sclerotiorum*	Y (5)	N	Y (local)	N	wide host range[6]
Beet						
Cercospora leaf spot	*Cercospora beticola*	Y (3)	Y	Y (local)	N	several[10]
Common scab	*Streptomyces* spp.	Y (3-4)	N	N	N	no records located
Phoma leaf spot	*Phoma betae*	Y (3)	Y	Y (local, rain)	N	no records located
Pocket rot	*Rhizoctonia solani*	Y	Y	N	N	wide host range[5]
Seed rot, damping-off, root rot	*Pythium ultimum, Rhizoctonia solani*	Y (3-4)	Y	N	N	wide host range[4,5]
Sugar beet cyst nematode	*Heterodera schachtii*	Y (4-5)	N	NA	N	field pennycress, tumble pigweed, common lambsquarters, hairy galinsoga
Cabbage, broccoli, cauliflower, and Brussels sprouts						
Alternaria leaf spot	*Alternaria* spp.	Y (3)	Y	Y (local)	N	field pepperweed, Virginia pepperweed, field pennycress
Black leg, seed decay	*Phoma lingam*	Y (4)	Y	Y (local)	N	weeds in the mustard family
Black rot	*Xanthomonas campestris* pv. *campestris*	Y (3)	Y	NA	N	mustard, shepherd's purse, some other weeds in the mustard family
Clubroot	*Plasmodiophora brassicae*	Y (7)	N	NA	N	several[11]
Downy mildew	*Peronospora parasitica*	Y (3)	N	Y	N	wild mustard, yellow rocket, hedge mustard, shepherd's purse, marsh yellowcress, field pennycress suspected; actual hosts might be affected by strain specificity
Fusarium yellows	*Fusarium oxysporum*	Y (7)	N	N	N	wide host range[3]
Head rot of broccoli	*Pseudomonas* spp.	Y (2)	N	NA	N	wide host range
Root-knot nematodes	*Meloidogyne hapla, M. incognita*	Y (long); small grains	N	NA	N	wide host range[9]
Root rot	*Pythium ultimum, Rhizoctonia solani*	Y (3)	Y	N	N	wide host range[4,5]
White mold	*Sclerotinia sclerotiorum*	Y (5)	N	Y (local)	N	wide host range[6]
Wirestem	*Rhizoctonia solani*	Y (4-5)	Y	N	N	wide host range[5]

Disease	Pathogen Name	Rotation (years)[1]	Seed Borne	Wind-blown Spores[2]	Insect Vectored	Weed Hosts
Carrot						
Alternaria leaf blight	*Alternaria dauci*	Y (2-3)	Y	Y (local)	N	no records located
Aster yellows	Aster yellows phytoplasma	NA	N	NA	Y (leafhopper)	wide host range[12]
Bacterial leaf blight	*Xanthomonas campestris* pv. *carotae*	Y (2-3)	Y	NA	N	mustard, shepherd's purse, some other weeds in the mustard family
Cavity spot	*Pythium* spp.	Y (3-4)	Y	N	N	several weed hosts[4]
Cercospora leaf spot	*Cercospora carotae*	Y (2-3)	Y	Y (local)	N	no records located
Common scab	*Streptomyces* spp.	Y (3-4)	N	N	N	no records located
Crater rot, foliar blight	*Rhizoctonia solani*	Y (4-5)	Y	N	N	wide host range[5]
Damping-off, seed decay	*Pythium* spp., *Rhizoctonia* spp.	N	N	N	N	wide host range[4,5]
Root-knot nematodes	*Meloidogyne hapla*, *M. incognita*, others	Y (long); small grains	N	NA	N	wide host range[9]
White mold, cottony rot	*Sclerotinia sclerotiorum*	Y (5)	N	Y (local)	N	wide host range[6]
Celery						
Aster yellows	Aster yellows phytoplasma	NA	N	NA	Y (leafhopper)	wide host range[12]
Bacterial leaf spot	*Pseudomonas syringae* pv. *apii*	Y (2-3)	Y	NA	N	wide host range
Early blight, cercospora leaf spot	*Cercospora apii*	Y	Y	Y (local)	N	no records located
Late blight, septoria leaf spot	*Septoria apiicola*	Y (2)	Y	Y (local)	N	no records located
Corn, sweet						
Anthracnose	*Colletotrichum graminicola*	Y	N	Y (local, rain)	N	several grasses[13]
Barley yellow dwarf luteovirus (BYDV-PAV)	Barley yellow dwarf luteovirus (BYDV-PAV)	NA	—	NA	Y (aphid)	witchgrass, Italian ryegrass, annual bluegrass
Common rust	*Puccinia sorghi*	NA	N	Y	N	yellow woodsorrel
Common smut	*Ustilago maydis*	Y	Y	Y (local)	Y (leafhopper)	no records located
Maize dwarf mosaic virus (MDMV)	Maize dwarf mosaic virus (MDMV)	NA	N	NA	Y (aphid)	witchgrass, johnsongrass, barnyardgrass
Northern corn leaf blight	*Exserohilum turcicum*	Y (1, 2 w/ no-till)	N	Y (local)	N	green foxtail, wild-proso millet
Seed rots	*Fusarium* spp., *Diplodia* spp., etc	N	N	N	Y	wide host range[3]
Stewart's wilt	*Erwinia stewartii*	NA	Y	NA	Y (flea beetle)	no records located

Disease	Pathogen Name	Rotation (years)[1]	Seed Borne	Wind-blown Spores[2]	Insect Vectored	Weed Hosts
Cucurbits (cucumber, melon, pumpkin, squash, watermelon)						
Alternaria leaf blight	*Alternaria cucumerina*	Y (2+)	Y	Y (local)	N	Virginia copperleaf is a host for *Alternaria* spp.
Angular leaf spot	*Pseudomonas syringae*	Y (2+)	Y	NA	N	wide host range
Anthracnose	*Colletotrichum orbiculare*	Y (2)	Y	Y (local, rain)	Y	no records located
Bacterial fruit blotch	*Xanthomonas campestris*	Y (2-3)	Y	NA	N	mustard, shepherd's purse, some other weeds in the mustard family
Bacterial leaf spot	*Acidovorax avenae* subsp. *citrulli*	Y (3)	Y	NA	Y? (bee)	no records located
Bacterial wilt	*Erwinia tracheiphila*	NA	N	NA	Y (cucumber beetle)	no records located
Belly rot	*Rhizoctonia solani*	Y (long)	N	N	N	wide host range[5]
Black rot, gummy stem blight	*Didymella bryoniae*	Y (2)	Y	Y (local)	N	no records located
Choanephora blossom blight or fruit rot	*Choanephora cucurbitarum*	Y (2)	N	Y (local)	N	redroot pigweed
Cottony leak	*Pythium* spp.	N	N	N	N	several weed hosts[4]
Cucumber mosaic virus (CMV)	Cucumber mosaic virus (CMV)	NA	N	NA	Y (aphid)	wide host range[8]
Damping-off, root rot	*Pythium* spp., *Phytophthora* spp.	N	N	N	N	common purslane, horsenettle, velvetleaf (*P. capsici*); eastern black nightshade (*P. capsici* and *P. infestans*)[4]
Downy mildew	*Pseudoperonospora cubensis*	NA	N	Y	N	no records located
Fusarium crown and root rot	*Fusarium solani* f. sp. *cucurbitae*	Y (5)	Y	N	N	no records located
Fusarium wilt (cucumber)	*Fusarium oxysporum* f. sp. *cucumerinum*	Y (5-7)	Y	N	N	no records located
Fusarium wilt (melon)	*Fusarium oxysporum* f. sp. *melonis*	Y (5-7)	Y	N	N	no records located
Fusarium wilt (watermelon)	*Fusarium oxysporum* f. sp. *niveum*	Y (5-7)	Y	N	N	no records located
Gummy stem blight (aka black rot)	*Didymella bryoniae*	Y (2)	Y	Y (local)	N	no records located
Papaya ring spot virus (PRSV)	Papaya ring spot virus (PRSV)	NA	N	NA	Y (aphid)	burcucumber
Phytophthora blight	*Phytophthora capsici*	Y (>3)	N	Y (local, rain)	N	common purslane, eastern black nightshade, horsenettle, velvetleaf
Powdery mildew	*Podosphaera xanthii*	N	N	Y	N	no records located

Disease	Pathogen Name	Rotation (years)[1]	Seed Borne	Wind-blown Spores[2]	Insect Vectored	Weed Hosts
Root-knot nematodes	*Meloidogyne hapla, M. incognita*	Y (long); small grains	N	NA	N	wide host range[9]
Scab	*Cladosporium cucumerinum*	Y (2+)	Y	Y (local)	N	common sunflower
Septoria leaf spot	*Septoria cucurbitacearum*	Y (2+)	N	Y (local)	N	no records located
Southern blight	*Sclerotium rolfsii*	Y (long); corn, small grains, grass	N	N	N	no records located
Ulocladium leaf spot	*Ulocladium cucurbitae*	Y (2)	N	Y (local)	N	no records located
Verticillium wilt	*Verticillium dahliae*	Y (5)	Y	N	N	velvetleaf, common sunflower, field pennycress
Watermelon mosaic virus (WMV)	Watermelon mosaic virus (WMV)	NA	N	NA	Y (aphid)	common lambsquarters, burcucumber, jimsonweed, eastern black nightshade, shepherd's purse
White mold	*Sclerotinia sclerotiorum*	Y (5)	N	Y (local)	N	wide host range[6]
Zucchini yellow mosaic virus (ZYMV)	Zucchini yellow mosaic virus (ZYMV)	NA	N	NA	Y (aphid)	no records located
Eggplant						
Anthracnose	*Colletotrichum coccodes*	Y	Y	Y (local, rain)	N	eastern black nightshade, velvetleaf
Alternaria early blight	*Alternaria solani, A. alternata*	Y (2-3)		Y (local)	N	jimsonweed, redroot pigweed, eastern black nightshade (*A. solani*)
Phytophthora crown or collar rot	*Phytophthora capsici*	Y (>3)	N	Y (local, rain)	N	field pepperweed, Virginia pepperweed, field pennycress
Phomopsis	*Phomopsis vexans*	Y (2-3)	N	Y (local)	N	no records located
Root-knot nematodes	*Meloidogyne hapla, M. incognita*	Y (long); small grains	N	NA	N	wide host range[9]
Verticillium wilt	*Verticillium albo-atrum, V. dahliae*	Y (4-5)	Y	N	N	wide host range[14]
Lettuce						
Anthracnose	*Microdochium panattonianum*	Y (1)	Y	Y (local, rain)	N	prickly lettuce
Aster yellows	Aster yellows phytoplasma	NA	N	NA	Y (leafhopper)	wide host range[12]
Botrytis gray mold-post harvest	*Botrytis cinerea*	Y	N	Y	N	common sunflower
Bottom rot	*Rhizoctonia solani*	Y (3)	N	N	N	wide host range[5]
Broadbean wilt virus (BBWV)	Broadbean wilt virus (BBWV)	NA	N	NA	Y (aphid)	no records located

Disease	Pathogen Name	Rotation (years)[1]	Seed Borne	Wind-blown Spores[2]	Insect Vectored	Weed Hosts
Cucumber mosaic virus (CMV)	Cucumber mosaic virus (CMV)	NA	N	NA	Y (aphid)	wide host range[8]
Damping-off	*Pythium* spp.	N	Y	N	N	several weed hosts[4]
Downy mildew	*Bremia lactucae*	Y (2-3)	N	Y	N	perennial sowthistle, annual sowthistle, prickly lettuce
Drop	*Sclerotinia sclerotiorum, S. minor*	Y (3)	N	Y (local)	N	wide host range[6]
Lettuce mosaic virus (LMV)	Lettuce mosaic virus (LMV)	NA	Y	NA	Y	common groundsel, common lambsquarters, annual sowthistle
Root-knot nematodes	*Meloidogyne hapla, M. incognita*	Y (long); small grains	N	NA	N	wide host range[9]
Onion						
Bacterial canker, sour skin	*Burkholderia cepacia*	N	N	NA	N	no records located
Bacterial soft rot	*Erwinia carotovora* subs. *carotovora*	N	N	NA	N	no records located
Botrytis leaf blight	*Botrytis squamosa*	Y (3-4)	N	Y	N	no records located
Botrytis net rot	*Botrytis allii*	Y (2-3)	Y	Y	N	no records located
Damping-off	*Pythium* spp., *Fusarium* spp.	Y (*Fusarium*; small grains)	Y (*Fusarium*)	N	N	wide host range[3,4]
Downy mildew	*Peronospora destructor*	Y (3-4)	Y	Y	N	no records located
Fusarium basal rot	*Fusarium oxysporum* f. sp. *cepae*	Y (4)	N	N	N	no records located
Lesion nematodes	*Pratylenchus* spp.	Y (long)	Y	NA	N	wide host range
Onion yellow dwarf virus (OYDV)	Onion yellow dwarf virus (OYDV)	Y	Y	NA	Y (aphid)	no records located
Pink rot	*Phoma terrestris*	Y (3-6)	N	Y (local)	N	barnyardgrass, green foxtail, shattercane, witchgrass, field pepperweed, horsenettle
Purple blotch	*Alternaria porri*	Y (long)	Y	Y (local)	N	Virginia copperleaf is a host for *Alternaria* spp.
Root-knot nematodes	*Meloidogyne hapla, M. incognita*	Y (long); small grains	Y	NA	N	wide host range[9]
Slippery skin	*Pseudomonas gladioli* pv. *allicola*	Y	N	NA	N	wide host range
Smut	*Urocystis colchici*	Y	Y	Y (local)	N	no records located
Stalk rot	*Stemphylium botryosum*	Y (long)	Y	Y (local)	N	green foxtail
Stemphylium leaf blight	*Stemphylium vesicarium*	Y (long)	Y	Y (local)	N	no records located
White rot	*Sclerotinia cepivorum*	N	N	N	N	no records located

Disease	Pathogen Name	Rotation (years)[1]	Seed Borne	Wind-blown Spores[2]	Insect Vectored	Weed Hosts
Parsnip						
Aster yellows	Aster yellows phytoplasma	NA	N	NA	Y (leafhopper)	wide host range[12]
Bacterial blight	*Pseudomonas marginalis, P. viridiflava*	Y	N	NA	N	wide host range
Pea						
Ascochyta leaf spot	*Ascochyta pisi*	Y (3)	Y	Y (local)	N	no records located
Bacterial blight	*Pseudomonas syringae* pv. *pisi*	NA	Y	NA	N	wide host range
Fusarium wilt	*Fusarium oxysporum* f. sp. *pisi*	Y (long)	N	N	N	no records located
Seed decay and root rot	*Pythium ultimum*	Y (3-4)	Y	N	N	wild-proso millet, shattercane, barnyardgrass, quackgrass
White mold	*Sclerotinia sclerotiorum*	Y (5)	N	Y (local)	N	wide host range[6]
Pepper						
Anthracnose fruit rot	*Colletotrichum gloeosporioides*	Y (2)	Y	Y (local, rain)	N	velvetleaf
Bacterial leaf spot	*Xanthomonas campestris* pv. *vesicatoria*	Y	Y	NA	N	mustard, shepherd's purse, some other weeds in the mustard family
Bacterial soft rot	*Erwinia carotovora*	N	N	NA	Y	no records located
Cucumber mosaic virus (CMV)	Cucumber mosaic virus (CMV)	NA	N	NA	Y (aphid)	wide host range[8]
Damping-off	*Phytophthora* spp., *Pythium* spp., *Rhizoctonia solani*	N	N	N	N	common purslane, horsenettle, velvetleaf (*P. capsici*); eastern black nightshade (*P. capsici* and *P. infestans*)[4,5]
Phytophthora blight	*Phytophthora capsici*	Y (>3)	Y	Y (local, rain)	N	field pepperweed, Virginia pepperweed, field pennycress
Root-knot nematodes	*Meloidogyne hapla, M. incognita*	Y (long); small grains	N	NA	Y	wide host range[9]
Southern blight	*Sclerotium rolfsii*	Y (long)	N	N	N	no records located
Tomato spotted wilt virus (TSWV)	Tomato spotted wilt virus (TSWV)	NA	N	NA	Y (thrips)	wide host range[15]
Verticillium wilt	*Verticillium albo-atrum, V. dahliae*	Y (long)	N	N	N	wide host range[14]

Disease	Pathogen Name	Rotation (years)[1]	Seed Borne	Wind-blown Spores[2]	Insect Vectored	Weed Hosts
Potato						
Bacterial ring rot	*Clavibacter michiganensis* subsp. *sepedonicum*	NA (regulated; 0 tolerance)	Y (seed tubers)	NA	N	no records located
Bacterial soft rot	*Erwinia* spp.	N	N	NA	N	no records located
Black dot root rot	*Colletotrichum coccodes*	Y (2)	Y (seed tubers)	N	N	eastern black nightshade, velvetleaf
Botrytis vine rot	*Botrytis cinerea*	N	N	Y	N	common sunflower
Canker and black scurf	*Rhizoctonia solani*	Y (3-4)	Y (seed tubers)	N	N	wide host range[5]
Common scab	*Streptomyces* spp.	Y (3-4)	N	N	N	no records located
Early blight	*Alternaria solani, A. tomatophila*	Y (2)	N	Y (local)	N	redroot pigweed, eastern black nightshade, jimsonweed (*A. solani*), Virginia copperleaf (*A. sp.*)
Fusarium dry rot	*Fusarium solani, F. sambucinum*	Y (long)	Y (seed tubers)	N	N	green foxtail (*F. solani*)
Fusarium wilt	*Fusarium* spp.	Y (long)	Y (seed tubers)	N	N	wide host range[3]
Golden nematode, Potato cyst nematode (quarantined, NY only)	*Globodera rostochiensis*	Y (5-9)	Y (seed tubers)	NA	N	no records located
Late blight	*Phytophthora infestans*	N	Y (seed tubers)	Y	N	eastern black nightshade
Leak	*Pythium* spp.	N (>4 if severe)	N	N	N	several weed hosts[4]
Lesion nematodes	*Pratylenchus* spp.	Y (long)	Y	NA	N	wide host range
Pink rot	*Phytophthora erythroseptica*	N (>4 if severe)	Y (seed tubers)	N	N	no records located
Powdery scab	*Spongospora subterranea*	Y (3-10)	Y (seed tubers)	N	N	no records located
Root-knot nematodes	*Meloidogyne hapla, M. incognita*	Y (long); small grains	N	NA	N	wide host range[9]
Silver scurf	*Helminthosporium solani*	Y (>3?)	Y (seed tubers)	N	N	no records located
Verticillium wilt	*Verticillium albo-atrum, V. dahliae*	Y (long)	N	N	N	wide host range[14]
White mold	*Sclerotinia sclerotiorum*	Y (5)	N	Y (local)	N	wide host range[6]
Spinach						
Anthracnose	*Colletotrichum spinaciae*	Y (3+)	Y	Y (local, rain)	N	no records located
Cucumber mosaic virus (CMV)	Cucumber mosaic virus (CMV)	NA	N	NA	Y (aphid)	wide host range[8]

Disease	Pathogen Name	Rotation (years)[1]	Seed Borne	Wind-blown Spores[2]	Insect Vectored	Weed Hosts
Damping-off and seed rot	*Pythium* spp.	N	N	N	N	several weed hosts[4]
Downy mildew, blue mold	*Peronospora effusa*	Y (2)	Y	Y	N	winter spinach, common lambsquarters
White rust	*Albugo occidentalis*	Y (3)	N	Y (local)	N	no records located
Sweet Potato						
Black rot	*Ceratocystis fimbriata*	Y (3-4)	Y (seed roots)	N	N	no records located
Fusarium wilt	*Fusarium oxysporum* f. sp. *batatas*	Y	Y (seed roots)	N	N	no records located
Pox, soil rot	*Streptomyces ipomoea*	Y (5)	Y (seed roots)	N	N	no records located
Root-knot nematodes	*Meloidogyne hapla*, *M. incognita*	Y (long); small grains	Y (seed roots)	NA	N	wide host range[9]
Sclerotial blight, southern blight, circular spot	*Sclerotium rolfsii*	Y (3-4)	Y (seed roots)	N	N	no records located
Scurf	*Monilochaetes infuscans*	Y (2-4)	Y (seed roots)	N	N	no records located
Soft rot, rhizopus soft rot	*Rhizopus stolonifer*	N	N	N	N	no records located
Surface rot, fusarium surface rot	*Fusarium oxysporum*	N	N	N	N	wide host range[3]
Sweet potato feathery mottle virus (SPFMV)	Sweet potato feathery mottle virus (SPFMV)	NA	Y (seed roots)	NA	Y (aphid)	no records located
Tomato						
Anthracnose	*Colletotrichum coccodes*	Y (3+)	Y	Y (local, rain)	N	eastern black nightshade, velvetleaf
Bacterial canker	*Clavibacter michiganensis* subsp. *michiganensis*	Y	Y	NA	N	no records located
Bacterial soft rot	*Erwinia carotovora* subsp. *carotovora*	N	N	NA	N	no records located
Bacterial speck	*Pseudomonas syringae* pv. *tomato*	Y (2)	Y	NA	N	no records located
Bacterial spot	*Xanthomonas campestris* pv. *vesicatoria*	Y (1-3)	Y	NA	N	mustard, sheperd's purse, some other weeds in the mustard family
Botrytis gray mold	*Botrytis cineria*	N	N	Y	N	common sunflower
Buckeye fruit rot	*Phytophthora parasitica*, *P. capsici*	Y (3+)	N	Y (local, rain)	N	common purslane, horsenettle, velvetleaf (*P. capsici*)
Cucumber mosaic virus (CMV)	Cucumber mosaic virus (CMV)	NA	N	NA	Y (aphid)	wide host range[8]
Damping-off	*Pythium* spp., *Rhizoctonia* spp.	N	N	N	N	wide host range[4,5]

Disease	Pathogen Name	Rotation (years)[1]	Seed Borne	Wind-blown Spores[2]	Insect Vectored	Weed Hosts
Double virus streak	Tomato mosaic virus (TMV) and potato virus X (PVX)	NA	Y	NA	Y (aphid)	no records located
Early blight	*Alternaria tomatophila, A. solani*	Y (long)	Y	Y (local)	N	redroot pigweed, eastern black nightshade, jimsonweed (*A. solani*), Virginia copperleaf (*A. sp.*)
Fusarium	*Fusarium oxysporum* f. sp. *lycopersici*	Y (5-7)	Y	N	N	no records located
Late blight	*Phytophthora infestans*	N	Y	Y	N	eastern black nightshade
Leaf mold	*Fulvia fulva*	Y (3+)	Y	Y	N	no records located
Phytophthora root rot	*Phytophthora parasitica, P. capsici*	Y (3+)	N	N	N	common purslane, horsenettle, velvetleaf (*P. capsici*)
Septoria leaf spot	*Septoria lycopersici*	Y (3)	Y	Y (local)	N	horsenettle, jimsonweed
Southern blight	*Sclerotium rolfsii*	Y (long); corn, cereal, grass	N	N	N	no records located
Tomato mosaic virus (TMV)	Tomato mosaic virus (TMV)	NA	N	NA	Y (aphid)	no records located
Tomato spotted wilt virus (TSWV)	Tomato spotted wilt virus (TSWV)	NA	N	NA	Y (thrips)	wide host range[15]
Verticillium wilt	*Verticillium albo-atrum, V. dahliae*	Y	N	N	N	wide host range[14]
White mold, timber rot	*Sclerotinia sclerotiorum*	N	N	Y (local)	N	wide host range[6]
Turnip, rutabaga and radish						
Alternaria leaf spot, brown spot	*Alternaria* spp.	Y (2+)	Y	Y (local)	N	field pepperweed, Virginia pepperweed, field pennycress
Black rot	*Xanthomonas campestris* pv. *campestris*	Y (3)	Y	NA	N	mustard, shepherd's purse, some other weeds in the mustard family
Blackleg	*Phoma lingam*	Y (4)	Y	Y (local, rain)	N	wild radish
Clubroot	*Plasmodiophora brassicae*	Y (7)	N	NA	N	wide host range[11]
Common scab	*Streptomyces* spp.	Y (3-4)	N	N	N	no records located
Damping-off	*Pythium* spp., *Rhizoctonia* spp., others	N	N	N	N	wide host range[4,5]
Downy mildew	*Peronospora parasitica*	Y (3)	N	Y	N	wild mustard, yellow rocket, hedge mustard, shepherd's purse, marsh yellowcress, field pennycress
Wirestem	*Rhizoctonia solani*	Y (4-5)	Y	N	N	wide host range[5]

Disease	Pathogen Name	Rotation (years)[1]	Seed Borne	Wind-blown Spores[2]	Insect Vectored	Weed Hosts
FIELD CROPS						
Alfalfa						
Anthracnose	*Colletotrichum trifolii*	Y (2-3)	Y	Y (local, rain)	N	no records located
Aphanomyces root rot	*Aphanomyces euteiches*	Y (2-3)	N	N	N	legumes
Bacterial wilt	*Clavibacter michiganensis* subsp. *insidiosus*	N	Y	NA	N	no records located
Brown root rot	*Phoma sclerotioides*	Y (3); non-legumes	Y	N	N	wide host range
Crown and root rot complex	*Fusarium* spp., *Phoma medicaginis*, *Pythium* spp., *Rhizoctonia solani*	Y (long)	Y	N	N	wide host range[3,4,5]
Fusarium wilt	*Fusarium oxysporum* f. sp. *medicaginis*	Y (long)	Y	N	N	no records located
Lepto leaf spot	*Leptosphaerulina trifolii*	N	N	Y (local)	N	medics, soybean
Lesion nematodes	*Pratylenchus* spp.	N	N	NA	N	wide host range
Phytophthora root rot	*Phytophthora medicaginis, P. megasperma* f. sp. *medicaginis*	Y (very long)	N	N	N	no records located
Sclerotinia crown and stem blight	*Sclerotinia trifoliorum, S. sclerotiorum*	Y (3-4)	Y	Y (local)	N	wide host range[6]
Spring black stem and leaf spot	*Phoma medicaginis*	Y (2-3)	Y	Y (local, rain)	N	legumes
Summer black stem and leaf spot	*Cercospora medicaginis*	Y (2-3)	Y	Y (local, rain)	N	legumes
Verticillium wilt	*Verticillium albo-atrum*	Y (3)	Y	N	Y (several)	wide host range[14]
Corn						
Anthracnose leaf blight and stalk rot	*Colletotrichum graminicola*	Y (2)	N	Y (local, rain)	N	several grasses[13]
Barley yellow dwarf virus	Barley yellow dwarf luteovirus (BYDV-PAV)	NA	N	NA	Y (aphid)	witchgrass, Italian ryegrass, annual bluegrass
Common rust	*Puccinia sorghi*	N	N	Y	N	yellow woodsorrel
Common smut	*Ustilago maydis*	Y (long)	Y	Y (local)	Y (leafhopper)	no records located
Diplodia ear rot, stalk rot, seed rot and seedling blight	*Stenocarpella maydis* (*Diplodia maydis*)	Y (2-3); worst in no-till continuous corn	N	Y	N	no records located

Disease	Pathogen Name	Rotation (years)[1]	Seed Borne	Wind-blown Spores[2]	Insect Vectored	Weed Hosts
Diplodia leaf spot, Diplodia leaf streak	*Stenocarpella macrospora* (*Diplodia macrospora*)	Y (2-3)	N	Y	N	no records located
Eyespot	*Aureobasidium zeae*	Y; worst in no-till continuous corn	N	Y (local, rain)	N	no records located
Fusarium stalk and ear rot	*Fusarium moniliforme*	Y; worst in no-till continuous corn	Y	Y (local)	Y (European corn borer, ear worm)	grasses
Gibberella stalk and ear rot[16]	*Fusarium* spp.	Y (2-3); worst in no-till continuous corn	Y	Y (local)	N	wide host range[3]
Gray leaf spot, Cercospora leaf spot	*Cercospora sorghi*	Y (1-2); worst in no-till continuous corn	N	Y (local)	N	a few grasses
Leaf blight	*Erwinia stewartii*	N	Y	NA	Y (corn flea beetle)	a few grasses
Lesion nematodes	*Pratylenchus* spp.	N	N	NA	N	wide host range
Maize dwarf mosaic virus (MDMV)	Maize dwarf mosaic virus (MDMV)	N	N	NA	Y (aphid)	witchgrass, johnsongrass, barnyardgrass, goosegrass
Northern corn leaf blight	*Exserohilum turcicum*	Y (2-3)	N	Y	N	johnsongrass, green foxtail, wild-proso millet
Seed rots	*Fusarium* spp., *Diplodia* spp., etc	N	N	N	Y	wide host range[3]
Soybean						
Asian soybean rust	*Pakospora pachyrhizi*	NA	N	Y	N	kudzu, clover, lupin
Brown spot	*Septoria glycines*	Y	Y	Y	N	no records located
Brown stem rot	*Phialophora gregata* (*Cephalosporium gregatum*)	Y (2-3)	N	N	N	unknown; likely
Damping-off, stem rot	*Rhizoctonia* spp., *Fusarium* spp., *Phytophthora sojae*, *Pythium* spp.	Y (long)	N	N	N	wide host range[3,4,5]
Diaporthe stem canker	*Diaporthe phaseolorum* (*Phomopsis phaseoli*)	Y	Y	Y (local, rain)	N	no records located
Green stem/soybean viruses	Bean pod mottle virus	NA	Y (low levels)	NA	Y (bean leaf beetle)	no records located
Phomoposis seed rot	*Phomopsis* spp.	Y	Y	Y (local, rain)	N	velvetleaf

Disease	Pathogen Name	Rotation (years)[1]	Seed Borne	Wind-blown Spores[2]	Insect Vectored	Weed Hosts
Phytophthora root rot	*Phytophthora sojae*	Y (long)	N	N	N	unknown; likely
Sclerotinia white mold, sclerotinia stem rot	*Sclerotinia sclerotiorum*	Y (long)	Y	Y (local)	N	wide host range[6]
Soybean cyst nematode	*Heterodera glycines*	Y (3+)	Y (in soil with seed)	NA	N	many
Sudden death syndrome	*Fusarium solani* f. sp. *glycines*	Y (3)	N	N	N	no records located
Wheat						
Barley yellow dwarf luteovirus (BYDV-PAV)	Barley yellow dwarf luteovirus (BYDV-PAV)	NA	N	NA	Y (aphid)	witchgrass, Italian ryegrass, annual bluegrass etc. (about 105 grass species)
Cephalosporium stripe	*Hymenula cerealis* (*Cephalosporium gramineum*)	Y (2-3)	N	N	N	perennial grasses
Common bunt, stinking smut	*Tilletia tritici*	NA	Y	NA	N	no records located
Common root rot	*Bipolaris sorokiniana* (*Cochliobolus sativus*)	Y (3-6); avoid oat	Y	Y	N	grasses
Eyespot foot rot	*Pseudocercosporella herpotrichoides*	Y (2+)	N	Y (local, rain)	N	likely grass weeds (esp. quackgrass)
Foot rot	*Fusarium* spp.	Y (2-3)	Y	Y (local, rain)	N	wide host range[3]
Fusarium scab, head blight[16]	*Fusarium* spp.	Y (2-3)	NA	Y (local, rain)	N	wide host range[3]
Leaf rust, brown rust	*Puccinia triticina*	Y	N	Y	N	no records located
Lesion nematodes	*Pratylenchus* spp.	Y (2-3)	N	NA	NA	wide host range
Loose smut	*Ustilago tritici*	NA	Y	Y (local)	N	no records located
Powdery mildew	*Blumeria gramini* (*Erysiphe graminis* f. sp. *tritici*)	Y (1-2)	N	Y	N	annual bluegrass
Septoria leaf blotch	*Septoria tritici* (*Mycosphaerella graminicola*)	Y (1-2)	N	Y (local, rain)	N	a few grasses
Stagonospora leaf and glume blotch	*Stagonospora nodorum*	Y (1-2)	Y	Y (local, rain)	N	annual bluegrass
Take-all	*Gaeumannomyces graminis* var. *tritici*	Y (2-3); avoid barley	N	NA	N	annual bluegrass, quackgrass
Tan spot	*Pyrenophora tritici-repentis*	Y (2-3)	Y	Y	N	a few grasses
Wheat spindle streak mosaic	Wheat spindle streak mosaic bymovirus (WSSM)	Y (3 or more)	N	NA	N (soilborne protozoan)	unknown; likely

Notes

Y indicates yes and N indicates no. For example, in the column labeled "Seed Borne" Y indicates that the pathogen is seed borne and N indicates it is not seed borne.

[1] Y=Yes, the disease can be managed by rotation. The number in parentheses is the minimum rotation return time needed for successful management of the disease (see sidebars 5.4 and 5.5, p. page 70–page 71). Long means more than just a few years. N=No, the disease cannot be managed through rotation because the pathogen survives too well in the soil or wind disperses the spores too widely. NA=not applicable as the pathogen does not survive in the soil.

[2] Y=Spores are dispersed by wind, commonly for several miles. Local=Spores are wind dispersed for short distances, rarely moving farther than adjacent fields. Rain=Spores are dispersed by splashing water and can be moved out of a field by wind during a rainstorm. N=Spores are not dispersed by wind. NA=Not applicable, as pathogen does not produce spores.

[3] Many common weeds host *Fusarium* species, including barnyardgrass, witchgrass, green foxtail, shattercane, annual bluegrass, wild-proso millet, corn cockle, common sunflower, perennial sowthistle, redroot pigweed, common purslane, and ivyleaf morningglory.

[4] Several common weeds host *Pythium* species, including wild-proso millet, shattercane, barnyardgrass, quackgrass (*P. ultimum*) and yellow foxtail (*P. graminicola*).

[5] Many common weeds host *Rhizoctonia solani*, including green foxtail, perennial sowthistle, tumble pigweed, redroot pigweed, prostrate pigweed, common ragweed, barnyardgrass, large crabgrass, goosegrass, kochia, common lambsquarters, eastern black nightshade, common purslane, prickly lettuce, annual bluegrass, wild mustard, shepherd's purse, Italian ryegrass, field bindweed, mouseear chickweed, field horsetail, Venice mallow, black medic, common milkweed, corn chamomile, wild buckwheat, and witchgrass.

[6] Many common weeds host *Sclerotinia sclerotiorum*, including common lambsquarters, prickly lettuce, wild mustard, eastern black nightshade, field pennycress, redroot pigweed, wild radish, common ragweed, shattercane, annual sowthistle, common sunflower, common chickweed, green foxtail, and Canada thistle. *S. minor* on lettuce is also hosted by yellow nutsedge.

[7] Bean yellow mosaic virus has both cultivated and wild host reservoirs. It can infect most species of the legume family, including herbaceous plants such as sicklepod and other *Cassia* species, chickpea, crotalaria, soybean, vetchling, sweet pea, lentil, lupine, alfalfa, medics, sweet clover, common bean, pea, clover, fenugreek, vetch, broad bean, and cowpea. It can also infect woody members of the family (pigeon pea, yellowwood, and black locust) and nonlegume species (lambsquarters, freesia, and gladiolus).

[8] Many common weeds host CMV, including common chickweed, corn cockle, hairy galinsoga, common groundsel, horsenettle, jimson-weed, common lambsquarters, prickly lettuce, wild mustard, eastern black nightshade, field pennycress, redroot pigweed, common purslane, wild radish, annual sowthistle, Canada thistle, common milkweed, common ragweed, shepherd's purse, prostrate pigweed, pitted morningglory, tall morningglory, corn speedwell, hedge bindweed, burcucumber, white campion, and marsh yellowcress.

[9] Many common weeds host the nematodes *Meloidogyne incognita* and *M. hapla*, including common lambsquarters, black medic, field pepperweed, tumble pigweed, velvetleaf, Canada thistle, shepherd's purse, field pennycress, wild buckwheat, prickly lettuce, wild mustard, yellow rocket, common groundsel, redroot pigweed, large crabgrass, purslane speedwell, hairy galinsoga, prostrate knotweed, and yellow nutsedge.

[10] Several weeds host *Cercospora beticola*, including redroot pigweed, common lambsquarters, roundleaf mallow, white sweetclover, and wild buckwheat.

[11] Several weeds host *Plasmodiophora brassicae*, including wild mustard, common lambsquarters, field pennycress, Virginia pepperweed, shepherd's purse, yellow woodsorrel, field pepperweed, and wild radish.

[12] Several species of leafhopper transmit aster yellows. It has many weed hosts, including dandelion, plantain, Russian thistle, perennial sowthistle, common purslane, shepherd's purse, Canada thistle, common ragweed, and wild lettuce. There are also ornamental hosts. More than 300 species are susceptible.

[13] Many common grasses host *Colletotrichum graminicola*, including barnyardgrass, quackgrass, witchgrass, johnsongrass, wild-proso millet, large crabgrass, goosegrass, and Italian ryegrass.

[14] Many weeds host *Verticillium albo-atrum*, including eastern black nightshade, common purslane, redroot pigweed, horsenettle, common lambsquarters, common cocklebur, common groundsel, and prickly sida. Hosts of *V. dahliae* include velvetleaf, common sunflower, and field pennycress.

[15] Many common weeds host the tomato spotted wilt virus (TSWV), including annual sowthistle, eastern black nightshade, redroot pigweed, shepherd's purse, field bindweed, prickly lettuce, prostrate pigweed, common purslane, common chickweed, jimsonweed, and wild buckwheat.

[16] The same pathogen causes fusarium scab (head blight) of wheat and gibberella stalk rot of corn.

APPENDIX 4 Characteristics of Common Agricultural Weeds Relevant to Crop Rotation
Compiled by Charles L. Mohler

Weed common name	Weed scientific name	Family	Life history	Seed weight (mg)[1,2]	Season of emergence	Seedbank longevity[3]
Barnyardgrass	*Echinochloa crus-galli* (L.) *Beauv.*	Grass	summer annual	1.7	spring to summer	3–8 yrs
Bedstraw, catchweed (cleavers)	*Galium aparine* L.	Madder	summer or winter annual	7.2	fall, spring, winter	1–5 yrs
Bedstraw, smooth	*Galium mollugo* L.	Madder	perennial	0.4–0.6, 0.7	seeds; early to late spring, fall in warm regions. Shoots: early spring	usu. 3–12 mos
Bindweed, field	*Convolvulus arvensis* L.	Morningglory	perennial spreading by deep, creeping fleshy roots	10	fall, spring	>20 yrs
Bindweed, hedge	*Calystegia sepium* (L.) R. Br.	Morningglory	perennial spreading by deep, creeping fleshy roots	40	spring, fall	>20 yrs
Bluegrass, annual	*Poa annua* L.	Grass	annual or short-lived perennial	0.26	spring, late summer to early fall	up to 4 yrs
Buckwheat, wild	*Polygonum convolvulus* L.	Buckwheat	summer annual	6	spring, some in summer and fall	up to 5 yrs
Burcucumber	*Sicyos angulatus* L.	Cucurbit	summer annual	81	mid spring to early summer	NA
Campion, white	*Silene alba* (Mill.) E.H.L. Krause	Pink	winter or summer annual, biennial or short-lived perennial	0.74	mid to late spring, late summer	5–20 yrs
Chamomile, corn	*Anthemis arvensis* L.	Lettuce	annual or biennial	0.5, 1.2	fall, spring	5–20 yrs
Chamomile, mayweed	*Anthemis cotula* L.	Lettuce	winter or summer annual	0.4	fall, spring	>20 yrs
Chickweed, common	*Stellaria media* (L.) Vill.	Pink	winter or summer annual	0.35, 0.67	fall, spring	20–60 yrs
Chickweed, mouseear	*Cerastium vulgatum* L.	Pink	perennial	0.13	late summer to fall, spring	NA
Cockle, corn	*Agrostemma githago* L.	Pink	winter annual	12, 15	fall, spring	usu. <3 mos
Cocklebur, common[4]	*Xanthium strumarium* L.	Lettuce	summer annual	small, 39; large, 54	spring to summer	up to 2.5 yrs
Copperleaf, Virginia	*Acalypha virginica* L.	Spurge	summer annual	0.73	late spring	NA
Crabgrass, large	*Digitaria sanguinalis* (L.) Scop.	Grass	summer annual	0.52	spring	several yrs
Dandelion	*Taraxacum officinale* Weber in Wiggers	Lettuce	perennial	0.6	spring	1–5 yrs
Foxtail, giant	*Setaria faberi* Herrm.	Grass	summer annual	1.3	late spring to midsummer	<5 yrs
Foxtail, green	*Setaria viridis* (L.) Beauv.	Grass	summer annual	11	throughout growing season	up to 21 yrs

Weed common name	Weed scientific name	Family	Life history	Seed weight (mg)[1,2]	Season of emergence	Seedbank longevity[3]
Foxtail, yellow	*Setaria glauca* (L.) Beauv.	Grass	summer annual	2.5, 3.4	spring, some during summer	up to 13 yrs
Galinsoga, hairy	*Galinsoga ciliata* (Raf.) Blake	Lettuce	summer annual	0.18	spring, also summer and fall	a few yrs
Galinsoga, smallflower	*Galinsoga parviflora* Cav.	Lettuce	summer annual	0.17	spring, also summer and fall	a few yrs
Goosegrass	*Eleusine indica* (L.) Gaertn.	Grass	summer annual	0.51	early to midsummer	<5 yrs
Groundcherry, smooth	*Physalis subglabrata* Mackenz. & Bush	Nightshade	perennial spreading by deep rhizomes	1.5	spring to summer	NA
Groundsel, common	*Senecio vulgaris* L.	Lettuce	summer or winter annual	0.18, 0.22	fall, spring, summer, winter	1–5 yrs
Henbit	*Lamium amplexicaule* L.	Mint	winter annual	0.53	fall, spring	>4 yrs
Horsenettle	*Solanum carolinense* L.	Nightshade	perennial spreading by deep, creeping roots	1.1–1.9	spring	up to 7 yrs
Horsetail, field	*Equisetum arvense* L.	Horsetail	perennial spreading by rhizomes	tiny spore	spring	spores short-lived
Jimsonweed	*Datura stramonium* L.	Nightshade	summer annual	5.6, 7.8	spring	>20 yrs
Johnsongrass	*Sorghum halpense* (L.) Pers.	Grass	perennial spreading by shallow rhizomes	6.2	spring	up to 7 yrs
Knotweed, prostrate	*Polygonum aviculare* L.	Buckwheat	summer annual	1.7	spring	NA
Kochia	*Kochia scoparia* (L.) Schrad.	Beet	summer annual	0.54	spring	<2 yrs
Lambsquarters, common	*Chenopodium album* L.	Beet	summer annual	0.7	spring to summer	>20 yrs
Lettuce, prickly	*Lactuca serriola* L.	Lettuce	summer or winter annual or biennial	0.45	fall, spring	1–5 yrs
Mallow, Venice	*Hibiscus trionum* L.	Mallow	summer annual	3.3	summer	NA
Medic, black	*Medicago lupulina* L.	Legume	winter or summer annual	1.2–2.5	fall, spring	1–5, 5–20 yrs
Milkweed, common	*Asclepias syriaca* L.	Milkweed	perennial spreading by deep, creeping roots	0.43–0.73	spring	up to 9 yrs
Millet, wild-proso	*Panicum miliaceum* L.	Grass	summer annual	14	spring through summer	>5 yrs
Morningglory, ivyleaf	*Ipomoea hederacea* (L.) *Jacq.*	Morningglory	summer annual	30, 32, 35	early summer	prob. many yrs
Morningglory, pitted	*Ipomoea lacunosa* L.	Morningglory	summer annual	27	early summer	>39 yrs

Weed common name	Weed scientific name	Family	Life history	Seed weight (mg)[1,2]	Season of emergence	Seedbank longevity[3]
Morningglory, tall	*Ipomoea purpurea* (L.) Roth	Morningglory	summer annual	25	early summer	prob. many yrs
Mustard, hedge	*Sisymbrium officinale* (L.) Scop.	Mustard	winter or summer annual, rarely biennial	1.5	spring to summer	>5 yrs
Mustard, wild	*Brassica kaber* (DC.) L. C. Wheeler (= *Sinapis arvensis* L.)	Mustard	summer or winter annual	1.6, 2.3	spring, late summer to early fall	up to 60 yrs
Nightshade, eastern black	*Solanum ptycanthum* Dun.	Nightshade	summer annual	0.43	spring to summer	up to 39 yrs
Nutsedge, yellow	*Cyperus esculentus* L.	Sedge	perennial with rhizomes and tubers	0.17	spring	most tubers <2 yrs
Panicum, fall	*Panicum dichotomiflorum* Michx.	Grass	summer annual	0.57	late spring to midsummer	10 yrs
Pennycress, field	*Thlaspi arvense* L.	Mustard	winter or summer annual	1.25	fall, spring	>20 yrs
Pepperweed, field	*Lepidium campestre* (L.) R. Br.	Mustard	winter annual	1.9	late summer to early fall	NA
Pepperweed, Virginia	*Lepidium virginicum* L.	Mustard	winter or summer annual, occasionally biennial	0.35	late summer to early fall, some spring	NA
Pigweed, Powell amaranth	*Amaranthus powellii* S. Wats.	Pigweed	summer annual	0.51	mid spring	NA
Pigweed, prostrate	*Amaranthus blitoides* S. Wats.	Pigweed	summer annual	0.89	late spring to early summer	NA
Pigweed, redroot	*Amaranthus retroflexus* L.	Pigweed	summer annual	0.39	mid spring	up to 20 yrs
Pigweed, smooth	*Amaranthus hybridus* L.	Pigweed	summer annual	0.37	mid to late spring	up to 40 yrs
Pigweed, tumble	*Amaranthus albus* L.	Pigweed	summer annual	0.28	late spring to early summer, some through fall	NA
Purslane, common	*Portulaca oleracea* L.	Purslane	summer annual	0.13	summer	>20 yrs
Quackgrass	*Elytrigia repens* (L.) Nevski	Grass	perennial spreading by shallow rhizomes	2.0	spring, fall	5–20 yrs
Radish, wild	*Raphanus raphanistrum* L.	Mustard	winter or summer annual	8	late summer to fall, early spring	up to 20 yrs
Ragweed, common	*Ambrosia artemisiifolia* L.	Lettuce	summer annual	3.2	early to late spring	up to 40 yrs
Ragweed, giant	*Ambrosia trifida* L.	Lettuce	summer annual	17, 31	early spring, diminishing through early summer	4–18% survive 1st yr

Weed common name	Weed scientific name	Family	Life history	Seed weight (mg)[1,2]	Season of emergence	Seedbank longevity[3]
Rocket, yellow	*Barbarea vulgaris* R. Br.	Mustard	biennial or short-lived perennial, occasionally a winter annual	0.5	fall, spring, winter	1–5 yrs
Ryegrass, Italian	*Lolium multiflorum* Lam.	Grass	winter annual	2	spring, late summer to mid fall	<4 yrs
Shattercane	*Sorghum bicolor* (L.) Moench	Grass	summer annual	14	mid spring to early summer	<13 yrs
Shepherd's purse	*Capsella bursa-pastoris* (L.) Medicus	Mustard	summer or winter annual	0.1	fall, spring, summer, winter	>20 yrs
Sida, prickly	*Sida spinosa* L.	Mallow	summer annual	2.3	spring to midsummer	up to 6 yrs
Smartweed, Pennsylvania	*Polygonum pensylvanicum* L.	Buckwheat	summer annual	4.5, 6.5	spring to early summer	up to 30 yrs
Sowthistle, annual	*Sonchus oleraceus* L.	Lettuce	winter or summer annual	0.27, 0.34	fall, spring	5–20 yrs
Sowthistle, perennial	*Sonchus arvensis* L.	Lettuce	perennial spreading by creeping roots	0.4–0.7	shoots: early spring; seedlings: late spring to early summer	<5 yrs
Speedwell, corn	*Veronica arvensis* L.	Snapdragon	annual	0.1	fall, spring	up to 20 yrs
Speedwell, Persian	*Veronica persica*	Snapdragon	winter or summer annual	0.38, 0.52	fall, spring, summer, winter	up to 30 yrs
Speedwell, purslane	*Veronica peregrina* L.	Snapdragon	annual	0.03	spring, fall	NA
Thistle, Canada	*Cirsium arvense* (L.) Scop.	Lettuce	perennial spreading by horizontal roots	1.2	spring, fall	5–20 yrs
Velvetleaf	*Abutilon theophrasti* Medicus	Mallow	summer annual	7	late spring to early summer	up to 50 yrs
Violet, field	*Viola arvensis* Murr.	Violet	annual	0.2	fall, spring	>5 yrs
Witchgrass	*Panicum capillare* L.	Grass	summer annual	0.35	late spring to midsummer	several decades
Woodsorrel, yellow	*Oxalis stricta* L.	Woodsorrel	perennial with short, shallow rhizomes	0.13	spring to summer	>5 yrs
Yellowcress, marsh	*Rorippa islandica* (Oeder) Borbas	Mustard	annual, biennial, short-lived perennial (rarely)	NA	spring	up to 10 yrs

Notes:
1. For comparison, one lettuce seed weighs about 1 milligram.
2. Multiple numbers are weights from different populations, except for common cocklebur.
3. Data are maximum survival of seeds in soil, often based on undisturbed burial experiments. Seeds usually die off at a constant rate, so that most are gone much more quickly than the numbers indicate. Also, they die off more quickly in regularly tilled soil. NA=Information not available.
4. Common cocklebur has one large and one small seed in each capsule.

Sources:
Compiled primarily from references 1, 7, 11, 12, 13, 15, 25, 32, 38, 49, 76, 77, 87, 88, 90, 91, 108, 109, 112, 116, 117, and data of the author.

APPENDIX 5 Crop Disease Pathogens Hosted by Common Agricultural Weeds
Compiled by Charles L. Mohler and Margaret Tuttle McGrath

Weed common name	Weed scientific name	Pathogens and crop diseases[1]
Barnyard grass	*Echinochloa crus-galli* (L.) Beauv.	*Pythium ultimum* (seed rot and root rot of pea, beet, and crucifer crops), *Fusarium oxysporum* (various diseases of many crops), *Colletotrichum graminicola* (anthracnose of corn), *Phoma terrestris* (onion pink rot), *Rhizoctonia solani* (various diseases of many crops) (31); alfalfa dwarf disease (*Xylella fastidiosa*); viruses including maize dwarf mosaic, barley stripe mosaic hordeivirus, oat pseudo-rostette tenuivirus, and wheat streak mosaic rymovirus (45).
Bedstraw, catchweed (cleavers)	*Galium aparine* L.	No records located for North America.
Bedstraw, smooth	*Galium mollugo* L.	No records located.
Bindweed, field	*Convolvulus arvensis* L.	*Rhizoctonia solani* (various diseases of many crops) (31); alfalfa mosaic alfamovirus, cucumber mosaic cucumovirus, potato virus Y potyvirus, tomato spotted wilt tospovirus (128).
Bindweed, hedge	*Calystegia sepium* (L.) R. Br.	
Bluegrass, annual	*Poa annua* L.	*Septoria nodorum* (stagnospora blotch of wheat), *Claviceps purpurea* (ergot), *Gaeumannomyces graminis* (take-all), *Erysiphe graminis* (powdery mildew) (77), but whether the strains that attack annual bluegrass can damage wheat is unclear; *Cephalosporium gramineum* (cephalosporium stripe) (84); *Fusarium* sp. (various diseases of many crops), *Rhizoctonia solani* (various diseases of many crops) (31); barley yellow dwarf virus (48).
Buckwheat, wild	*Polygonum convolvulus* L.	*Rhizoctonia solani* (various diseases of many crops) (31); *Meloidogyne hapla* (northern root-knot nematode) (113); tomato spotted wilt tospovirus (128).
Burcucumber	*Sicyos angulatus* L.	Cucumber mosaic virus, papaya ring spot potyvirus, watermelon mosaic potyvirus (128).
Campion, white	*Silene alba* (Mill.) E.H.L. Krause	Cucumber mosaic cucumovirus, turnip mosaic potyvirus, tobacco mosaic tobamovirus (128).
Chamomile, corn	*Anthemis arvensis* L.	*Rhizoctonia solani* (various diseases of many crops) (31).
Chamomile, mayweed	*Anthemis cotula* L.	No records located.
Chickweed, common	*Stellaria media* (L.) Vill.	*Sclerotinia sclerotiorum* (white mold and cottony rot of potato, tomato, beans, cabbage, and carrot; lettuce drop) (31); *Phoma exigua* var. *foveata* (potato rot fungus) (77); cucumber mosaic cucumovirus, turnip mosaic potyvirus, bean yellow mosaic potyvirus, potato virus Y potyvirus, tomato spotted wilt tospovirus (128). Many additional viruses affecting crops are reported on common chickweed in the United Kingdom and may be present in North America as well (100).
Chickweed, mouseear	*Cerastium vulgatum* L.	*Rhizoctonia solani* (various diseases of many crops) (31).
Cockle, corn	*Agrostemma githago* L.	*Fusarium* sp. (various diseases of many crops) (31); cucumber mosaic cucumovirus, turnip mosaic potyvirus (128).
Cocklebur, common	*Xanthium strumarium* L.	*Verticillium albo-atrum* (verticillium wilt of nightshade crops) (26).
Copperleaf, Virginia	*Acalypha virginica* L.	*Alternaria* spp. (alternaria leaf spot) (37).

Weed common name	Weed scientific name	Pathogens and crop diseases[1]
Crabgrass, large	*Digitaria sanguinalis* (L.) Scop.	*Colletotrichum graminicola* (anthracnose of corn), *Rhizoctonia solani* (various diseases of many crops) (31); barley stripe hordeivirus (45); southern root-knot nematode (*Meloidogyne incognita*) (29).
Dandelion	*Taraxacum officinale* Weber in Wiggers	*Sclerotinia sclerotiorum* (white mold of potato, tomato, beans, cabbage, and carrot, lettuce drop), *Rhizoctonia solani* (various diseases of many crops) (31); *Verticillium albo-atrum* (verticillium wilt) (26); aster yellows phytoplasma, (46); alfalfa mosaic alfamovirus, cucumber mosaic cucumovirus, turnip mosaic potyvirus, potato virus Y potyvirus (128); dandelion yellow mosaic virus of lettuce (36).
Foxtail, giant	*Setaria faberi* Herrm.	No records located.
Foxtail, green	*Setaria viridis* (L.) Beauv.	*Sclerotinia sclerotiorum* (white mold and cottony rot of potato, tomato, beans, cabbage, and carrot; lettuce drop), *Exserohilum turcicum* (northern corn leaf blight), *Fusarium oxysporum* (various diseases of several crops), *Fusarium solani* (fusarium dry rot of potato, fusarium crown and root rot of cucurbits), *Stemphylium botryosum* (onion stalk rot), *Phoma terrestris* (onion pink rot), *Rhizoctonia solani* (various diseases of many crops) (31).
Foxtail, yellow	*Setaria glauca* (L.) Beauv.	*Claviceps purpurea* (ergot), *Pythium graminicola* (browning root rot), *Sclerospora graminicola* (downy mildew), *Ustilago neglecta* (smut) (17).
Galinsoga, hairy	*Galinsoga ciliata* (Raf.) Blake	Alfalfa mosaic alfamovirus, cucumber mosaic cucumovirus, turnip mosaic potyvirus (128); several nematodes including *Meloidogyne hapla* (northern root-knot nematode) and *Heterodera schachtii* (beet cyst nematode) (77).
Goosegrass	*Eleusine indica* (L.) Gaertn.	*Colletotrichum graminicola* (anthracnose of corn), *Rhizoctonia solani* (various diseases of many crops) (31); corn dwarf mosaic (45).
Groundcherry, smooth	*Physalis subglabrata* Mackenz. & Bush	Alfalfa mosaic alfamovirus, potato virus Y potyvirus, tobacco etch potyvirus (128).
Groundsel, common	*Senecio vulgaris* L.	*Verticillium albo-atrum* (verticillium wilt) (26, 31); alfalfa mosaic alfamovirus, cucumber mosaic cucumovirus, lettuce mosaic virus (128); *Meloidogyne hapla* (northern root-knot nematode) (113).
Horsenettle	*Solanum carolinense* L.	*Phoma terrestris* (onion pink rot), *Septoria lycopersici* (septoria leaf spot of tomato) (31); *Verticillium albo-atrum* (verticillium wilt) (26, 31); *Phytophthora capsici* (phytophthora blight) (35); cucumber mosaic cucumovirus, tobacco etch potyvirus (128).
Horsetail, field	*Equisetum arvense* L.	*Rhizoctonia solani* (various diseases of many crops) (31).
Jimsonweed	*Datura stramonium* L.	*Alternaria solani* (early blight), *Septoria lycopersici* (septoria leaf spot of tomato) (31); alfalfa mosaic alfamovirus, cucumber mosaic cucumovirus, potato virus X potyvirus, tobacco etch potyvirus, tobacco mosaic tobamovirus, tomato spotted wilt tospovirus, turnip mosaic potyvirus, watermelon mosaic potyvirus (128).
Johnsongrass	*Sorghum halpense* (L.) Pers.	*Exserohilum turcicum* (northern corn leaf blight), *Colletotrichum graminicola* (corn anthracnose) (31); beet yellows closterovirus, wheat streak mosaic rymovirus (45); maize dwarf mosaic, maize chlorotic dwarf mosaic virus (77).
Knotweed, prostrate	*Polygonum aviculare* L.	*Meloidogyne hapla* (northern root-knot nematode) (113).
Kochia	*Kochia scoparia* (L.) Schrad.	*Cercospora beticola* (cercospora leaf spot of beet), *Rhizoctonia solani* (various diseases of many crops) (31).

Weed common name	Weed scientific name	Pathogens and crop diseases[1]
Lambsquarters, common	*Chenopodium album* L.	*Peronospora effusa* (downy mildew of spinach), *Sclerotinia sclerotiorum* (white mold and cottony rot of potato, tomato, beans, cabbage, and carrot; lettuce drop), *Cercospora beticola* (cercospora leaf spot of beet), *Rhizoctonia solani* (various diseases of many crops) (31); clubroot (*Plasmodiophora brassicae*) (36); *Verticillium albo-atrum* (verticillium wilt) (26); alfalfa mosaic alfamovirus, cucumber mosaic cucumovirus, bean yellow mosaic potyvirus, clover yellow vein potyvirus, potato virus Y potyvirus, soybean mosaic potyvirus, tobacco etch potyvirus, turnip mosaic potyvirus, watermelon mosaic potyvirus, lettuce mosaic virus (128); barley stripe mosaic hordeivirus, beet yellows virus, beet curly top virus (45); beet nematode (*Heterodera schachtii*) (20); *Meloidogyne hapla* (northern root-knot nematode) (113); *Meloidogyne incognita* (southern root-knot nematode) (29).
Lettuce, prickly	*Lactuca serriola* L.	*Microdochium panattonianum* (lettuce anthracnose), *Verticillium dahliae* (verticillium wilt) (13); *Cercospora longissima* (cercospora leaf spot), *Erysiphe cichoracearum* (powdery mildew), and *Septoria lactucae* (septoria leaf spot of lettuce), *Bremia lactucae* (downy mildew of lettuce), *Sclerotinia sclerotiorum* (white mold and cottony rot of potato, tomato, beans, cabbage, and carrot; lettuce drop), *Rhizoctonia solani* (various diseases of many crops), *Sclerotium rolfsii* (southern blight) (31); cucumber mosaic cucumovirus, tomato spotted wilt tospovirus (31); *Meloidogyne hapla* (northern root-knot nematode) (113).
Mallow, Venice	*Hibiscus trionum* L.	*Rhizoctonia solani* (various diseases of many crops) (31).
Medic, black	*Medicago lupulina* L.	*Rhizoctonia solani* (various diseases of many crops) (31); alfalfa mosaic alfamovirus, bean yellow mosaic potyvirus, clover yellow vein potyvirus (128); *Meloidogyne hapla* (northern root-knot nematode) (113).
Milkweed, common	*Asclepias syriaca* L.	*Rhizoctonia solani* (various diseases of many crops) (31); alfalfa mosaic alfamovirus, cucumber mosaic cucumovirus (128).
Millet, wild-proso	*Panicum miliaceum* L.	*Pythium ultimum* (seed decay and root rot of many crops), *Exserohilum turcicum* (northern corn leaf blight), *Fusarium oxysporum* (various diseases of many crops), *Colletotrichum graminicola* (corn anthracnose) (31).
Morningglory, ivyleaf	*Ipomoea hederacea* (L.) Jacq.	*Fusarium* sp. (various diseases of many crops) (31).
Morningglory, pitted	*Ipomoea lacunosa* L.	Cucumber mosaic cucumovirus (128).
Morningglory, tall	*Ipomoea purpurea* (L.) Roth	Cucumber mosaic cucumovirus (128).
Mustard, hedge	*Sisymbrium officinale* (L.) Scop.	*Peronospora parasitica* (downy mildew of crucifer crops) (31).
Mustard, wild	*Brassica kaber* (DC.) L. C. Wheeler (= *Sinapis arvensis* L.)	*Peronospora parasitica* (downy mildew of crucifer crops), *Sclerotinia sclerotiorum* (white mold and cottony rot of potato, tomato, beans, cabbage, and carrot; lettuce drop), *Rhizoctonia solani* (various diseases of many crops) (31); *Cystopus candidus* = *Albugo candida* (white blister) (36); *Plasmodiophora brassicae* (clubroot), *Bacterium campestre* (77); cucumber mosaic cucumovirus, turnip mosaic potyvirus (128); *Meloidogyne hapla* (northern root-knot nematode) (113).
Nightshade, eastern black	*Solanum ptycanthum* Dun.	*Phytophthora infestans* (late blight), *Sclerotinia sclerotiorum* (white mold and cottony rot of potato, tomato, beans, cabbage, and carrot; lettuce drop), *Alternaria solani* (early blight), *Verticillium albo-atrum* (verticillium wilt of solanaceous crops), *Colletotrichum coccodes* (anthracnose of tomato and eggplant, potato black dot), *Rhizoctonia solani* (various diseases of many crops) (31); *Phytophthora capsici* (phytophthora blight) (35); alfalfa mosaic alfamovirus, cucumber mosaic cucumovirus, potato virus Y potyvirus, tobacco etch potyvirus, tomato spotted wilt tospovirus, turnip mosaic potyvirus, watermelon mosaic potyvirus (128).

Weed common name	Weed scientific name	Pathogens and crop diseases[1]
Nutsedge, yellow	*Cyperus esculentus* L.	*Sclerotinia minor* on lettuce and peanut (44a and appendix 3); alfalfa mosaic virus (45); *Meloidogyne incognita* (southern root-knot nematode) (29).
Panicum, fall	*Panicum dichotomiflorum* Michx.	No records located.
Pennycress, field	*Thlaspi arvense* L.	*Verticillium dahliae* (verticillium wilt), *Peronospora parasitica* (downy mildew), *Alternaria brassicicola* (alternaria leaf spot) (13); *Sclerotinia sclerotiorum* (white mold and cottony rot of potato, tomato, beans, cabbage, and carrot; lettuce drop) (31); *Plasmodiophora brassicae* (clubroot) (36, 31); cucumber mosaic cucumovirus, turnip mosaic potyvirus (128); *Meloidogyne hapla* (northern root-knot nematode) (113); *M. incognita* (southern root-knot nematode), *Pratylenchus penetrans* (meadow nematode), *Heterodera schachtii* (sugar beet cyst nematode), *H. glycines* (soybean cyst nematode) (11).
Pepperweed, field	*Lepidium campestre* (L.) R. Br.	*Plasmodiophora brassicae* (clubroot) (36); *Phoma terrestris* (onion pink rot), *Alternaria brassicae* (alternaria leaf spot of mustard family crops) (31); *Meloidogyne hapla* (northern root-knot nematode) (113).
Pepperweed, Virginia	*Lepidium virginicum* L.	*Plasmodiophora brassicae* (clubroot), *Alternaria brassicae* (alternaria leaf spot of mustard family crops) (31).
Pigweed, Powell amaranth	*Amaranthus powellii* S. Wats.	*Albugo bliti* (white rust), *Alternaria* spp. (various leaf spots and blights), *Fusarium* spp. (various wilts and rots) (11).
Pigweed, prostrate	*Amaranthus blitoides* S. Wats.	*Rhizoctonia solani* (various diseases of many crops) (31); alfalfa mosaic alfamovirus, potato virus Y potyvirus, cucumber mosaic cucumovirus, tomato spotted wilt tospovirus (128).
Pigweed, redroot	*Amaranthus retroflexus* L.	*Albugo bliti* (white rust), *Alternaria solani* (early blight), *Choanephora cucurbitarum* (choanephora blossom blight and fruit rot of cucurbits), *Sclerotinia sclerotiorum* (white mold and cottony rot of potato, tomato, beans, cabbage, and carrot; lettuce drop), *Sclerotium rolfsii* (southern blight), *Verticillium albo-atrum* (verticillium wilt of nightshades), *Verticillium dahliae* (verticillium wilt of cucurbits, nightshades), *Rhizoctonia solani* (various diseases of many crops, *Fusarium oxysporum* f. sp. *betae* (fusarium wilt of beet) (11); alfalfa mosaic alfamovirus, cucumber mosaic cucumovirus, tomato spotted wilt tospovirus, turnip mosaic potyvirus (128); *Meloidogyne incognita* (southern root-knot nematode) (29); *Heterodera schachtii* (sugar beet cyst nematode), *Pratylenchus penetrans* (lesion nematode) (11).
Pigweed, smooth	*Amaranthus hybridus* L.	*Albugo bliti* (white rust), *Rhizoctonia solani* (various diseases of many crops), *Fusarium oxysporum* f. sp. *radicis-lycopersici* (tomato fusarium wilt) (11); alfalfa mosaic alfamovirus, potato virus Y potyvirus (128); tobacco mosaic virus (45); *Meloidogyne incognita* (southern root-knot nematode) (11).
Pigweed, tumble	*Amaranthus albus* L.	*Rhizoctonia solani* (various diseases of many crops) (11); overwintering host for alfalfa mosaic virus (51); *Meloidogyne incognita* (southern root-knot nematode), *Heterodera schachtii* (sugar beet cyst nematode) (11).
Purslane, common	*Portulaca oleracea* L.	*Fusarium* sp. (various diseases of many crops), *Verticillium albo-atrum* (verticillium wilt of solanaceous crops), *Rhizoctonia solani* (various diseases of many crops) (31); *Phytophthora capsici* (phytophthora blight) (35); aster yellows phytoplasma, clover big vein virus (45); alfalfa mosaic alfamovirus, cucumber mosaic cucumovirus, potato virus Y potyvirus, turnip mosaic potyvirus, tomato spotted wilt tospovirus (128).
Quackgrass	*Elytrigia repens* (L.) Nevski	*Pythium ultimum* (seed rot and root rot of pea, beet, and crucifer crops), *Colletotrichum graminicola* (anthracnose of corn), *Rhizoctonia solani* (various diseases of many crops) (31); *Gaeumannomyces graminis* (take-all) (52).

Weed common name	Weed scientific name	Pathogens and crop diseases[1]
Radish, wild	*Raphanus raphanistrum* L.	*Sclerotinia sclerotiorum* (white mold and cottony rot of potato, tomato, beans, cabbage, and carrot; lettuce drop), *Phoma lingam* (black leg and seed decay of crops in the mustard family) (31); *Plasmodiophora brassicae* (clubroot) (36); cucumber mosaic cucumovirus, turnip mosaic potyvirus (128).
Ragweed, common	*Ambrosia artemisiifolia* L.	*Sclerotinia sclerotiorum* (white mold and cottony rot of potato, tomato, beans, cabbage, and carrot; lettuce drop), *Rhizoctonia solani* (various diseases of many crops) (31); rusts of wheat, rye, and barley, aster yellows phytoplasma (77).
Rocket, yellow	*Barbarea vulgaris* R. Br.	*Peronospora parasitica* (downy mildew of crucifer crops) (31); *Meloidogyne hapla* (northern root-knot nematode) (113).
Ryegrass, Italian	*Lolium multiflorum* Lam.	*Colletotrichum graminicola* (corn anthracnose), *Rhizoctonia solani* (various diseases of many crops) (31); *Claviceps purpurea* (ergot), barley yellow dwarf virus, oat sterile dwarf virus (6).
Shattercane	*Sorghum bicolor* (L.) Moench	*Pythium ultimum* (seed decay and root rot of several crops), *Sclerotinia sclerotiorum* (white mold and cottony rot of potato, tomato, beans, cabbage, and carrot; lettuce drop), *Fusarium oxysporum* (various diseases of several crops), *Phoma terrestris* (onion pink rot), *Rhizoctonia solani* (various diseases of many crops) (31); *Peronosclerospora sorghi* (sorghum downy mildew of corn) (123).
Shepherd's purse	*Capsella bursa-pastoris* (L.) Medicus	*Plasmodiophora brassicae* (clubroot) and *Cystopus candidus* = *Albugo candida* (white blister), which attack most crops in the mustard family, *Rhizoctonia solani* (black scurf and stem canker of potato) (36); *Xanthomonas campestris* pv. *campestris* (bacterial wilt), *Peronospora parasitica* (black rot and downy mildew of crops in the mustard family) (31); aster yellows phytoplasma (45); viruses including alfalfa mosaic alfamovirus, cucumber mosaic cucumovirus, turnip mosaic potyvirus, tomato spotted wilt tospovirus, watermelon mosaic potyvirus (128); aster yellows phytoplasma, beet curly top hybrigeminivirus, beet mosaic potyvirus, beet yellows closterovirus, cauliflower mosaic virus (45); *Meloidogyne hapla* (northern root-knot nematode) (113).
Sida, prickly	*Sida spinosa* L.	*Verticillium albo-atrum* (verticillium wilt) (26).
Smartweed, Pennsylvania	*Polygonum pensylvanicum* L.	No records located.
Sowthistle, annual	*Sonchus oleraceus* L.	*Bremia lactucae* (lettuce downy mildew), *Sclerotinia sclerotiorum* (white mold and cottony rot of potato, tomato, beans, cabbage, and carrot; lettuce drop) (31); aster yellows phytoplasma, beet curly top hybrigeminivirus (45); alfalfa mosaic alfamovirus, cucumber mosaic cucumovirus, tomato spotted wilt tospovirus, lettuce mosaic virus (128).
Sowthistle, perennial	*Sonchus arvensis* L.	*Bremia lactucae* (downy mildew of lettuce). Diseased roots can act as a source of *Fusarium oxysporum* (various diseases of many crops), *Rhizoctonia solani* (various diseases of many crops), and *Sclerotinia sclerotiorum* (white mold and cottony rot of potato, tomato, beans, cabbage, and carrot; lettuce drop); aster yellows phytoplasma (12).
Speedwell, corn	*Veronica arvensis* L.	Cucumber mosaic cucumovirus (128).
Speedwell, Persian	*Veronica persica*	Arabis mosaic and strawberry latent ring spot viruses carried by the nematode *Xiphinema diversicaudatum* (111).
Speedwell, purslane	*Veronica peregrina* L.	*Meloidogyne hapla* (northern root-knot nematode) (113).
Sunflower, common	*Helianthus annuus*	*Erysiphe cichoracearum* (powdery mildew), *Sclerotinia sclerotiorum* (white mold and cottony rot of potato, tomato, beans, cabbage, and carrot; lettuce drop), *Botrytis cineria* (gray mold blight), *Cladosporium cucumerinum* (scab of cucurbits), *Fusarium oxysporum* (various diseases of many crops), *Verticillium dahliae* (verticillium wilt), *Rhizoctonia solani* (various diseases of many crops) (31).

Weed common name	Weed scientific name	Pathogens and crop diseases[1]
Thistle, Canada	*Cirsium arvense* (L.) Scop.	*Sclerotinia sclerotiorum* (white mold and cottony rot of potato, tomato, beans, cabbage, and carrot; lettuce drop) (31); rusts of rye and barley (77); cucumber mosaic cucumovirus, bean yellow mosaic potyvirus, turnip mosaic potyvirus (128); aster yellows phytoplasma (76); *Meloidogyne hapla* (northern root-knot nematode) (113).
Velvetleaf	*Abutilon theophrasti* Medicus	*Phomopsis sojae* (pod and stem blight of soybean), *Colletotrichum dematium* and *C. gloeosporioides* (soybean anthracnose), *Verticilium dahliae* (verticillium wilt) (12); *Colletotrichum coccodes* (tomato anthracnose and potato black dot), *C. gloeosporioides* (pepper anthracnose) (31); *Phytophthora capsici* (phytophthora blight) (29); *Meloidogyne hapla* (northern root-knot nematode) (12); turnip mosaic potyvirus (128).
Violet, field	*Viola arvensis* Murr.	No records located.
Witchgrass	*Panicum capillare* L.	*Fusarium oxysporum* (various vegetable diseases), *Colletotrichum graminicola* (corn anthracnose), *Phoma terrestris* (onion pink rot), *Rhizoctonia solani* (various diseases of many crops) (31); wheat streak mosaic rymovirus, barley yellow dwarf luteovirus, barley stripe mosaic hordeivirus, maize chlorotic mottle machlomovirus, maize dwarf mosaic potyvirus, sugarcane mosaic potyvirus, wheat American striate mosaic nucleorhabdovirus; also susceptible to bromegrass mosaic virus but whether it hosts this virus in the field is unknown (13).
Woodsorrel, yellow	*Oxalis stricta* L.	Sexual stages of *Puccinia sorghi* and *P. polysora* (corn rusts) and *P. purpurea* (sorghum rust) (11).
Yellowcress, marsh	*Rorippa islandica* (Oeder) Borbas	*Plasmodiophora brassicae* (clubroot), *Peronospora parasitica* (downy mildew of crucifer crops) (31); cucumber mosaic cucumovirus (128).

[1] Both common and scientific names are given where possible. Note that diseases with the same common name are sometimes caused by different organisms in different crops (for example, downy mildew), and the weed may only host one of the pathogens with that common name.

APPENDIX 6 Linking a Field Map and Spreadsheet in Microsoft Excel
Jody Bolluyt, Peter Lowy, and Charles L. Mohler

Creating management maps of your fields using Excel is easy and allows you to link a spreadsheet similar to tables 5.2 and 5.3 (pages 62–67) to the maps. Once you have a map and spreadsheet set up in a workbook, entering crop names on the spreadsheet causes them to appear on the map at the same time. The map and spreadsheet can also be set up to place additional information, like target planting dates, on the map. Updating the map as the season progresses is as simple as entering the changes in the spreadsheet. Moreover, for subsequent years, you can duplicate the workbook, rename it with the appropriate year, and enter the crops for that year into the spreadsheet. The map has to be created only once.

A sample map and spreadsheet called **Example_field_map_07** can be downloaded from HTTP://WWW.NEON. CORNELL.EDU/CROPROTATION/INDEX.HTML. An example of a field map in use on a real farm can be viewed at HTTP:// WWW.ROXBURYFARM.COM and click on "Roxbury Farm Manuals." In the section "Mapping of Crop Rotations" click on either *sample database* to see the table or *sample map* to see the map. The web site does not support the dynamic linkage between the table and map that you can achieve on your own computer, so click "No" when asked if you want to update linked information.

To Create the DATA Sheet:
1. Open a new Excel workbook and save it with an appropriate name.
2. To name the first sheet of the workbook, double click on the **Sheet1** tab at the bottom of the page and name it Field_nameDATA (for example, NorthDATA).
3. At the top of the table enter your column headings. In the example, they are Section, MU, Crops, Date, and Date2.
4. Enter the data for each management unit, or copy and paste columns from the FieldWork1 spreadsheet if you are following the detailed planning procedure.
5. Columns containing dates need to be formatted: Select those columns, go to **Format** menu, choose **Cells**, click on the **Number** tab, choose **Date**, and select the date format you prefer.
6. If you break up crop fields into sections that are physically separated by driveways, as shown in the example, leaving blank lines between sections on the DATA sheet will make using the workbook easier.

To Create the MAP Sheet:
1. Click on the **Sheet2** tab at the bottom of the page to go to that sheet. Then double click that tab to select it, and enter the name Field_nameMAP (for example, NorthMAP).
2. Select cell C3 and in the formula bar (a toolbar available under **View** that appears above the workbook) enter =Field_nameDATA!A2 and click on the checkmark in the toolbar. The value that appears in cell A2 of the DATA sheet should appear. Leaving rows 1 and 2 and columns A and B free gives you room to draw in landmarks later.
3. Including cell C3, choose as many cells to the right as you have data that you want to include on the map. In the example, we selected Cells C3–G3. Then hit Ctrl-R to fill those cells.
4. Select enough cells down to cover the number of rows in your DATA sheet, and hit Crtl-D to fill them. Delete any zeros that appear where data are absent on the DATA sheet.
5. Outline the sections and management units using the **Outline box ▾** ⊞ on the formatting toolbar, or choose **Cells** from the **Format** menu and select **Borders**. First outline a section (a group of management units) with a thick line, then select the rows within that outline and underline them with a thin line.
6. Adjust the column widths (**Columns** on the **Format** menu) until all of the information is visible and pleasantly spaced. Widen or narrow the column containing the crop species information to make the management units appear more or less the shape they are in the field. If necessary, adjust the row height (**Rows** on the **Format** menu) to help get the shape right. You will want the map to print nicely on one or possibly two pages, and this may also require adjusting column widths and row heights. If necessary, change the font size in some columns to make the information fit. Use **Print Preview** on the **File** menu to see how the map will appear on the printed page.

7. *PC users:* Go to **Tools** on the menu bar and select **Options**. Then click on the **Gridlines** box to make the checkmark disappear. This will eliminate the pale gridlines, so that the page looks more maplike.

   Mac users: Go to **Excel** on the menu bar and select **Preferences**. Verify that **View** is highlighted among the options on the left. If not, click **View**. Then, click on the box next to **Gridlines** to make the checkmark disappear. Click OK.

8. Finally, use the **Borders** and **Patterns** tabs within **Cells** on the **Format** menu to add landmarks like roadways, hedgerows, etc.

Note that maps of many fields can be coordinated with a single DATA sheet that contains information on all management units on the farm. To make additional maps, click on the **Sheet3** tab at the bottom of the page. Then choose **Worksheet** on the **Insert** menu repeatedly to create as many additional sheets as you have fields to map. For each field, follow the instructions above for making a map.

REFERENCES

Note: In the text, reference numbers are given in parentheses.

1. Abbas, H. K., D. J. Pantone, and R. N. Paul. 1999. Characteristics of multiple-seeded cocklebur: A biotype of common cocklebur (*Xanthium strumarium* L.). *Weed Technology* 13:257–63.

2. Andow, D. 1991. Vegetational diversity and arthropod population response. *Annual Review of Entomology* 36:561–86.

3. APS Press. Diagnostic compendia for alfalfa, barley, corn, soybean, and wheat. HTTP://WWW.SHOPAPSPRESS. ORG/DISEASE-DIAGNOSTIC-SERIES.HTML.

4. APS Press. Diagnostic compendia for bean, beet, carrot, cucurbit, lettuce, onion, pea, pepper, potato, sweet potato, and tomato. HTTP://WWW.SHOPAPSPRESS. ORG/DISEASE-DIAGNOSTIC-SERIES.HTML.

5. Baskin, C. C., and J. M. Baskin. 1998. *Seeds: Ecology, Biogeography, and Evolution of Dormancy and Germination.* San Diego: Academic Press.

6. Beddows, A. R. 1973. Biological flora of the British Isles. *Lolium multiflorum* Lam. (*L. perenne* L., ssp. *multiflorum* (Lam) Husnot, *L. italicum* A. Braun). *Journal of Ecology* 61:587–600.

7. Bell, R. S., W. H. Lachman, E. M. Rahn, and R. D. Sweet. 1962. *Life History Studies as Related to Weed Control in the Northeast. 1. Nutgrass.* Bulletin 364. Kingston: University of Rhode Island, Agricultural Experiment Station.

8. Boucher, T. J., and R. Durgy. 2003. Perimeter trap cropping works! University of Connecticut, Integrated Pest Management, HTTP://WWW.HORT. UCONN.EDU/IPM/VEG/HTMS/PTCWORKS.HTM.

9. Brainard, D. C., and R. R. Bellinder. 2004. Weed suppression in a broccoli–winter rye intercropping system. *Weed Science* 52:281–90.

10. Bruehl, G. W. 1987. *Soilborne Plant Pathogens.* New York: Macmillan.

11. Cavers, P. B., ed. 1995. *The Biology of Canadian Weeds, Contributions 62–83.* Ottawa: Agricultural Institute of Canada.

12. Cavers, P. B., ed. 2000. *The Biology of Canadian Weeds, Contributions 84–102.* Ottawa: Agricultural Institute of Canada.

13. Cavers, P. B., ed. 2005. *The Biology of Canadian Weeds, Contributions 103–129.* Ottawa: Agricultural Institute of Canada.

14. Cavigelli, M. A., S. R. Deming, L. K. Probyn, and R. R. Harwood. 1998. *Michigan Field Crop Ecology: Managing Biological Processes for Productivity and Environmental Quality.* Extension Bulletin E-2646. East Lansing: Michigan State University.

15. Chancellor, R. J. 1986. Decline of arable weed seeds during 20 years in soil under grass and the periodicity of seedling emergence after cultivation. *Journal of Applied Ecology* 23:631–37.

16. Clements, D. R., A. DiTommaso, S. J. Darbyshire, P. B. Cavers, and A. D. Sartonov. 2004. The biology of Canadian weeds. 127. *Panicum capillare* L. *Canadian Journal of Plant Science* 84:327–41.

17. Conners, I. L. 1967. *An Annotated Index of Plant Diseases in Canada and Fungi Recorded on Plants in Alaska, Canada and Greenland, Publication* 1251. Ottawa: Canada Department of Agriculture.

18. Cornell University. Vegetable MD Online, HTTP://VEGETABLEMDONLINE.PPATH.CORNELL.EDU/ NEWSARTICLES/MCNABROTATIONS.HTM.

19. Cunningham, S. J. 1998. *Great Garden Companions.* Emmaus, PA: Rodale Press.

20. Curl, E. A. 1963. Control of plant diseases by crop rotation. *Botanical Review* 29:413–79.

21. Davis, R. M., and J. J. Nunez. 1999. Influence of crop rotation on the incidence of *Pythium*- and *Rhizoctonia*-induced carrot root dieback. *Plant Disease* 83:146–48.

22. Davis, R. M., K. V. Subbarao, R. N. Raid, and E. A. Kurtz, eds. 1997. *Compendium of Lettuce Diseases.* St. Paul, MN: APS Press.

23. Dillard, H. R., and A. C. Cobb. 1998. Survival of *Colletotrichum coccodes* in infected tomato tissue and in soil. *Plant Disease* 82:235–38.

24. Doran, J. W., and M. S. Smith. 1991. Role of cover crops in nutrient cycling. In *Cover Crops for Clean*

Water, W. L. Hargrove, ed., pp. 85–90. Ankeny, IA: Soil and Water Conservation Society.

25. Ecological Flora of the British Isles at the University of York. http://www.ecoflora.co.uk

26. Engelhard, A. W. 1957. Host index of *Verticillium albo-atrum* Einke & Berth. (including *Verticillium dahliae* Kleb.). *Plant Disease Reporter*, Supplement 244.

27. Entz, M. H., W. J. Bullied, and F. Katepa-Mupondwa. 1995. Rotational benefits of forage crops in Canadian prairie cropping systems. *Journal of Production Agriculture* 8:521–29.

28. Epps, J. M., and A. Y. Chambers. 1958. New host records for *Heterodera glycines*: including one host in the Labiatae. *Plant Disease Reporter* 42:194.

29. Everts, K., University of Maryland. Personal communication.

30. Everts, K. 2003. Development and evaluation of management alternatives for root knot nematodes and volunteer potatoes. SARE final project report LNE00-131. http://www.sare.org/reporting/report_viewer.asp.

31. Farr, D. F., G. F. Bills, G. P. Chamuris, and A. Y. Rossman. 1989. *Fungi on Plants and Plant Products in the United States*. St. Paul, MN: APS Press.

32. Fenner, M. 1983. Relationships between seed weight, ash content and seedling growth in twenty-four species of Compositae. *New Phytologist* 95:697–706.

33. Ferro, D. N. 1996. Cultural control. Radcliffe's IPM World Textbook, University of Minnesota, http://ipmworld.umn.edu/chapters/ferro.htm.

34. Foster, R., and B. Flood, eds. 1995. *Vegetable Insect Management: With Emphasis on the Midwest*. Willoughby, OH: Meister Publishing.

35. French-Monar, R. D. 2006. Characterization of *Phytophthora capsici* associated with roots of weeds on Florida vegetable farms. *Plant Disease* 90:345–50.

36. Gram, E., and A. Weber. 1953. *Plant Diseases in Orchard, Nursery and Garden Crops*. New York: Philosophical Library.

37. Greene, H. C. 1945. Notes on Wisconsin parasitic fungi VII. *American Midland Naturalist* 34:258–70.

38. Grime, J. P., J. G. Hodgson, and R. Hunt. 1988. *Comparative Plant Ecology: A Functional Approach to Common British Species*. London: Unwin Hyman.

39. Grubinger, V. P. 1999. *Sustainable Vegetable Production from Start-up to Market*. Ithaca, NY: Cornell University, Natural Resource, Agriculture and Engineering Service (NRAES).

40. Håkansson, S. 1982. Multiplication, growth and persistence of perennial weeds. In *Biology and Ecology of Weeds*, W. Holzner and N. Numata, eds., pp. 123–35. The Hague: Dr. W. Junk.

41. Hall, R., ed. 1991. *Compendium of Bean Diseases*. St. Paul, MN: APS Press.

42. Hanson, A. A. 1990. *Practical Handbook of Agricultural Science*. Boca Raton, FL: CRC Press.

43. Hao, J. J., K. V. Subbarao, and S. T. Koike. 2003. Effects of broccoli rotation on lettuce drop caused by *Sclerotinia minor* and on the population density of sclerotia in soil. *Plant Disease* 87:159–66.

44. Høgh-Jensen, H., and J. K. Schjoerring. 1997. Interactions between white clover and ryegrass under contrasting nitrogen availability: N_2 fixation, N fertilizer recovery, N transfer and water use efficiency. *Plant and Soil* 197:187–99.

44a. Hollowell, J.E. and B.B. Shaw. 2001. Yellow nutsedge (*cyperus esculentus* L.) as a host for *Sclerotinia minor*. *Plant Disease* 85:562.

45. Holm, L. G., D. L. Plucknett, J. V. Pancho, and J. P. Herberger. 1977. *World's Worst Weeds: Distribution and Biology*. Honolulu, HI: University Press of Hawaii, East-West Center.

46. Holm, L., J. Doll, E. Holm, J. Pancho, and J. Herberger. 1997. *World Weeds: Natural Histories and Distribution*. New York: John Wiley.

47. Hunt, D.W. A., and R. S. Vernon. 2001. Portable trench barrier for protecting edges of tomato fields from Colorado potato beetle (Coleoptera: Chrysomelidae). *Journal of Economic Entomology* 94:204–7.

48. Hutchinson, C. S., and G. B. Seymour. 1982. Biological flora of the British Isles. Poa annua L. *Journal of Ecology* 70:887–901.

49. Ilnicki, R. D., and S. N. Fertig. 1962. *Life History Studies as Related to Weed Control in the Northeast. 3. Horse Nettle*. Bulletin 368. Kingston: University of Rhode Island, Agricultural Experiment Station.

50. Ingerson-Mahar, J., M. Huffaker, and S. Eck-Jones. 1997. Managing wireworms in New Jersey's field crops. Rutgers Cooperative Extension Fact Sheet, FS880. http://njaes.rutgers.edu/pubs/publication.asp?pid=FS880.

51. Kaiser, W. J., and R. M. Hannan. 1983. Additional hosts of alfalfa mosaic virus and its seed transmission in tumble pigweed and bean. *Plant Disease* 67:1354–57.

52. Kirby, R. S. 1922. The take-all disease of cereals and grasses. *Phytopathology* 12:67–88.

53. Koike, S. T., R. F. Smith, L. E. Jackson, L. J. Wyland, J. I. Inman, and W. E. Chaney. 1996. Phacelia, Lana

woollypod vetch, and Austrian winter pea: Three new cover crop hosts of *Sclerotinia minor* in California. *Plant Disease* 80:1409–12.

54. Kraft, J. M., and F. L. Pfleger, eds. 2000. *Compendium of Pea Diseases and Pests*, 2nd ed. St. Paul, MN: APS Press.

55. Landis, D. A., S. D. Wratten, and G. M. Gurr. 2000. Habitat management to conserve natural enemies of arthropod pests in agriculture. *Annual Review of Entomology* 45:175–201.

56. Ledingham, R. J. 1961. Crop rotations and common rootrot in wheat. *Canadian Journal of Botany* 41:479–86.

57. Levine, E., and H. Oloumi-Sadeghi. 1991. Management of diabroticite rootworms in corn. *Annual Review of Entomology* 36:229–55.

58. Liebhardt, W. C., R. W. Andrews, M. N. Culik, R. R. Harwood, R. R. Janke, J. K. Radke, and S. J. Rieger-Schwartz. Crop production during conversion from conventional to low-input methods. *Agronomy Journal* 81:150–59.

59. Liebman, M., Iowa State University. Personal communication.

60. Liebman, M., and E. Dyck. 1993. Crop rotation and intercropping strategies for weed management. *Ecological Applications* 3:92–122.

61. Liebman, M., and E. R. Gallandt. 1997. Many little hammers: Ecological management of crop-weed interactions. In *Agricultural Ecology*, L. E. Jackson, ed., pp. 291–343. San Diego, CA: Academic Press.

62. Liebman, M., and C. P. Staver. 2001. Crop diversification for weed management. In *Ecological Management of Agricultural Weeds*, M. Liebman, C. L. Mohler, and C. P. Staver, eds., pp. 322–74. New York: Cambridge University Press.

63. Lovett Doust, L., A. MacKinnon, and J. Lovett Doust. 1985. Biology of Canadian weeds. 71. *Oxalis stricta* L., *O. corniculata* L., *O. dillenii Jacq.* ssp. *dillenii* and *O. dillenii Jacq.* ssp. *filipes* (Small) Eiten. *Canadian Journal of Plant Science* 65:691–709.

64. Luna, J., and P. Jepson. 2002. Enhancement of Biological Control with Insectary Plantings. Information Bulletin 11. Santa Cruz, CA: Organic Farming Research Foundation.

65. Maas, E. M. C. 1990. Crop rotation and take-all of wheat in South Africa. *Soil Biology and Biochemistry* 22:489–94.

66. MacNab, A. A., and T. A. Zitter. 2000. Do rotations matter within disease management programs? *Vegetable MD Online*, Cornell University,

HTTP://VEGETABLEMDONLINE.PPATH.CORNELL.EDU/ NEWSARTICLES/MCNABROTATIONS.HTM.

67. MacNab, A. A., and T. A. Zitter.

HTTP://VEGETABLEMDONLINE.PPATH.CORNELL.EDU/ NEWSARTICLES/MCNABROTATIONS.HTM.

68. Magdoff, F., and H. Van Es. 2000. *Building Soils for Better Crops*. Beltsville, MD: Sustainable Agriculture Network.

69. Maynard, D., G. Hochmuth. 1997. *Knott's Vegetable Handbook*, 4th ed. New York: John Wiley.

70. McLenaghen, R. D., K. C. Cameron, N. H. Lampkin, M. L. Daly, and B. Deo. 1996. Nitrate leaching from ploughed pasture and the effectiveness of winter catch crops in reducing leaching losses. *New Zealand Journal of Agricultural Research* 39:413–20.

71. Metcalf, R. L., and W. H. Luckmann. 1982. *Introduction to Insect Pest Management*, 2nd ed. New York: John Wiley.

72. Mitkowski, N. A., J. G. Van der Beek, and G. S. Abawi. 2002. Characterization of root-knot nematode populations associated with vegetables in New York State. *Plant Disease* 86:840–47.

73. Mohler, C. L. 2001a. Weed life history: Identifying vulnerabilities. In *Ecological Management of Agricultural Weeds*, M. Liebman, C. L. Mohler, and C. P. Staver, eds., pp. 40–98. New York: Cambridge University Press.

74. Mohler, C. L. 2001b. Enhancing the competitive ability of crops. In *Ecological Management of Agricultural Weeds*, M. Liebman, C. L. Mohler, and C. P. Staver, eds., pp. 269–321. New York: Cambridge University Press.

75. Muller, J. C., D. Denys, G. Morlet, and A. Mariotta, 1988. Influence of catch crops on mineral nitrogen leaching and its subsequent plant use. In *Nitrogen Efficiency in Agricultural Soils*, vol. 2, D. S. Jenkinson and K. A. Smith, eds., pp. 85–98. New York: Elsevier Applied Science.

76. Mulligan, G. A., ed. 1979. *The Biology of Canadian Weeds, Contributions 1–32*. Publication 1693. Ottawa: Agricultural Institute of Canada.

77. Mulligan, G. A., ed. 1984. *The Biology of Canadian Weeds, Contributions 33–61*. Publication 1765. Ottawa: Agricultural Institute of Canada.

78. Plant Nutrient Content Database, HTTP://WWW.NRCS. USDA.GOV/TECHNICAL/ECS/NUTRIENT/TBB2.HTML. U.S. Department of Agriculture, Natural Resources Conservation Service.

78a. DACUM & SCID Training Information. Center for Education and Training for Development, College of Education and Human Ecology, Ohio State University, HTTP://WWW.DACUMOHIOSTATE.COM/.

79. Ominski, P. D., M. H. Entz, and N. Kenkel. 1999. Weed suppression by *Medicago sativa* in subsequent cereal crops: A comparative survey. *Weed Science* 47:282–90.

80. Observation of growers at the DACUM expert farmer workshop, Jan. 30–Feb. 1, 2002.

81. Observation of growers at Northeast Organic Farmers Association of New Jersey workshop "Identifying Problems in Crop Rotation Sequences," Feb. 2003.

82. Observation of growers at Northeast Organic Farmers Association of New York workshop "Identifying Problems in Crop Rotation Sequences," Jan. 26, 2003.

83. Observation of growers at Northeast Organic Network (NEON) meeting, Jan. 29, 2003.

84. An Online Guide to Plant Disease Control. Oregon State University Extension, HTTP://PLANT-DISEASE.IPPC.ORST.EDU/INDEX.CFM.

85. Papavizas, G. C. 1966. Suppression of aphanomyces root rot of peas by cruciferous soil amendments. *Phytopathology* 56:1071–75.

86. Pedersen, L., and C. Eckenrode. 1980. Predicting Cabbage Maggot Flights in New York Using Common Wild Plants, FLS 87. Geneva: New York State Agricultural Experiment Station, Cornell University.

87. Peters, R. A., and S. Dunn. 1971. *Life History Studies as Related to Weed Control in the Northeast. 6. Large and Small Crabgrass*. Bulletin 415. Storrs: University of Connecticut, College of Agriculture and Natural Resources, Storrs Agricultural Experiment Station.

88. Peters, R. A., J. A. Meade, and P. W. Santelmann. 1963. *Life History Studies as Related to Weed Control in the Northeast. 2. Yellow Foxtail and Giant Foxtail*. Bulletin 369. Kingston: University of Rhode Island, Agricultural Experiment Station.

89. Radke, J. K., and R. T. Hagstrom. 1976. Strip intercropping for wind protection. In *Multiple Cropping*, R. I. Papendick, P. A. Sanchez, and G. B. Triplett, eds., pp. 201–22. Madison, WI: American Society of Agronomy.

90. Rahn, E. M., R. D. Sweet, J. Vengris, and S. Dunn. 1968. *Life History Studies as Related to Weed Control in the Northeast. 5. Barnyardgrass*. Bulletin 368. Newark: University of Delaware, Agricultural Experiment Station.

91. Raleigh, S. M., T. R. Flanagan, and C. Veatch. 1962. *Life History Studies as Related to Weed Control in the Northeast. 4. Quackgrass*. Bulletin 365. Newark: University of Delaware, Agricultural Experiment Station.

92. Reeves, D.W. 1994. Cover crops and rotations. In *Crops Residue Management*, J. L. Hatfield and B. A. Stewart, eds., pp. 125–58. Ann Arbor, MI: CRC Press.

93. Reichert, S. E. 1998. The role of spiders and their conservation in the agroecosystem. In *Enhancing Biological Control: Habitat Management to Promote Natural Enemies of Agricultural Pests*, C. H. Pickett and R. L. Bugg, eds., pp. 211–37. Berkeley: University of California Press.

94. Robak, J. 1994. Crop rotation effect on clubroot disease decrease. *Acta Horticulturae* 371:223–26.

95. Sarantonio, M. 1992. *Northeast Cover Crop Handbook*. Soil Health Series. Emmaus, PA: Rodale Institute.

96. Scott, T. W., J. Mt. Pleasant, R. F. Burt, and D. J. Otis. 1987. Contributions of ground cover, dry matter, and nitrogen from intercrops and cover crops in a corn polyculture system. *Agronomy Journal* 79:792–98.

97. Sherf, A. F., and A. A. MacNab. 1986. *Vegetable Diseases and Their Control*, 2nd ed. New York: John Wiley.

98. Skoglund, L. G., H. F. Schwartz, and W. M. Brown. 1999. Cultural approaches to managing plant pathogens. In *Handbook of Pest Management*, J. R. Ruberson, ed., pp. 291–307. New York: Marcel Dekker.

99. Smith, H. A., and R. McSorley. 2000. Intercropping and pest management: A review of major concepts. *American Entomologist* 46:154–61.

100. Sobey, D. G. 1981. Biological flora of the British Isles. *Stellaria media* (L.) Vill. *Journal of Ecology* 69:311–35.

101. Sorenson, K. A., and J. R. Baker. eds. Insects and Related Pests of Vegetables. AG-295. Raleigh: North Carolina State University, HTTP://IPM.NCSU.EDU/AG295/HTML/.

102. Stivers-Young, L. J. 1998. Growth, nitrogen accumulation and weed suppression by fall cover crops following early harvest of vegetables. *HortScience* 33:60–63.

103. Stoner, K. A. 1997. Influence of mulches on the colonization by adults and survival of larvae of the Colorado potato beetle (Coleoptera: Chrysomelidae) in eggplant. *Journal of Entomological Science* 32:7–16.

104. Stoner, K. A., ed. 1999. Alternatives to Insecticides for Managing Vegetable Insects. NRAES-138. State of Connecticut, Agricultural Experiment Station, HTTP://WWW.CT.GOV/CAES/CWP/VIEW.ASP?A=2797&Q=345156

105. Subbarao, K. V., J. C. Hubbard, and S. T. Koike. 1999. Evaluation of broccoli residue incorporation into field soil for Verticillium wilt control in cauliflower. *Plant Disease* 83:124–29.

106. Subbarao, K. V. 2001. Rotations with broccoli—A sustainable alternative to soil chemical fumigants. SARE final project report SW99-009. HTTP://WWW.SARE.ORG/REPORTING/REPORT_VIEWER.ASP?PN=SW99-009.

107. Sustainable Agriculture Network (SAN). 1998. Managing Cover Crops Profitably, 2nd ed. Beltsville, MD: Sustainable Agriculture Network (SAN).

108. Sweet, R. D. 1986. *Life History Studies as Related to Weed Control in the Northeast. 9. Galinsoga.* Ithaca, NY: Cornell University Agricultural Experiment Station, New York State College of Agriculture and Life Sciences.

109. Sweet, R. D., Veatch, C., and S. Dunn. 1978. *Life History Studies as Related to Weed Control in the Northeast. 8. Common Ragweed.* Bulletin 1033. Ithaca, NY: Cornell University Agricultural Experiment Station, New York State College of Agriculture and Life Sciences.

110. Tahvanainen, J. O., and R. B. Root. 1972. The influence of vegetational diversity on the population ecology of a specialized herbivore, *Phyllotreta cruciferae* (Coleoptera: Chrysomelidae). *Oecologia* (Berlin) 10:321–46.

111. Thomas, P. R. 1970. Host status of some plants for *Xiphinema diversicaudatum* (Micol.) and their susceptibility to viruses transmitted by this species. *Annals of Applied Biology* 65:169–78.

112. Thompson, K., S. R. Band, and J. G. Hodgson. 1993. Seed size and shape predict persistence in soil. *Functional Ecology* 7:236–41.

113. Townshend, J. L., and T. R. Davidson. 1962. Some weed hosts of the northern root-knot nematode, *Meloidogyne hapla* Chitwood, 1949, in Ontario. *Canadian Journal of Botany* 40:543–48.

114. Turkington, T. K., and G. W. Clayton. Crop Rotation and Plant Disease Management. HTTP://SSCA.CA/CONFERENCE/2000PROCEEDINGS/TURKINGTON.HTML.

115. University of Connecticut, Integrated Disease Management. Having problems controlling vegetable crop diseases? Try rotation. HTTP://WWW.HORT.UCONN.EDU/IPM/VEG/HTMS/ROTATE.HTM.

116. Uva, R. H., J. C. Neal, and J. M. DiTomaso. 1997. *Weeds of the Northeast.* Ithaca, NY: Cornell University Press.

117. Vengris, J., S. Dunn, and M. Stacewicz-Sapuncakis. 1972. *Life History Studies as Related to Weed Control in the Northeast. 7. Common Purslane.* Research Bulletin 598. Amherst: University of Massachusetts, College of Food and Natural Resources, Agricultural Experiment Station.

118. Virginia Cooperative Extension. Integrated Disease Management in Small Grains. Diseases and management practices. HTTP://WWW.PPWS.VT.EDU/STROMBERG/SMALLGRAIN/SGPRACTICES.HTML.

119. Wallace, J., ed. 2001. *Organic Field Crop Handbook*, 2nd ed. Ottawa: Canadian Organic Growers.

120. Warwick, S. I., A. Francis, and D. J. Susko. 2002. The biology of Canadian weeds. 9. *Thlaspi arvense* L. (updated). *Canadian Journal of Plant Science* 82:803–23.

121. Weiner J., H.-W. Griepentrog, and L. Kristensen. 2001. Increasing the suppression of weeds by cereal crops. *Journal of Applied Ecology* 38:784–90.

122. Weisz, R., A. Smilowitz, and B. Christ. 1994. Distance, rotation and border crops affect Colorado potato beetle (Coleoptera: Chrysomelidae) colonization and population density and early blight (*Alternaria solani*) severity in rotated potato fields. *Journal of Economic Entomology* 87:723–29.

123. White, D. G., ed. 1999. *Compendium of Corn Diseases*, 3rd ed. St. Paul, MN: APS Press.

124. Wiggins, B. E., and L. L. Kinkel. 2005. Green manures and crop sequences influence potato diseases and pathogen inhibitory activity of indigenous streptomycetes. *Phytopathology* 95:178–85.

125. Wijands, F. G. 1999. Crop rotation in organic farming: Theory and practice. In *Designing and Testing Crop Rotations for Organic Farming*, J. E. Olesen, R. Eltun, M. J. Gooding, E. S. Jensen, and U. Köpke, eds. Tjele: Danish Research Center for Organic Farming.

126. Wiley, R. W. 1981. *Proceedings of the International Workshop on Intercropping, 10–13 January 1979.* Hyderabad, India: International Crops Research Institute for the Semi-Arid Tropics.

127. Wright, R. J. 1999. Use of Cultural Practices in Crop Insect Pest Management. Nebraska Cooperative Extension EC95-1560-B. HTTP://WWW.IANR.UNL.EDU/PUBS/INSECTS/EC1560.HTM.

128. Zitter, T. A. 2001. A Checklist of Major Weeds and Crops as Natural Hosts for Plant Viruses in the Northeast. HTTP://VEGETABLEMDONLINE/PPATH.CORNELL.EDU/TABLES/WEEDHOSTTABLE.HTML.

About SARE

SARE
Sustainable Agriculture
Research & Education

SARE is a grant making and outreach program. Its mission is to advance—to the whole of American agriculture—innovations that improve profitability, stewardship and quality of life by investing in groundbreaking research and education. SARE provided financial resources to lower the cost of this book, thus ensuring its vital information is accessible to as many people as possible.

For more information about SARE's grant making program and information products, visit WWW.SARE.ORG or contact:

SARE Outreach Associate
10300 Baltimore Ave., BARC, Bldg. 046
Beltsville, MD 20705
INFO@SARE.ORG
(301) 504-5236

SARE Regions

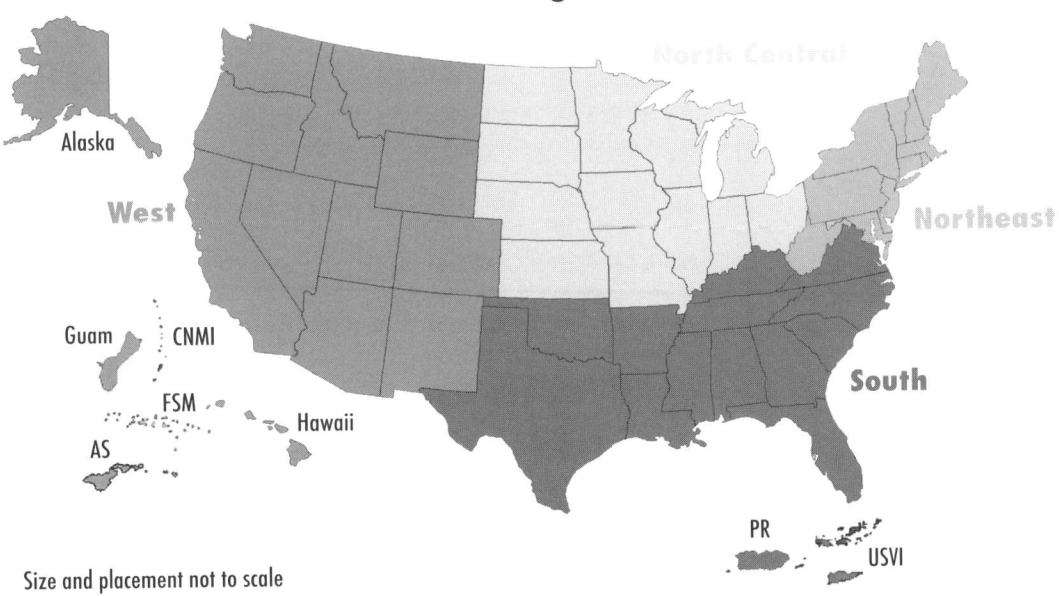

Size and placement not to scale

SARE's four regional offices and outreach office work to advance sustainable innovations to the whole of American agriculture.

About NRAES

NRAES, the Natural Resource, Agriculture, and Engineering Service, is a not-for-profit program dedicated to assisting land grant university faculty and others in increasing the public availability of research- and experience-based knowledge. NRAES is sponsored by eight land grant universities in the eastern United States. Administrative support is provided by Cornell University, the host university.

NRAES publishes practical books of interest to fruit and vegetable growers, landscapers, dairy and livestock producers, natural resource managers, SWCD (soil and water conservation district) staff, consumers, landowners, and professionals interested in agricultural waste management and composting. NRAES books are used in cooperative extension programs, in college courses, as management guides, and for self-directed learning.

NRAES member universities are:
University of Connecticut
University of Delaware
University of Maine
University of Maryland
University of New Hampshire
Rutgers University
Cornell University
West Virginia University

Contact NRAES for more information about membership.

NATURAL RESOURCE, AGRICULTURE, AND ENGINEERING SERVICE (NRAES)
Cooperative Extension, PO Box 4557
Ithaca, New York 14852-4557

Phone: (607) 255-7654
Fax: (607) 254-8770
E-mail: NRAES@CORNELL.EDU
Web site: WWW.NRAES.ORG